Elements of Decision Theory

Elements of Decision Theory

B. W. Lindgren

DEPARTMENT OF STATISTICS, UNIVERSITY OF MINNESOTA

The Macmillan Company, New York
Collier-Macmillan Limited, London

The Macmillan Company
866 Third Avenue, New York, New York 10022

Collier-Macmillan Canada, Ltd., Toronto, Ontario

Library of Congress catalog card number: 72–123530
First Printing

Preface

This book is intended as a text for a one-quarter or one-semester course in elementary decision theory. Despite its relatively low mathematical prerequisite, the material is perhaps most profitably studied by those in the third or later year of college, although in principle it is accessible to a reasonably sophisticated high school student.

The elements of decision theory can be understood without prior study of the infinitesimal calculus, but in my opinion a course in college algebra is almost essential. The basic ideas of decision theory and of decision theoretic methods, although requiring only those mathematical *tools* introduced in high school algebra, also require the mathematical maturity and familiarity and comfort that come either from more advanced mathematics courses or from being led through some mathematics in the course at hand. Indeed, studying this text and solving the problems will increase the student's mathematical maturity; the motivation of the application to decision theory may make this increase somewhat less painful than it is in a course in mathematics.

I have not emphasized methods to the extent of giving nomographs or tabular forms for solving certain problems, for such specialized techniques are soon (and perhaps best) forgotten. It seems to me that the function of a college course in decision theory should be to communicate basic principles and concepts, rather than to give the student computational devices. He should learn the kinds of problems with which the theory deals, the assumptions that are made as well as the necessary prior evaluations, and surely the limitations and pitfalls.

Many problems and examples are included, but it may be that not as many of these as some instructors would like are what are called "real" problems. Indeed, illustrations and examples drawn from a student's experience are helpful in teaching him concepts and principles. The best examples are straightforward and simply stated, so that wrestling with the complexities of the illustrative setting does not obscure the concept or principle being illustrated. However, in the realm of making decisions, problems from "real" life are seldom simple and straightforward. To present an example in a reasonable space and in such a way as to put a new idea into focus usually requires stripping it of those interdependencies and side effects that make it "real." One ends up with an example that is clearly artificial, though presented in terminology that pretends to make it seem real. I have included such examples, but I have also included examples that are more sterile or abstract. This is partly because the latter do contribute toward the student's mathematical education and partly because they can present an idea clearly without the distractions that the real setting might provide. An essential part of understanding how a mathematical method works is being able to view it somewhat abstractly, as a mathematical phenomenon; this ability also helps a student to see that the idea might have application in areas other than the one he is interested in at the moment.

Although probability is essential to decision theory, I have not included a thorough treatment of probability. I think it would be best if a student had some contact with probability—perhaps a course in it—prior to embarking on the study of decision theory. With current trends in mathematics curricula and in the curricula of the various professional schools, it is unlikely that a student ready for decision theory would not have been already exposed to probability. It is taught in many high schools, in college algebra courses, and in elementary statistics courses. An instructor teaching decision theory from this book might either require a prerequisite of probability or make appropriate supplementary material available to his class according to the particular needs and the available time.

At any rate, to avoid the risk of not reaching decision theory by the time the course ends, I have deliberately chosen to introduce ideas of probability as they are needed. This results, for example, in delaying the notion of independence until Chapter 7, a phenomenon that should not seem anomalous in a text devoted to decision theory rather than probability theory.

The material need not be studied in the order presented. The dependencies are perhaps most easily exhibited in the following diagram, the numerals denoting chapter numbers:

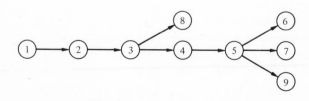

Moreover, there are certain sections that could be omitted, or passed by with only a slight reference, namely, Sections 2.2, 4.9, 6.7, 8.5, 8.6, 9.5, and perhaps some others.

I am much indebted, quite naturally, to the important earlier books dealing with decision theory, in particular to those in the list of references on page 275. I am indebted to my colleagues in the Department of Statistics at the University of Minnesota for many helpful discussions and criticisms. My thanks to these various authors and friends.

B. W. L.

Contents

Chapter 1   Preliminaries

Analyzing the process of making decisions involves a consideration of the following: (**a**) the set of possible actions from which one must choose; (**b**) the circumstances and basic "laws" that prevail; and (**c**) the consequences that result from taking a given action in the face of a given set of circumstances. It is up to the decision maker to select an action in such a way as to make the consequences as favorable as he can.

The combination of prevailing circumstances and governing laws will be referred to as the *state of nature*. If this state is known, it is then usually a simple matter to select the action according to the degree of desirability of the consequences resulting from the various actions and the known state. The real problems of decision theory are those in which the state of nature is *not* completely known. In such a case the correct decision is not obvious, since an action that results in favorable consequences under one state of nature may result in disaster under another state of nature.

Even in cases in which the state of nature is completely known, however, the analysis is usually clouded by the difficulty of accurately determining the consequences of the various actions in such a way that they can be compared. The consequences of an action are frequently quite complicated and involve many diverse ingredients. They may involve a loss or gain of money, of good will, of satisfaction or pride, of security, and so forth—some of which can actually be assessed and some of which may never even be known to the decision maker, let alone evaluated. Nevertheless, in order to construct a mathematical framework in which to study the decision problem, so as to provide a rational basis for making decisions, it is necessary to assume that consequences can be measured, on a *numerical scale*. Because *monetary* gain is often neither an adequate nor an accurate measure of consequences, the

1

notion of *utility* will be introduced to quantify preferences among various prospects with which the decision maker is faced.

Ordinarily one knows at least something about the state of nature and can consider some well-defined set of states as being *admissible*, or theoretically possible, thereby ruling out many that are not. It is natural in making decisions to try to get as much information as possible about the state of nature; and sometimes it is possible (by making measurements, or performing certain experiments, for instance) to obtain rather complete information about the state. A decision process becomes *statistical* when one is permitted (often at some cost) to perform certain experiments of *chance* related to the state of nature. The results of such experiments are called *observations*, or *data*; and a *statistical* decision rule is one that gives a prescription for the selection of an action on the basis of the data. Sometimes it is fruitful to consider, as part of the overall decision problem, the decision as to how much and what data to gather.

Example 1–1. A hospital receives a shipment of a certain drug from a manufacturer. It must decide whether to accept and use the drug, or to return or destroy it. If the drug does not meet certain specifications, its use may be harmful—even fatal. On the other hand, if it is safe but is discarded or returned, there is a loss of investment or of good will. The state of nature in this instance can be taken to be the state or quality of the drug; the available actions are to accept or to reject the shipment. The consequences depend both on the action taken and on the state of nature. To learn something about the quality of the shipment it may be possible to make certain tests on part of the shipment—or even on all of it, although sometimes such testing destroys the item being tested. The resulting data from the tests may well be useful in that they presumably would carry certain information about the state of nature, and so make the decision process less blind. Unless all of the shipment be tested, however, the information in the data about the quality of the shipment is still incomplete.

Example 1–2. A research chemist is charged with analyzing a new organic compound. He is faced with the task of deciding what to announce as the solubility of the substance, for instance. In such a case he would rarely choose a value to announce without conducting some tests, but it is characteristic of physical and chemical tests that there is a degree of uncertainty—owing to irregularities of the substance or to inadequacies of the testing processes. So he would gather some data and on the basis of this data announce a certain figure as specifying the degree of solubility. The state of nature is the "actual," or true, solubility of the substance. The consequences of the decision would be very difficult to assess, inasmuch as the result is probably to be given in a research journal, available to persons countless and unknown. The testing process, incidentally, would ordinarily involve some expense, which could perhaps be figured into the cost of the decision making.

Example 1-3. An instructor is about to place an order for the duplication of sets of class notes, which are to be on hand for the first day of classes. The cost of reproducing them is $1 per copy plus a $40 set-up cost. If he runs short and has to request a rush job for the initially unfilled demand, there is an additional $20 charge (plus the usual $40 and $1 per copy) for the second run. He does not know how many sets are needed, because he does not know the enrollment until just before classes begin. The notes are sold to the students for $2 per copy, but unsold copies are of no value since the course will be different the next year. The state of nature can be thought of as the actual enrollment, and for each assumed value of this unknown number and each number of copies ordered in the first run one can compute the net profit (or loss). The problem is to choose a number for the first (and perhaps only) run in a way that is advantageous in some sense. The instructor may have some hunches or beliefs about the number that will enroll, and he may be able to obtain some preliminary enrollment figures (as of the date on which he has to place the first run order) that are related in a known way to the ultimate enrollment.

Example 1-4. A grocer has a lot of fifty gross of eggs (purchased by his partner for a given amount) that he must classify as Jumbo, to sell for 65¢ a dozen; Large, to sell for 59¢ a dozen; or Medium, to sell for 53¢ a dozen. It is assumed that the quality of the lot can be adequately described by θ, the (unknown) average weight per dozen eggs in the lot. The grocer has some prior evidence as to the quality of the lot, namely, the amount that his partner paid for the lot, and his past experience with the particular egg producer from whom the lot was purchased. The grocer is also willing to take the time and trouble to pick five dozen eggs at random from the lot and weigh them. On the basis of this experiment and his prior convictions about θ, he is to make the classification. He might be tempted to ignore his prior convictions and his data and (looking for the maximum profit) simply call the lot Jumbo; however, if the average weight is small, the retail customer will tend to think the price is too high for the size of the eggs and not buy—or if he buys without looking, the customer will discover the underweight at home and complain or take his business to another market. Similarly, if he calls the lot Medium, and the value of θ is really big enough for Jumbo, he foregoes a significant potential profit. With such reflections as this the grocer can perhaps determine, for each grade of classification, the profit he can count on if the quality is actually θ, as a function of θ.

In summary, the ingredients of a decision problem are

(a)   a set of available actions,

(b)   a set of admissible states of nature, and

(c)   a loss associated with each combination of a state of nature and an action.

With these ingredients, **(a)** to **(c)**, the problem of picking an action will be referred to as a "no-data" decision problem. The fourth ingredient

(d)   observations from an experiment defined by the state of nature,

will combine with **(a)** to **(c)** to define the general statistical decision problem, that of choosing the most propitious action on the basis of the data, knowing the loss structure but not knowing the state of nature. To restrict the scope of the mathematical methods required, the set of available actions as well as the set of admissible states of nature will be assumed finite (or at most countably infinite) in number, throughout the first several chapters.

Some elementary probability and analytic geometry will be given in this first chapter. The former will provide the basis for treating the random aspects of a decision problem, those introduced as a device for making decisions, and those inherent in the nature of data. The second chapter will discuss the idea of utility, the scale on which consequences of actions will be measured. The actual decision problem will then be taken up in the third and subsequent chapters.

1.1 Discrete Random Variables

The term *experiment* is used to denote a process or procedure that happens or is carried out, coming to some final conclusion or definite outcome that can be measured or discerned and recorded. It is said to be an *experiment of chance* when the factors influencing the outcome are so complex that one cannot predict the outcome on the basis of what is known of the prevailing circumstances. When the outcome of an experiment of chance is or can be identified with a number, this numerical outcome is referred to as a *random variable*. A random variable will be denoted by a capital letter, such as X; and when dealing in generalities, possible values are denoted by lower case letters with subscripts: x_1, x_2, and so forth. (In specific examples, of course, these x's are specific numbers.)

Example 1–5. When two coins are tossed so as to fall on a flat surface, the outcome can be described according to the number of coins that show heads. This number is a random variable:

$$X = \text{number of heads in a toss of two coins.}$$

One cannot predict the value of this variable, but it is clear at the outset that the result will be either 0 heads, 1 head, or 2 heads. These numbers, 0, 1, and 2, are the possible values of X.

When an experiment of chance is repeated under superficially identical conditions, the results are found to vary from one trial to the next—as is implied in the term *variable*. However, experience with such experiments shows that there is something regular or systematic over long sequences of repeated trials, something that usefully characterizes the experiment and for which it is helpful to have a mathematical structure or model. It is this: Over a long sequence of trials of an experiment of chance, the proportion of trials in which a specific outcome is observed to occur is found to tend toward a limiting proportion as the number of trials is increased without limit. This limiting proportion is called the *probability* of the outcome. In case the outcome is the random variable X, the probability of $X = x_i$ is the limiting proportion of trials in which the value x_i is the result. One writes $P(X = x_i)$ for this probability.

Limiting proportions cannot be determined in practice, since one cannot carry out infinitely many trials, but it is useful to assume that such ideal quantities exist, as characteristics of the experiment being performed. A mathematical model for an experiment of chance consists of a list of the possible outcomes together with corresponding *probabilities* intended to embody the corresponding limiting proportions. For a random variable, the model is simply a list of possible values and corresponding probabilities.

Example 1–6. The number of heads showing when two coins are tossed is a random variable with possible values 0, 1, and 2. Experience in tossing ordinary coins has shown that the value 0 will occur about $\frac{1}{4}$ of the time in a long sequence of tosses, the value 1 in about $\frac{1}{2}$ of the tosses, and the value 2 in the remaining $\frac{1}{4}$ of the tosses. (Observe that these proportions add up to 1, representing all of the proportions that make up a whole.) The appropriate probability model would then appear to consist of the values and corresponding probabilities, often given in tabular form as in the following:

x_i	0	1	2
p_i	$\frac{1}{4}$	$\frac{1}{2}$	$\frac{1}{4}$

(Here p_i denotes the probability that X takes on the value x_i.)

Example 1–7. The demand for a product in a given period of time can often be considered to be a random variable. For example, the number of boxes of a certain brand of cereal sold by a certain small grocer in a week's time is unpredictable, but the proportion of weeks in which a given number is the number sold may be considered to have an ideal or limiting value. If Y denotes the number of boxes sold in a week, the possible values of Y are 0, 1, 2, . . .—perhaps up to some limit imposed by the size of the store and the practical limit on how many customers can be served. Each of these values is assumed to have an associated probability, or ideal proportion of weeks in which that number of boxes is sold.

For a given random variable X, the term *probability distribution* or simply *distribution* of X is used to describe the pattern of possible values $x_1, x_2, \ldots, x_n$ and corresponding probabilities $p_1, p_2, \ldots, p_n$. In this distribution the probabilities must add up to 1, being proportions of a whole. Moreover, they cannot exceed 1 and cannot be negative. Thus, they satisfy these conditions:

(1) $0 \le p_i \le 1$,   for $i = 1, 2, \ldots, n$.

(2) $p_1 + p_2 + \cdots + p_n = 1$.

(In the few instances in which it will be desirable to have a countably infinite set of possible values, the sum in **(2)** above will be an infinite series.) Any set of numbers postulated to represent probabilities of the values of a random variable must then satisfy properties **(1)** and **(2)**.

Assuming the existence of limiting proportions or probabilities for a given random phenomenon, one cannot then really construct or postulate a model for the phenomenon with arbitrary probabilities satisfying the properties **(1)** and **(2)**—since the correct or true probabilities already exist. What he can do is either to try to learn something about the true probabilities, or to see what the consequences of a model he constructs would be, and how well these consequences agree with what he can observe.

Example 1-8. In a certain school, there are 150 first-year students, 100 second-year students, 85 third-year students, and 75 fourth-year students. Let Z denote the year in school of a student selected at random from the list of all of the 410 students. The values that Z can take on are 1, 2, 3, and 4. A probability model would be defined by any set of four nonnegative numbers that add up to 1, but a model often assumed is that in which the probabilities are proportional to the sizes of each class in the school. That is,

$$P(Z = 1) = \frac{150}{410},$$

$$P(Z = 2) = \frac{100}{410},$$

$$P(Z = 3) = \frac{85}{410}, \quad \text{and}$$

$$P(Z = 4) = \frac{75}{410}.$$

Whether the model defined by these probabilities actually describes or represents the actual process of selection faithfully, or not, is a matter that only experience could determine—and even then, not with certainty.

There are two types of situations in which the probabilities of specific values of a random variable can be postulated with reasonable success. These involve a geometrical symmetry that suggests the values of the probabilities to use, and experience has shown that the suggestions turn out to be rather good. One situation is that of the toss of a "die" shaped like a regular polyhedron of n sides, resulting in a final position in which the die rests on one of its n sides. If the sides are numbered $1, 2, \ldots, n$, the number of the side that is considered to be the result is a random variable with these possible values; the probabilities or long run proportions of trials in which these numbers are the results are taken on intuitive grounds to be *equal*. If they are equal, and add up to 1, then each must be $1/n$:

$$P(X = i) = \frac{1}{n}, \quad \text{for } i = 1, 2, \ldots, n.$$

Of course, assuming them to be equal does not necessarily make it so; flaws in the die and quirks in the tossing of the die could result in long-run proportions different from $1/n$. But usually $1/n$ is pretty close.

Example 1–9. In the toss of an ordinary die (a cube, whose six sides are marked with 1, 2, 3, 4, 5, and 6 dots, respectively), the number X of dots on the face that turns up is a random variable with possible values 1, 2, 3, 4, 5, or 6 and probabilities $P(X = i) = \frac{1}{6}$, for $i = 1, 2, \ldots, 6$. A "loaded" die might well have probabilities slightly different from these—a situation that could be taken advantage of by one who knows the nature of the loading.

Regular polyhedrons do not exist for some values of n; there is a regular polyhedron of 4 sides, one of 6 sides, one of 12, and so forth, but none with, say, 5 sides. However, regular plane polygons do exist having any specified number of sides, and if one used such a polygon as the base of a long cylinder, this cylindrical solid could be rolled on a flat surface and would come to rest on one of the n sides. If the sides are numbered from 1 to n, the number of the side on which the cylinder stops would be a random variable with values $1, 2, \ldots, n$; and the corresponding probabilities would be $P(X = i) = 1/n$ in the ideal model in which all sides are equally likely. Figure 1–1 pictures a cylinder corresponding to $n = 7$.

A second situation in which a useful model can be postulated from *a priori* considerations is that in which chips numbered $1, 2, \ldots, n$ are placed in a bowl and mixed thoroughly. One chip is selected blindly, and the number drawn is a random variable X taking on one of the values $1, 2, \ldots, n$. These values are again considered equally probable, so that each has probability $1/n$ in the ideal model. Somewhat more generally, if there are n_1 chips numbered x_1, n_2 chips numbered $x_2, \ldots$, and n_k chips numbered x_k, then the

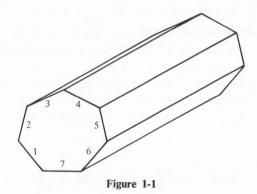

Figure 1-1

ideal model for the blind selection of a chip is that in which the individual chips are considered equally likely, whereas the probabilities of the values $x_1, \ldots, x_k$ are proportional to the numbers of chips $n_1, \ldots, n_k$. Example 1–8 above illustrates the latter type of model.

In both types of models—for tossing symmetrical solids, and for selecting blindly from a bowl of chips—the probabilities assigned from *a priori* considerations, and termed *ideal*, may or may not accurately represent an actual process of tossing or selection. What one does is to carry out the experiment taking such precautions as intuition would suggest to make it ideal. That is, in selecting one from several beads in a bowl, there should be thorough mixing so that the one doing the selecting is in complete ignorance of the locations of the beads; and in tossing an object one gives a reasonably vigorous toss and an appreciable spin, so that the object's initial orientation is really lost track of—effectively "shuffling" the sides and selecting one blindly.

One reason for making specific mention of the two types of ideal models is that either one may be used in constructing an experiment whose result is a discrete random variable with any arbitrarily specified distribution. Thus, if one wants to create an experiment resulting in a random variable X with values $x_1, x_2, \ldots, x_k$ and corresponding probabilities $p_1, p_2, \ldots, p_k$, he can do it in either of two ways. Either he can build a cylindrical die with n_1 sides marked $x_1, \ldots,$ and n_k sides marked x_k, where the n_i's are proportional to the p_i's (and toss this die); or he can put into a bowl n_1 chips marked $x_1, \ldots,$ and n_k chips marked x_k, where again the n_i's are proportional to the p_i's (and select a chip blindly from the bowl). Actually, to do this requires that the p's be rational numbers, but certainly one can get an arbitrarily good approximation by using a finite decimal approximation to the p's. Also, the number of values k has to be finite; but, if it is countably infinite, one can again build an approximating experiment with finitely many values.

Example 1–10. Suppose it is desired to realize, in an actual experiment, the probability model consisting of a random variable X with possible values and probabilities as given in the following table:

x_i	2	4	5	8
p_i	.12	.26	.30	.32

A cylindrical die with 50 sides, 6 marked 2, 13 marked 4, 15 marked 5, and 16 marked 8 could be constructed and tossed, the number on the side on which the die comes to rest then being the random variable having the given distribution. Alternatively, the number on a chip drawn blindly from a bowl containing 6 chips marked 2, 13 marked 4, 15 marked 5, and 16 marked 8 would also be such a random variable.

It is useful to have the notion of an *event*, relating to a random variable X: *An event is a set of possible values of X.* For instance, if the set of all possible values of X is the list $x_1, x_2, \ldots, x_k$, (in which, just to be clear on the matter, these x_i's are all distinct), then the set $\{x_2, x_5, x_6\}$ is such a set of values and is called an event. This particular event is said to "happen" if the random variable X assumes (in carrying out the experiment) either the value x_2, the value x_5, or the value x_6. The *probability* that a given event will happen, or more briefly, the probability of that event, is defined to be the sum of the probabilities of the values which constitute it. The motivation for this is that the probability of an event is intended to be simply the long-run proportion, in an infinite sequence of trials of the underlying experiment, of the trials in which the event actually happens; this proportion is clearly the sum of the proportions in which the individual values in the event happen. Thus, the probability of the event $\{x_2, x_5, x_6\}$ is

$$P(\{x_2, x_5, x_6\}) = p_2 + p_5 + p_6,$$

where as usual $p_i = P(X = x_i)$.

An event can be specified, as above, by making a list of the values in it, but it is often more convenient to specify an event by giving some condition satisfied by the values in it and only those values. Thus, the condition $X < 3$ defines the event consisting of all values x_i that are in fact less than 3; the probability of this event is then written $P(X < 3)$.

Example 1–11. When an ordinary die (a cube whose six sides are marked with 1, 2, 3, 4, 5, and 6 dots) is tossed, the number X of dots on the face that turns up is a random variable with values 1, 2, 3, 4, 5, 6. In the *ideal* model, the probabilities assigned to the values are all $\frac{1}{6}$. The condition that the number of points showing is an odd number defines an event, namely, the set of values $\{1, 3, 5\}$. And then

$$P(X \text{ is odd}) = P(X = 1) + P(X = 3) + P(X = 5)$$
$$= \frac{1}{6} + \frac{1}{6} + \frac{1}{6} = \frac{1}{2}.$$

Similarly, for the event $X > 4$, consisting of the values 5 and 6, one has

$$P(X > 4) = P(X = 5) + P(X = 6)$$
$$= \frac{1}{6} + \frac{1}{6} = \frac{1}{3}.$$

Problems

1–1 Toss two ordinary coins fifty times. Let X denote the number of heads that turn up in a given toss, and record the value of X for each toss.

    (a) Make a plot of f_k/k, for $k = 1, 2, \ldots, 50$, where f_k is the number of tosses in which *two* heads turn up. Notice the tendency toward stability, and infer from your plot the probability that $X = 2$.

    (b) If there is an argument as to whether the proper model for X should be the first or the second of the following probability tables, which side would you be on after your experience in tossing?

Model 1:

x_i	0	1	2
p_i	$\frac{1}{3}$	$\frac{1}{3}$	$\frac{1}{3}$

Model 2:

x_i	0	1	2
p_i	$\frac{1}{4}$	$\frac{1}{2}$	$\frac{1}{4}$

1–2 The face cards are extracted from an ordinary deck of cards, leaving four cards in each of ten denominations: Ace (1), 2, 3, ..., 10. The deck is shuffled well and then a card is drawn blindly from the deck; let X denote the denomination of that card.

    (a) Determine the probability distribution of X. (An adequate answer consists of a table of values and corresponding probabilities.)

    (b) Compute $P(X \text{ is even})$.

    (c) Compute $P(X \le 3)$.

    (d) Compute $P(2 < X < 6)$.

1–3 The "Goren system" of point-count bidding in contract bridge assigns values to cards as follows: ace:4, king:3, queen:2, jack:1, and anything else:0. (A deck of bridge cards contains four aces, four kings, four queens, four jacks, and 36 other cards.) Let Y denote the number of points assigned to a card selected blindly from a well-shuffled deck.

    (a) Give the probability distribution of Y.

    (b) Compute $P(Y < 3)$.

    (c) Compute $P(Y = 0 \text{ or } 4)$.

1–4 A random variable Z has possible values 0, 1, 2, 3, ... with corresponding probabilities $\frac{1}{2}, \frac{1}{4}, \frac{1}{8}, \frac{1}{16}, \ldots$. That is, $P(Z = k) = \frac{1}{2}^{k+1}$, for any nonnegative integer k. Determine the following:

    (a) $P(Z \text{ is an even number})$.

    (b) $P(Z < 4)$.

    (c) $P(Z \ge 3)$.

1–5 An ordinary lead pencil is frequently in the shape of a cylinder with a hexagonal cross-section. If the sides are numbered 1, 2, 3, 4, 5, 6, and U denotes the number showing on the top side when the pencil comes to rest after being rolled, what is the appropriate distribution for U? Roll such a pencil 24 times, recording the outcome each time; do you believe the ideal model of equal likelihood of the values?

1.2 Expected Value

Averaging the observations in a sequence of trials of an experiment of chance leads, by idealization, to the notion of the *mean value*, or *expected value*, or *expectation* of the random variable. (The various terms are synonymous.) An example will help motivate the definition.

Example 1–12. In a certain gambling house, a game consists of the toss of a coin, with a $1 payoff for heads and a $2 payoff for tails. If the game is to be fair, with no profit to the house (which would be an unusual situation in practice), the customers should be charged in such a way that the total take in a large number of plays of the game is equal to the total payoff. In N plays of the game, where N is a large number, there will be approximately $N/2$ plays that result in heads, with a payoff of $1 each, and $N/2$ plays that result in tails, with a payoff of $2 each. The house therefore must pay out $$N/2$ (total) to those players who get heads and about $$2N/2$ (total) to those players who get tails, or in all

$$\text{Total paid out} = \$1 \cdot \frac{N}{2} + \$2 \cdot \frac{N}{2} = \$3 \cdot \frac{N}{2}.$$

If this is exactly the total paid out, the house should then also *collect* $3N/2$ (total) from the N players, in order to break even. If the charge is made prior to the play of the game, it would be unreasonable to charge different players different amounts; if the N players are all charged the same amount, that amount would be $1.50 for each. This is an "average" amount won, distributed over all N players:

$$\text{Average payoff} = \$1 \cdot \frac{1}{2} + \$2 \cdot \frac{1}{2}.$$

It is called the *expectation*, or sometimes *mathematical expectation*, of the game, the adjective "mathematical" referring to the fact that the expectation is an idealization as N becomes large without limit, so that the proportions converge to probabilities.

The payoff in the example above, as a number of dollars won, is a particular example of a random variable. The notion of average is extended to an arbitrary random variable as follows.

DEFINITION　*The expected value of a random variable X with possible values $x_1, \ldots, x_k$ and corresponding probabilities $p_1, \ldots, p_k$ is the weighted average of those values, with the probabilities as weights:*

$$E(X) \equiv x_1 p_1 + x_2 p_2 + \cdots + x_k p_k = \sum_{i=1}^{k} x_i p_i.$$

The synonymous terms *expectation*, *average value*, and *mean value* are also used for this quantity. Observe that whereas in calculating a weighted average it is usual to divide by the sum of the weights, the weights in the present kind of average are already relative—they add up to 1, being probabilities.

The term "expected" may be a bit misleading. The expected value of a random variable may not be even a possible value, let alone anything one expects (in a single trial). For instance, in Example 1–12 above the expected number of dollars won was 1.5, whereas in a single play of the game, the payoff would be either 1 or 2 dollars—never 1.5 dollars.

The notion of expected value is ascribed to the probability distribution of X as well as to X itself. Thus, one speaks of the expected value or mean of a distribution, meaning the defining weighted sum above; it would be, of course, the mean value of a random variable X having that probability distribution.

It is convenient to realize that if a constant c is added to each value of a random variable, yielding a new random variable $Y = X + c$, the mean of this new variable is just

$$E(Y) = \sum (x_i + c) p_i = \sum x_i p_i + c \sum p_i = E(X) + c.$$

And if, on the other hand, each value of X is multiplied by a constant b, the mean of the new variable $Z = bX$ would be

$$E(Z) = \sum b x_i p_i = b \sum x_i p_i = bE(X).$$

Combining these one obtains

$$E(bX + c) = bE(X) + c.$$

That is, if the values of X undergo a linear transformation, the mean value undergoes the same linear transformation.

Example 1–13. Consider the random variable X, the number of heads in two tosses of a coin, and the model of Example 1–6, in which the distribution of X is given in the following table

x_i	0	1	2
p_i	$\frac{1}{4}$	$\frac{1}{2}$	$\frac{1}{4}$

The expected value, said to be the "expected number of heads in two tosses," is

$$E(X) = 0 \cdot \frac{1}{4} + 1 \cdot \frac{1}{2} + 2 \cdot \frac{1}{4} = 1.$$

This happens to be one of the possible values. If one subtracts this mean from each value, obtaining a new variable

$$Y = X - E(X) = Y - 1,$$

the mean of the new variable is

$$E(Y) = E(X - 1) = E(X) - 1 = 1 - 1 = 0.$$

The last computation in Example 1–13 can be generalized. If X has mean value $E(X) = \mu$, then

$$E(X - \mu) = E(X) - \mu = \mu - \mu = 0.$$

This fact is significant in the interpretation of a probability distribution in terms of a mass analogue, which in turn gives a good intuitive feeling for the significance of an expected value.

A distribution of probability is quite analagous to a distribution of *mass*. Suppose that a mass $m(x_1)$ is placed at the point x_1, a mass $m(x_2)$ is placed at the point x_2, and so on, where $x_1, x_2, \ldots$ are coordinates, with respect to some reference origin, of points on an axis of x-values. The sum of the quantities $m(x_j)$ is the total mass:

$$\text{Total mass} = \sum_j m(x_j) \equiv M.$$

The *relative* masses, $m(x_j)/M$, that is, the proportion of the total mass placed at the point x_j, have the property that their sum is 1:

$$\sum_j \frac{m(x_j)}{M} = \frac{1}{M} \sum_j m(x_j) = \frac{M}{M} = 1.$$

Moreover, mass is inherently a nonnegative quantity, so the relative masses are analogous to probabilities. Indeed, given such a distribution of point masses on a line, one could define a corresponding probability distribution by simply taking the relative masses as probabilities:

$$p(x_j) = \frac{m(x_j)}{M}.$$

Conversely, a given probability model could be realized by any mass distribution having point masses in proportion to the probabilities.

In this analogy between mass and probability, the *center of gravity* of the system of masses corresponds to the *expected value* of the probability distribution:

$$\text{Center of gravity} = \frac{\sum_j x_j m(x_j)}{\sum_j m(x_j)} = \sum_j x_j \frac{m(x_j)}{M}$$

$$= \sum_j x_j p(x_j) = E(X),$$

where X is a random variable taking on values x_j with probabilities $p(x_j)$. Thus, it is correct, as well as helpful, to think of the expected value of a probability distribution as the center of gravity of a corresponding mass distribution. The center of gravity measures the *center* of a mass distribution, or its *location* along the line, and so the expected value measures the center or location of a probability distribution.

The center of a mass distribution, as measured by its center of gravity, is a "center" in the sense that if the point masses are conceived of as attached to a stiff, weightless wire or rod, that system of masses would *balance* at the center of gravity. This property of the center of gravity of a mass distribution, or of the expected value of a probability distribution, is precisely the property encountered in and just after Example 1–13 above, namely, that $E(X - \mu) = 0$ if $\mu = E(X)$. That is, the quantities $x_i - \mu$ are distances from the mass locations x_i to the center of gravity; multiplying these by masses gives *moments* which add up to zero, indicating that the positive moments (from masses to the right of the center of gravity) exactly balance the negative moments (from masses to the left). This kind of computation is usually encountered in elementary arithmetic in problems of balancing teeter-totters.

Example 1–14. Consider point masses of 2 gms placed at $x = -1$, 3 gms placed at $x = 1$, 1 gm placed at $x = 2$, and 4 gms placed at $x = 5$. The total mass is 10 gms, and so the center of gravity is

$$cg = -1 \times .2 + 1 \times .3 + 2 \times .1 + 5 \times .4 = 2.3.$$

The point $x = 2.3$ is the balance point. Notice, then, that

$$(-1 - 2.3) \times .2 + (1 - 2.3) \times .3 + (2 - 2.3) \times .1 + (5 - 2.3) \times .4 = 0,$$

indicating that the positive moments about 2.3 cancel the negative ones, which establishes the balance:

$$-10.8 + 10.8 = 0.$$

Experiments of chance in which the outcomes are not necessarily numbers are common, and probability models for these are similar to those used above in the case of random variables. This will be discussed more in detail in a later chapter. For the present suffice it to say that the more general model again assigns probabilities to outcomes in such a way that their total is 1, and each is nonnegative. The probability of an outcome (as above) is intended to represent the long-run relative frequency of occurrence of that outcome in an infinitely long sequence of independent trials.

Problems

1–6 A random variable X has values $1, 2, \ldots, 10$, and these values are equally likely (see Problem 1–2). Determine the expected value of X.

1-7   A random variable Y has values and probabilities as follows:

y_j	0	1	2	3	4
p_j	$\dfrac{9}{13}$	$\dfrac{1}{13}$	$\dfrac{1}{13}$	$\dfrac{1}{13}$	$\dfrac{1}{13}$

(This is the number of points assigned to a card drawn at random from a bridge deck, in the Goren system, as in Problem 1–3.)

(a) Determine the expected value of Y.

(b) Calculate $E(Y - E(Y))$ directly, as the weighted sum of the differences $y_j - E(Y)$.

1-8   Calculate $E(X)$ for the random variable X of Problem 1–1, the number of heads that turn up in a toss of two coins, using each of the models proposed in that problem.

1-9   Compute the expected value of the random variable U in Problem 1–5, using the model with equal probabilities. Suppose that you were to take instead the relative frequencies in your 24 rolls of the pencil as the probabilities; what then would be the expected value?

1-10 A baker counts the number of raisins in each of 1,000 raisin cookies, with the results shown in the following table

Number of raisins	0	1	2	3	4	5	6	7	8	9	10	11	12
Frequency	18	74	146	195	196	156	104	60	30	13	5	2	1

If the corresponding relative frequencies were taken as the probabilities for the various numbers of raisins per cookie (which is not unnatural, since the probabilities are supposed to be long-run limiting relative frequencies), what would be the expected number of raisins per cookie?

1.3 Lines in the Cartesian Plane

The reader is assumed to be familiar with rectangular or Cartesian coordinates in the plane, which both provide an analytical means for studying geometrical relationships and permit the representation of algebraic concepts geometrically to aid one's intuition. He may not, however, be accustomed to writing the point (x, y) in the form* $\begin{pmatrix} x \\ y \end{pmatrix}$. In this new notation the following

---

* This is called a column matrix.

conventions will be employed, *defining* (respectively) "equality," "addition," and "multiplication" by a constant:

(i) $\begin{pmatrix} x \\ y \end{pmatrix} = \begin{pmatrix} a \\ b \end{pmatrix}$ means $x = a$ *and* $y = b$;

(ii) $\begin{pmatrix} x \\ y \end{pmatrix} + \begin{pmatrix} u \\ v \end{pmatrix} \equiv \begin{pmatrix} x + u \\ y + v \end{pmatrix}$;

(iii) $k\begin{pmatrix} x \\ y \end{pmatrix} \equiv \begin{pmatrix} kx \\ ky \end{pmatrix}$.

Definition (i) states that two points will be considered equal if and only if they are precisely the same point—agreeing in both coordinates. Definition (ii) has a geometrical interpretation: it is a simple exercise in geometry to show that the point $(x + u, y + v)$ is a fourth vertex of a *parallelogram*, three of whose vertices are $(0, 0)$, (x, y), and (u, v). Figure 1–2 shows two points and their *sum*, together with quantities used in the derivation of the fact that the sum is the fourth vertex of a parallelogram, as asserted.

Definition (iii) says that the point $k\begin{pmatrix} x \\ y \end{pmatrix}$ is along the same line through the origin as is $\begin{pmatrix} x \\ y \end{pmatrix}$, being k times as far out (in the same direction if $k > 0$ and in the opposite direction if $k < 0$). This is illustrated in Figure 1–3.

It is often convenient to identify the point (x, y) with the directed line segment or *vector* from the origin $(0, 0)$ out to that point. Thus, the operation $+$ is referred to as *vector addition*, and multiplication by a constant is called

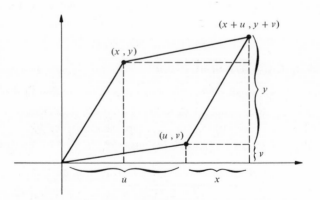

Figure 1–2

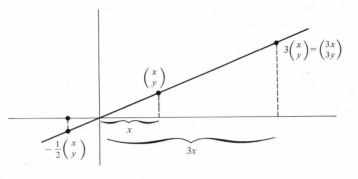

Figure 1–3

multiplication of a vector by a *scalar*. (An ordinary number is said to be a scalar, in contradistinction to a vector.) In terms of this identification of points with vectors, the sum of two points or vectors is the vector which is the diagonal of the parallelogram formed with the two given vectors as adjacent sides, as in Figure 1–4.

It can be verified that the operations defined by (ii) and (iii) satisfy these properties:

(a) $\begin{pmatrix} x \\ y \end{pmatrix} + \begin{pmatrix} u \\ v \end{pmatrix} = \begin{pmatrix} u \\ v \end{pmatrix} + \begin{pmatrix} x \\ y \end{pmatrix}$;

(b) $\begin{pmatrix} x \\ y \end{pmatrix} + \left[\begin{pmatrix} u \\ v \end{pmatrix} + \begin{pmatrix} z \\ w \end{pmatrix} \right] = \left[\begin{pmatrix} x \\ y \end{pmatrix} + \begin{pmatrix} u \\ v \end{pmatrix} \right] + \begin{pmatrix} z \\ w \end{pmatrix}$;

(c) $a\begin{pmatrix} x \\ y \end{pmatrix} + b\begin{pmatrix} x \\ y \end{pmatrix} = (a + b)\begin{pmatrix} x \\ y \end{pmatrix}$,   and $a\begin{pmatrix} x \\ y \end{pmatrix} + a\begin{pmatrix} u \\ v \end{pmatrix} = a\left[\begin{pmatrix} x \\ y \end{pmatrix} + \begin{pmatrix} u \\ v \end{pmatrix} \right]$.

(These properties have names in algebra: The first says that vector addition is *commutative*, the second says that it is *associative*, and those in (c) are *distributive laws* for multiplication by a scalar and vector addition. Properties (a) to (c) justify, in a sense, the appropriation of the terms "addition" and

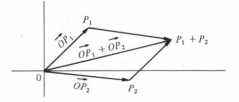

Figure 1–4

"multiplication," and the symbols for these operations, which are experienced first in the realm of ordinary numbers.)

To be considered next is the relationship between the solving of a pair of simultaneous linear equations in two variables or unknowns and the representation of an arbitrary point as a certain combination of two given points. The relationship will be introduced first in an example, and then considered in more generality.

Example 1–15. Consider the following system of equations in the unknowns a and b:

$$\begin{cases} 3a + 2b = 12 \\ a - b = -1. \end{cases}$$

This pair of equations can be replaced by the equivalent, single equation

$$a\begin{pmatrix} 3 \\ 1 \end{pmatrix} + b\begin{pmatrix} 2 \\ -1 \end{pmatrix} = \begin{pmatrix} 12 \\ -1 \end{pmatrix}.$$

The problem, geometrically, is that of finding a scalar multiple of $(3, 1)$ and a scalar multiple of $(2, -1)$, the sum of which multiples is $(12, -1)$. Figure 1–5 shows how this can be done, namely, by drawing lines parallel to the vectors $(3, 1)$ and $(2, -1)$ through $(12, -1)$ until they meet the extensions of those vectors. The solution, $a = 2$ and $b = 3$, found easily by elementary algebra, says that twice $(3, 1)$ plus three times $(2, -1)$ yields $(12, -1)$, and this is evident in Figure 1–5.

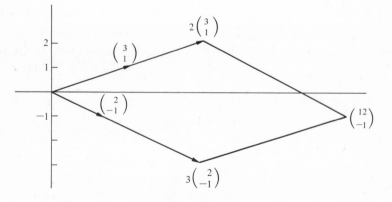

Figure 1–5

Consider now a more general simultaneous system of two equations in the unknowns a and b:

$$\begin{cases} x_1 a + x_2 b = x_3 \\ y_1 a + y_2 b = y_3. \end{cases}$$

This can be written in the equivalent form

$$a \binom{x_1}{y_1} + b \binom{x_2}{y_2} = \binom{x_3}{y_3},$$

or, denoting (x_i, y_i) by P_i, in the form

$$a P_1 + b P_2 = P_3.$$

As in the example above, the problem is that of determining a and b such that $a P_1 + b P_2$ is equal to, or is, the point or vector P_3.

The combination $a P_1 + b P_2$ is said to be a *linear combination* of P_1 and P_2, and the question is then whether it is possible to express an arbitrary point P_3 as a linear combination of given points P_1 and P_2. This question can be answered geometrically and algebraically—and the answers are, of course, equivalent.

A theorem from algebra states that a system of two linear equations in two unknowns has a unique solution if and only if the determinant formed from the coefficients is not zero:

$$\begin{vmatrix} x_1 & x_2 \\ y_1 & y_2 \end{vmatrix} = x_1 y_2 - x_2 y_1 \neq 0.$$

(This actually becomes evident upon solving the system by the method of elimination.) The condition can also be written in the form

$$\frac{x_1}{x_2} \neq \frac{y_1}{y_2},$$

which says that the coefficients of a and b are not in proportion. Geometrically it says that the points P_1 and P_2 are not on the same line through the origin;

that is, the vectors from the origin to P_1 and to P_2 are not parallel. For, if it holds, then there is no k such that

$$\begin{pmatrix} x_1 \\ y_1 \end{pmatrix} = k \begin{pmatrix} x_2 \\ y_2 \end{pmatrix}.$$

In summary, then, an arbitrary point P_3 can be represented as a linear combination of given points P_1 and P_2 if and only if P_1 and P_2 are not on the same line through the origin. In such a case the points P_1 and P_2 are said to *generate* the plane, which is then precisely the collection of all linear combinations of these points.

An interesting subset of points of the plane is generated by those linear combinations of the particular form

$$P = \alpha P_1 + (1 - \alpha) P_2,$$

in which the coefficients add up to 1: $\alpha + (1 - \alpha) = 1$. With coordinates as before: $P_1 = (x_1, y_1)$, $P_2 = (x_2, y_2)$, and $P = (x, y)$, the equation can be written in the form of a system of equations:

$$\begin{cases} x = \alpha x_1 + (1 - \alpha) x_2 \\ y = \alpha y_1 + (1 - \alpha) y_2, \end{cases}$$

or equivalently

$$\begin{cases} x - x_2 = \alpha(x_1 - x_2) \\ y - y_2 = \alpha(y_1 - y_2). \end{cases}$$

Thinking of these as conditions imposed on the coordinates x and y of P gives what are called *parametric equations* of a line through P_1 and P_2, in which α is called a parameter. That is, the conditions are satisfied by points P lying on that line, and only those points. This is seen by dividing one equation by the other:

$$\frac{x - x_2}{y - y_2} = \frac{x_1 - x_2}{y_1 - y_2},$$

which is a condition for similarity of triangles $P_1 P_2 Q$ and $P_2 PR$ in Figure 1–6. But these triangles are similar if and only if $\overline{P_1 P_2}$ is parallel to $\overline{P_2 P}$, equivalent to the condition that P lies on $\overline{P_1 P_2}$ (or on the extension of that segment).

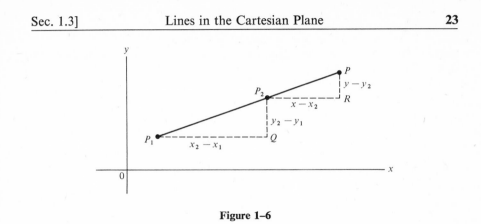

Figure 1–6

What has just been shown, then, is the very useful result that an arbitrary point P lies on the line through P_1 and P_2 if and only if it is expressible as a linear combination of those points in which the coefficients add up to 1:
$P = \alpha P_1 + (1 - \alpha)P_2$.

Specifying a value of the parameter α fixes the values of x and y, so each choice of α determines a point P. In particular, $\alpha = 1$ yields the point P_1, and $\alpha = 0$ the point P_2. A little experimentation should convince the reader that as α ranges over the real numbers from $-\infty$ to ∞, the corresponding point P ranges over the line through P_1 and P_2 from one end to the other.

Example 1–16. Consider the points $P_1 = (3, 1)$ and $P_2 = (2, -1)$. Linear combinations of the form

$$\begin{pmatrix} x \\ y \end{pmatrix} = \alpha \begin{pmatrix} 3 \\ 1 \end{pmatrix} + (1 - \alpha) \begin{pmatrix} 2 \\ -1 \end{pmatrix}$$

lie on the line through P_1 and P_2. Writing this out as a system yields the parametric equations of that line

$$\begin{cases} x = 3\alpha + 2(1 - \alpha) = \alpha + 2 \\ y = \alpha + (-1)(1 - \alpha) = 2\alpha - 1. \end{cases}$$

Notice that $\alpha = 1$ gives the point $(3, 1)$ and $\alpha = 0$ gives $(2, -1)$. The system can also be written

$$\begin{cases} x - 2 = \alpha \\ y + 1 = 2\alpha, \end{cases}$$

which implies that

$$\frac{y + 1}{x - 2} = 2,$$

or that

$$y + 1 = 2(x - 2),$$

which is the ordinary form of the equation of the line through P_1 and P_2.

Problems

1–11 Write the system

$$\begin{cases} 4a - 3b = 2 \\ a + 2b = 5 \end{cases}$$

as a single vector equation. Is there a unique solution? Are the vectors $(4, 1)$ and $(-3, 2)$ parallel?

1–12 An arbitrary point $P = (x, y)$ on the line joining $P_1 = (4, 1)$ and $P_2 = (-3, 2)$ can be expressed as the linear combination $\alpha P_1 + (1 - \alpha)P_2$. Obtain equivalent equations for x and y in terms of the parameter α. Eliminate α and so obtain the usual equation of the line through P_1 and P_2. Verify that the coordinates of P_1 and also the coordinates of P_2 satisfy the equation of the line.

1–13 Consider the points $P_1 = (2, -1)$ and $P_2 = (-4, 2)$.

(a) Does the equation $P_3 = aP_1 + bP_2$ have any solutions? (Or, can you find a and b so that the linear combination $aP_1 + bP_2$ yields a given point P_3?) If, for some P_3, it has a solution, is that solution unique?

(b) Obtain, as was done in the preceding problem, the equation of the line through P_1 and P_2. Is there anything unusual about this equation? (Is there anything unusual about the line?)

1–14 By using the formula $d = [(x_2 - x_1)^2 + (y_2 - y_1)^2]^{\frac{1}{2}}$ for the distance between two points P_1 and P_2, show that the parameter α in the parametric equation $P = \alpha P_1 + (1 - \alpha)P_2$ of the line through P_1 and P_2 is equal to the ratio of the distance from P_2 to P to the distance from P_2 to P_1. (That is, α is proportional to the distance from P_2 to P.)

1–15 Show directly that if the point $\alpha P_1 + (1 - \alpha)P_2$ lies to the right of both P_1 and P_2, then either α or $1 - \alpha$ is negative.

1.4 Convex Sets

Of particular interest and importance are those linear combinations $\alpha P_1 + (1 - \alpha)P_2$ in which the coefficients are both nonnegative:

$$\alpha \geq 0 \quad \text{and} \quad 1 - \alpha \geq 0,$$

or

$$0 \leq \alpha \leq 1.$$

If α is positive, and if (say) $x_1 < x_2$, then $\alpha x_1 < \alpha x_2$, and from $P = \alpha P_1 + (1 - \alpha)P_2$ there follows

$$x = \alpha x_1 + (1 - \alpha)x_2 = (\alpha x_1 - \alpha x_2) + x_2 < x_2.$$

Similarly, if $\alpha < 1$, then $(1 - \alpha)x_1 < (1 - \alpha)x_2$, and

$$x = \alpha x_1 + (1 - \alpha)x_2 = (1 - \alpha)(x_2 - x_1) + x_1 > x_1.$$

That is, if $0 \leq \alpha \leq 1$, then $x_1 \leq x \leq x_2$. (If it had been assumed that $x_1 > x_2$, this would be reversed.) So P lies between P_1 and P_2 horizontally, which means that P must lie *on the line segment joining P_1 and P_2.* (Analogous manipulation of the y-coordinates would have shown that P lies between P_1 and P_2 vertically.) Moreover, the argument can be reversed: If P lies between P_1 and P_2 on the line segment joining them, and $P = \alpha P_1 + (1 - \alpha)P_2$, then $0 \leq \alpha \leq 1$.

DEFINITION *A linear combination of the form* $\alpha P_1 + (1 - \alpha)P_2$ *with* $0 \leq \alpha \leq 1$ *is called a* convex combination *of P_1 and P_2.*

The argument above shows that the set of all convex combinations of two given points is precisely the set of points which make up the line segment joining those points.

It is worth pointing out that numbers α and $1 - \alpha$, which are both between 0 and 1, can be interpreted as *probabilities*. A convex combination of P_1 and P_2 will then sometimes be referred to as a *probability combination*. Moreover, the x-coordinate of such a combination is just the expected value of the x-coordinates of P_1 and P_2, and the y-coordinate of the combination is the expected value of their y-coordinates! Indeed, if one places a point mass m_1 at the point P_1 in the plane and a point mass m_2 at the point P_2, then the convex combination

$$\frac{m_1}{m_1 + m_2} P_1 + \frac{m_2}{m_1 + m_2} P_2$$

is just the center of gravity* of the system of two point masses. Thus, the

---

* The center of gravity of point masses in the plane is computed by carrying out the computations, given in Section 1.2 for points on a line, for the x and y coordinates separately, to obtain the x and y coordinates of the cg in the plane.

center of gravity is a point on the line segment joining the points where the two masses are placed. And a line segment joining two points can be thought of as the collection of all possible centers of gravity, corresponding to various distributions of masses at the two points.

The concept of linear combination, and in particular the notion of a convex combination, can be extended to the case of several points in the plane, as follows: A *linear combination* of points $P_1, P_2, \ldots, P_k$ is a combination of the form

$$\alpha_1 P_1 + \alpha_2 P_2 + \cdots + \alpha_k P_k.$$

If the α's are nonnegative and add up to 1, that is, if the coefficients define a probability distribution on k values, then the combination is said to be a *convex combination*:

$$0 \leq \alpha_i \leq 1, \qquad i = 1, \ldots, k$$

$$\alpha_1 + \alpha_2 + \cdots + \alpha_k = 1.$$

The term "convex combination" is used because the set of *all* such combinations is what is called a *convex set*.

DEFINITION   *A set of points is said to be convex if and only if the line segment joining each pair of its points is contained entirely in the set.*

The definition actually applies for sets in any number of dimensions, but will be applied here principally in the case of two dimensions (and incidentally in the case of one dimension).

Some examples of convex and nonconvex sets are shown in Figure 1–7. In the nonconvex examples, line segments are drawn with ends in the set, but which are not contained *entirely* in the set.

Convex

Nonconvex

Figure 1–7

It is asserted above that the set of all convex combinations of a finite set of points is a convex set. Another way of saying this is that the line segment joining any two convex combinations of a finite set of points consists only of convex combinations of that set of points. To show this it suffices to show that if P and Q are each convex combinations of $P_1, \ldots, P_k$, then the convex combination $\alpha P + (1 - \alpha)Q$, for $0 \le \alpha \le 1$, is *also* a convex combination of $P_1, \ldots, P_k$. Consider then these points:

$$P = a_1 P_1 + \cdots + a_k P_k, \qquad 0 \le a_i \le 1, \quad \sum a_i = 1,$$

$$Q = b_1 P_1 + \cdots + b_k P_k, \qquad 0 \le b_i \le 1, \quad \sum b_i = 1.$$

A linear combination of P and Q is

$$R = \alpha P + (1 - \alpha)Q = \alpha \sum a_i P_i + (1 - \alpha) \sum b_i P_i$$

$$= \sum [\alpha a_i + (1 - \alpha)b_i]P_i.$$

Thus, R is also a linear combination of $P_1, \cdots, P_k$; it remains to show that if $0 \le \alpha \le 1$, R is a convex combination—which simply requires showing that the coefficients in the expression for R in terms of the P_i's are nonnegative and add up to 1. They are surely nonnegative, being made up of sums and products of a_i, b_i, α, and $1 - \alpha$, which are all nonnegative. Their sum is

$$\sum [\alpha a_i + (1 - \alpha)b_i] = \alpha \sum a_i + (1 - \alpha) \sum b_i$$

$$= \alpha + 1 - \alpha = 1,$$

and so they are indeed coefficients that define a convex combination. So R is a convex combination of the P_i's, as was to be shown.

The set of convex combinations of $P_1, \ldots, P_k$ has an interesting interpretation in terms of mass. If mass m_1 is placed at $P_1, \ldots$ and mass m_k at P_k, then the center of gravity is precisely the convex combination:

$$cg = \frac{\sum m_i P_i}{\sum m_i} = \sum \left(\frac{m_i}{\sum m_i}\right) P_i.$$

If the relative mass $m_i / \sum m_i$ is called α_i, then $0 \le \alpha_i \le 1$, and

$$cg = \sum \alpha_i P_i.$$

Thus, the set of convex combinations of $P_1, \ldots, P_k$ is simply the set of possible centers of gravity corresponding to the various possible ways of depositing masses m_i at the points P_i.

Example 1–17. Let there be given the points $P_1 = (-1, 1)$, $P_2 = (2, 1)$, $P_3 = (3, 3)$, $P_4 = (1, 3)$, and $P_5 = (2, -1)$. The convex set of all convex combinations will have to include all line segments $\overline{P_i P_j}$, because a convex combination of two of these points is automatically a convex combination of all of them. Thus, if

$$P = \frac{1}{3} P_1 + \frac{2}{3} P_4,$$

then also

$$P = \frac{1}{3} P_1 + 0 \cdot P_2 + 0 \cdot P_3 + \frac{2}{3} P_4 + 0 \cdot P_5.$$

So the set of all convex combinations includes all of the quadrilateral that is shown in Figure 1–8 as a shaded set, because it includes all of the edges—and is convex. Moreover, a point outside that quadrilateral is *not* a convex combination, since it could not be the center of gravity of a mass system with masses only at $P_1, \ldots, P_5$. The point Q in Figure 1–8, for instance, could not be a center of gravity—unless one permitted negative masses; surely, if the masses were affixed to a weightless thin, stiff sheet, the balance point could not be at Q for any combination of masses at $P_1, \ldots, P_5$. Indeed, any set bigger than the indicated quadrilateral and including it would have in it points that are not convex combinations of the given points.

Although the argument in the example above is based on intuition about centers of gravity, the following result is general, and can be proved: *The convex set of all convex combinations of k given points is the smallest convex set containing those points.* This set is called the convex set *generated* by the k points. It can be visualized, in the case of points in the plane, by putting a peg at each point and stretching a rubber band so as to enclose all of the points.

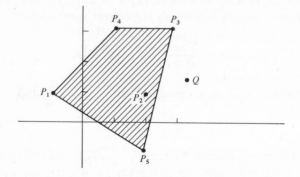

Figure 1–8

The region enclosed by the rubber band when it is released (and stretched around the most extreme points) is the set generated by the given points. It is a convex polygon of at most k sides.

That the set of convex combinations of $P_1, \ldots, P_k$ is the smallest convex set containing those points is seen by showing that it is included in any convex set containing them. Thus, suppose that T is a convex set including the points $P_1, P_2, \ldots, P_k$, and let P denote any convex combination of those points

$$P = \alpha_1 P_1 + \cdots + \alpha_k P_k, \qquad \text{where } 0 \leq \alpha_i \leq 1, \quad \sum \alpha_i = 1.$$

Then since T is convex, the point

$$Q_2 = \frac{\alpha_1 P_1 + \alpha_2 P_2}{\alpha_1 + \alpha_2}$$

belongs to T, being a convex combination of P_1 and P_2. And the point

$$Q_3 = \frac{(\alpha_1 + \alpha_2) Q_2 + \alpha_3 P_3}{\alpha_1 + \alpha_2 + \alpha_3} = \frac{\alpha_1 P_1 + \alpha_2 P_2 + \alpha_3 P_3}{\alpha_1 + \alpha_2 + \alpha_3}$$

belongs to T, being a convex combination of Q_2 and P_3. This process can be continued, with Q_4 a convex combination of Q_3 and P_4, and so on, until finally one obtains

$$Q_k = \frac{(\alpha_1 + \cdots + \alpha_{k-1}) Q_{k-1} + \alpha_k P_k}{\alpha_1 + \cdots + \alpha_k} = \frac{\alpha_1 P_1 + \cdots + \alpha_k P_k}{1}$$

belongs to T, being a convex combination of Q_{k-1} and P_k. But Q_k is just P, and so P belongs to T, as was to be shown.

The *convex hull* of an arbitrary set of points, finite in number or not, is defined to be the smallest convex set containing them. The convex hull can be visualized by the rubber band approach of the paragraph above. Figure 1–9

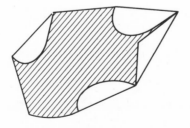

Figure 1–9

shows a set (shaded) and its convex hull (the set of all points included within the larger outline).

Problems

1–16 Each condition below defines a set of points in the plane. Determine (in each case) whether or not the set is convex.

(a) $x^2 + y^2 = 1$. (e) $y < x^2$. (i) $x + 2y \geq 3$.

(b) $x^2 + y^2 \geq 1$. (f) $xy = 0$. (j) $|x| + |y| \leq 1$.

(c) $x^2 + y^2 \leq 1$. (g) $xy > 0$. (k) $y = 2$.

(d) $y > x^2$. (h) $x + 2y = 3, 0 < x < 1$. (l) $x^2 + y^2 \leq 4, y \geq 1$.

1–17 Prove that the set defined by $x + y \leq 1, y \geq 0, x \geq 0$ is convex, as follows: Let P_1 and P_2 be points satisfying these conditions and show that if $0 \leq \alpha \leq 1$, then $\alpha P_1 + (1 - \alpha)P_2$ also satisfies the conditions.

1–18 Sketch the convex set generated by

(a) $\begin{pmatrix} 1 \\ 0 \end{pmatrix}, \begin{pmatrix} 0 \\ 1 \end{pmatrix}$.

(b) $\begin{pmatrix} 1 \\ 0 \end{pmatrix}, \begin{pmatrix} 0 \\ 1 \end{pmatrix}, \begin{pmatrix} -1 \\ 0 \end{pmatrix}, \begin{pmatrix} 0 \\ -1 \end{pmatrix}, \begin{pmatrix} 0 \\ 0 \end{pmatrix}$.

1–19 What is the convex hull of the indicated set in each part of Figure 1–10 below?

(a)

(b)

(c)

Figure 1–10

Chapter 2 Utility

An analytical study of a decision problem seems to require the assumption of a mathematical model or structure of *ordering* among the various possible consequences of taking an action in the face of a particular state of nature. These consequences, or future histories, or prospects are thus arranged in a row, one end being thought of as associated with desirable consequences— gains, rewards, happiness, or usefulness, and the other end of the scale as associated with undesirable consequences—losses, or payments, or discomfiture, or disaster. With such an ordering, it is the aim of the decision maker—really by definition of the word "desirable"—to achieve a consequence that is *maximal,* or as far toward the desirable end of the row of possible consequences as can be achieved.

In speaking about what one is faced with as the result of making a decision when nature is in a certain state, the term *consequence* has been used, because the situation has been brought about in part by the making of the decision. In discussing utility, it will be preferable to use the term *prospect*, without the implication that the future history has necessarily been brought upon one by his decision—which happens to be the case in decision theory but is not generally so in the theory of utility.

A prospect, or complete future history, is quite involved and just about impossible to specify precisely in a given case, if one really takes everything into account. Indeed, it is frequently impossible to take everything into account. For example, the prospect of receiving a million dollars implies a host of possible future histories, depending on what one then does with all that money. And it may be that the sudden wealth will affect mental health in an unforseeable way.

On the other hand, suppose one is sitting in a restaurant, choosing an entree from the choices steak, chicken, and fish. He may consider what the future history of the prospect "steak" for that particular meal will be. It could affect his digestion in a certain way, and it might infinitesimally ripple the beef market, which in turn affects the economy, and so in turn the diner. But the main part of the future history is simply in the enjoyment of that meal —at any rate, this is so as would concern the problem of decision among the entrees. Thus, it is practical to consider that a *prospect* is really a small aspect of all of future history that one can isolate as being pertinent to a given problem.

A mathematical analysis is simpler if it is possible to put prospects, not just in order, but on a *numerical* scale—to assign a numerical measure to each prospect. With reasonable assumptions about one's preferences among the various prospects, such an assignment, or *function*, can be achieved; it will be called *utility*. Utility is a function defined on the various prospects (or consequences) with which one is faced, measuring the relative desirability of these prospects on a numerical scale. Although it can be shown mathematically that such an assignment or function exists when one behaves according to a certain type of rationality, it is indeed not always easy to determine with precision just what that function is in a given case. (This difficulty is sometimes taken as substantially detracting from the usefulness of the theory.)

2.1 Preference Axioms

Every mathematical or logical structure is based on *axioms*—propositions so basic and elementary that they must be accepted without proof. Acceptance of the axioms then binds one, by rules of logic, to accept a whole string of consequences, or *theorems*, that follow from the axioms. The axioms to be presented here, dealing with preferences, will imply the existence of a *utility function*, which provides a numerical scale in terms of which the consequences of actions will be assumed to be measured.

A notion of preference, or relative desirability, among prospects will be assumed. In particular, the basic binary relation will be taken to be *at least as desirable as*, with this notation:

$P_1 \gtrsim P_2$ means: *Prospect P_1 is at least as desirable as prospect P_2.*

This relation can be used to define the equal desirability of two prospects; the notation is as follows:

$P_1 \sim P_2$ means: *Prospects P_1 and P_2 are equally desirable,* which is defined to mean that both $P_1 \succsim P_2$ and $P_2 \succsim P_1$. And then (strict) preference is expressed in terms of these:

$P_1 \succ P_2$ means: *Prospect P_1 is preferred over prospect P_2,*

a condition that (by definition) exists when and only when $P_1 \succsim P_2$, but P_1 and P_2 are not equally desirable.

The symbols $\succ$ and $\succsim$ will occasionally be used in the other direction, with the obvious meaning, namely, that the prospect on the small end of the symbol is the less desirable. The relation $\sim$ is clearly reflexive, that is, $P_1 \sim P_1$, if it is understood that a prospect is at least as good as itself. Moreover, it is by its very definition symmetric; that is, $P_1 \sim P_2$ is equivalent to $P_2 \sim P_1$.

Transitivity of these relations will have to be assumed; it will be one of the basic axioms to be given below. In particular, it will be *assumed* (as Axiom 2) that

$$P_1 \succsim P_2 \quad \text{and} \quad P_2 \succsim P_3 \quad \text{imply} \quad P_1 \succsim P_3.$$

From this can be shown the following consequences

(i)   If $P \sim Q$ and $Q \sim R$, then $P \sim R$.

(ii) If $P \succsim Q$ and $Q \sim R$, then $P \succsim R$.

(iii) If $P \succ Q$ and $Q \sim R$, then $P \succ R$.

(iv) If $P \succ Q$ and $Q \succ R$, then $P \succ R$.

These follow readily from the above axiom and from the definitions of the relations $\sim$ and $\succ$. Proofs are left as exercises (Problems 2–2 through 2–5).

It also will be necessary to have the concept of a "mixture" of prospects. If one is faced with the chance or probability p of a prospect P_1 and a probability $1 - p$ of a prospect P_2, this will be called a *random prospect*, and in particular it is said to be a *mixture* of the prospects P_1 and P_2. This mixture will be denoted by $[P_1, P_2]_p$.

More generally, if one faces P_1 with probability p_1, P_2 with probability $p_2, \ldots,$ and P_k with probability p_k, this is again a random prospect, called a mixture of $P_1, \ldots, P_k$ and denoted

$$[P_1, \ldots, P_k]_{(p_1, \ldots, p_k)}.$$

(In the particular case $k = 2$, the notation (p_1, p_2) in the subscript is simplified to just a p_1 since $p_2 = 1 - p_1$.) It will also be useful to consider random prospects composed of a countable infinite of prospects, P_1 with probability p_1, P_2 with probability p_2, and so forth; where $p_1 + p_2 + \cdots = 1$. Such a mixture will be written with the notation

$$[P_1, P_2, \ldots]_{(p_1, p_2, \ldots)}.$$

Example 2-1. Suppose that a gambling house (for a suitable entry fee) will pay off a number of dollars equal to the number of tosses of a fair coin necessary to get a heads. The probability of heads on the first toss is $\frac{1}{2}$, of tails on the first and heads on the second is $\frac{1}{4}$, of tails on the first two and heads on the third is $\frac{1}{8}$, and so on. Thus, the prospect facing the bettor is

$$[\$1, \$2, \$3, \ldots]_{(\frac{1}{2}, \frac{1}{4}, \frac{1}{8}, \ldots)}.$$

The axioms to be adopted are as follows:

AXIOM 1: *Given any prospects P and Q, then either*

$$P \succ Q, \quad or \quad P \prec Q, \quad or \quad P \sim Q.$$

AXIOM 2: *If $P \succsim Q$ and $Q \succsim R$, then $P \succsim R$.*

AXIOM 3: *If $P_1 \succ P_2$, then for any probability p and any prospect P, it follows that*

$$[P_1, P]_p \succ [P_2, P]_p.$$

AXIOM 4: *Given three prospects in the order $P_1 \succ P_2 \succ P_3$, there are mixtures $[P_1, P_3]_p$ and $[P_1, P_3]_r$ such that*

$$P_1 \succ [P_1, P_3]_p \succ P_2 \succ [P_1, P_3]_r \succ P_3.$$

A somewhat stronger assumption than Axiom 3 is the following:

AXIOM 3': *If $P_1, P_2, \ldots$ and $Q_1, Q_2, \ldots$ are sequences of prospects such that $P_i \succ Q_i$ for $i = 1, 2, \ldots$, then for any set of probabilities $\alpha_1, \alpha_2, \ldots$ ($\sum \alpha_i = 1$)*

$$[P_1, P_2, \ldots]_{(\alpha_1, \alpha_2, \ldots)} \succ [Q_1, Q_2, \ldots]_{(\alpha_1, \alpha_2, \ldots)}.$$

The significance of these axioms will be discussed next.

Axiom 1 states that, given any two prospects, either one is preferred over the other, or the other over the one, or they are equally desirable. It may be, especially in considering prospects that are rather involved and to some extent unknown, that an individual is hard put to say that one prospect is preferred or that they are equally desirable. For instance, a widower of fifty may find that two women are eager to marry him: one a twenty-eight-year-old who would like to raise a family, and the other a forty-seven-year-old who is quite companionable and sophisticated; is it then more or less or equally desirable to marry the younger one, with the tribulations of another crop of offspring, but the joys of youthful exuberance, or to marry the older one, who is content to make an interesting life for two? Perhaps the widower can order these prospects—but maybe he can't.

Axiom 2 is the axiom of *transitivity* of the preference relation. Its assumption precludes a type of inconsistency in the mathematical structure that may or may not accurately describe one's preferences. That is, people do sometimes act inconsistently—it may be that one will choose coffee over tea, tea over milk, and yet choose milk over coffee!

Axiom 3 says that improving one of the prospects in a finite mixture improves the mixture, and Axiom 3′ extends this notion to countably infinite mixtures. It is difficult to imagine a situation or context in which at least the version for finite mixtures would not be accepted.

The significance of Axiom 4 is not quite so obvious. Consider first an example.

Example 2–2. A young man just finishing school and about to embark on a career considers these three prospects

P_1: A cash balance of $10,000,000,

P_2: A cash balance of $1,000,

P_3: In debt to the amount $5,000.

(Perhaps he has a very rich father who can arrange any of these three prospects.) It is likely that the young may would order the prospects as follows:

$$P_1 \succ P_2 \succ P_3,$$

although it is indeed conceivable that another person might consider that P_3 is really the way to start out life that is best for building character. The question is this: Is there any mixture of P_1 and P_3 that is worse than P_2? That is, does every prospect that involves even the slightest chance of P_1, the millionaire prospect, rate higher than P_2? More specifically, does a probability of .01 of facing P_1 and .99 of facing P_3 involve P_1 enough so that this mixture is better than P_2? It will, of course, depend on the young man, but most young men would find some small but positive p (perhaps $p = .000001$) such that P_2 is better than $[P_1, P_3]_p$, even though P_1 is a rather delightful prospect. The further question then arises: Is there any prospect so absolutely magnificent (perhaps much more than \$10,000,000, and more than just money) that every mixture of P_1 and P_3 with a positive chance of getting P_1 is better than P_2?

A complementary or converse question can also be asked. Is there any prospect P_3 so terrible (worse than just being \$5,000 in debt, no doubt) that a positive chance of facing it as opposed to P_1 is always worse than P_2?

Axiom 3 says, when $P_1 \succ P_2 \succ P_3$, that there is no P_1 so wonderful that the slightest chance of encountering it instead of P_3 is better than any ordinary P_2; and that there is no P_3 so terrible that the slightest chance of encountering it instead of P_1 is worse than any ordinary P_2.

The axioms imply a number of useful and interesting consequences. For instance, if $P_1 \succ P_0$, it then follows that

(v) $P_1 \succ [P_1, P_0]_p \succ P_0$, for $0 < p < 1$.

That is, every nontrivial mixture of two *unequal* prospects lies between them. This is because P_1 can be thought of as $[P_1, P_1]_p$ and P_0 as $[P_0, P_0]_p$, so that (by Axiom 3)

$$P_1 = [P_1, P_1]_p \succ [P_1, P_0]_p \succ [P_0, P_0]_p = P_0.$$

(The equality of two prospects means that they are precisely the same prospect.)

Another consequence is that one mixture of two prospects is preferred over another if there is a stronger probability of the more desirable prospect in the first mixture

(vi) $[P_1, P_0]_p \succ [P_1, P_0]_q$, if $P_1 \succ P_0$ and $0 \le q < p \le 1$.

That is, as p increases from 0 to 1, the mixture $[P_1, P_0]_p$ becomes increasingly more desirable. To see that this is the case simply observe that

$$[P_1, P_0]_q = [[P_1, P_0]_p, P_0]_{q/p} \prec [[P_1, P_0]_p, [P_1, P_0]_p]_{q/p} = [P_1, P_0]_p.$$

The first equality in this series of relations is considered in Problem 2–6; the preference in the middle follows from Axiom 3, since $[P_1, P_0]_p$ is preferred to P_0.

A further consequence of the axioms is the existence of a *utility function*, to be taken up in the next section.

Problems

2–1 Show, for every prospect P, that $P \sim P$.

2–2 Prove Consequence (i), the transitivity of "equally desirable:" If $P \sim Q$ and $Q \sim R$, then $P \sim R$. (*Hint:* Write out what is meant by these relations, and apply the transitivity of $\gtrsim$.)

2–3 Prove Consequence (ii): If $P \gtrsim Q$ and $Q \sim R$, then $P \gtrsim R$.

2–4 Prove Consequence (iii): If $P \succ Q$ and $Q \sim R$, then $P \succ R$. (*Hint:* Observe what would follow if $P \sim R$.)

2–5 Prove Consequence (iv): If $P \succ Q$ and $Q \succ R$, then $P \succ R$. (*Hint:* Note the contradiction that would arise if $P \sim R$.)

2–6 Show that if $p \neq 0$, $q \le p$, and $P_0 \prec P_1$, then the mixture $[P_1, P_0]_q$ can be thought of as a mixture of $[P_1, P_0]_p$ and P_0 in which the probability of encountering $[P_1, P_0]_p$ is q/p.

$$[P_1, P_0]_q = [[P_1, P_0]_p, P_0]_{q/p}.$$

2.2 Coding Intermediate Prospects

It has been seen that given any two distinct prospects P_0 and P_1 with $P_0 \prec P_1$, all mixtures of these prospects lie between them in order of desirability:

$$P_0 \prec [P_1, P_0]_p \prec P_1.$$

Moreover, the larger the p the more desirable is the mixture. It will be shown next that if P is an arbitrary prospect between P_0 and P_1:

$$P_0 \prec P \prec P_1,$$

then there is some mixture of P_0 and P_1 equivalent to P.

THEOREM 1 *Given any two prospects P_0 and P_1 such that $P_0 \prec P_1$, and given any prospect P such that $P_0 \prec P \prec P_1$, then there is a unique number p between 0 and 1 such that $[P_1, P_0]_p$ is equivalent to P.*

This result means that the prospects intermediate to two given prospects can be thought of as lined up on the scale of numbers from 0 to 1, each being identified with a number on that scale. Equivalent prospects are located at the same point on the scale, and the ordering of prospects in desirability corresponds to ordering on the scale—with more desirable prospects being farther to the right.

PROOF OF THEOREM 1: Let P be an arbitrary prospect between P_0 and P_1:

$$P_0 \prec P \prec P_1.$$

It is known, from Axiom 4, that there is at least one nontrivial mixture of P_1 and P_0, which is preferred to P, and at least one nontrivial mixture over which P is preferred. (By *nontrivial* is meant a mixture in which both prospects enter with positive probability.) Thus, some of the numbers on the range from 0 to 1 yield mixtures that are worse than P, and some of them yield mixtures that are better than P; and the former are all to the left of each of the latter— that is, the probabilities for P_1 in the mixtures worse than P are all smaller than the probabilities for P_1 in the mixtures better than P.

Now, the set of probabilities r for which $[P_1, P_0]_r \prec P$ is a set of numbers. For this set of numbers there are lots of "upper bounds"—numbers greater than all of them; define p to be the *smallest* upper bound on the r's that give mixtures $[P_1, P_0]_r$ worse than P. (The smallest upper bound for any bounded set of numbers can be shown to exist.) This p is the probability that gives a mixture precisely as desirable as P:

$$[P_1, P_0]_p \sim P.$$

If this were not so, then by Axiom 1 the mixture $[P_1, P_0]_p$ is either more or less desirable than P. Each possibility will be considered, and it will be seen that each leads to a contradiction; thus, equal desirability is the only tenable conclusion.

First, suppose that $P \succ [P_1, P_0]_p$. Then (by Axiom 4) there is a nontrivial mixture of P_1 and $[P_1, P_0]_p$ which is between $[P_1, P_0]_p$ and P

$$[P_1, P_0]_p \prec [[P_1, P_0]_p, P_1]_s \prec P.$$

But this middle mixture can be seen to be equivalent to a mixture of P_1 and P_0, namely

$$[[P_1, P_0]_p, P_1]_s = [P_1, P_0]_{ps+1-s}.$$

Here, since $s < 1$ and $p < 1$, it follows that

$$ps + 1 - s > p.$$

This means that p is *not an upper bound* on r's that give mixtures $[P_1, P_0]_r$ worse than P. (A bigger r, namely $ps + 1 - s$, has been found.) Thus, the definition of p is contradicted.

Second, suppose that $P \prec [P_1, P_0]_p$. Then (by Axiom 4) there is a non-trivial mixture of $[P_1, P_0]_p$ and P_0 which is between P and $[P_1, P_0]_p$:

$$P \prec [[P_1, P_0]_p, P_0]_t \prec [P_1, P_0]_p,$$

where $t < 1$. This middle mixture is precisely a mixture of P_0 and P_1 with the probability pt for P_1, and $pt < p$. This means that p is not the *least* upper bound it was defined to be, again a contradiction. (For, pt is also an upper bound, yielding as it does a mixture of P_1 and P_0 which is preferred to P.)

That the p now defined is the *only* probability that gives a mixture equal to the given P follows from the fact that a different p would give a mixture that is either better or worse than P. (This completes the proof of Theorem 1.)

Having seen that all prospects intermediate to two given prospects can be thought of as lined up on the scale of numbers from 0 to 1, one can easily construct a *utility function*—a coding of utilities that gives a numerical representation of preferences—by taking the utility of a prospect to be just the number on the scale from 0 to 1 where it happens to fall (according to Theorem 1). Thus, if $P \sim [P_1, P_0]_p$, define

$$u(P) = p.$$

This works for all prospects between P_0 and P_1, as well as for P_0 and P_1 themselves

$$u(P_0) = 0, \quad \text{and} \quad u(P_1) = 1.$$

Example 2–3.   A diner is to choose between beef, chicken, and fish. His preferences are as follows

$$\text{fish} \prec \text{chicken} \prec \text{beef}.$$

Upon introspection, he decides that a random prospect offering him beef with probability $\frac{1}{4}$ and fish with probability $\frac{3}{4}$ is precisely as desirable as the (nonrandom) prospect of chicken:

$$[\text{beef, fish}]_{\frac{1}{4}} \sim \text{chicken}.$$

If he assigns utility 0 to fish and utility 1 to beef, then the utility assigned to the random prospect is $\frac{1}{4}$; this in turn is also his utility for chicken, which is precisely as desirable as the random prospect. Thus,

$$u(\text{fish}) = 0, \qquad u(\text{chicken}) = \tfrac{1}{4}, \qquad u(\text{beef}) = 1.$$

The utility function, defined for any P between given P_0 and P_1 as the value p in the mixture $[P_1, P_0]_p$, which is equivalent to P, satisfies certain important properties:

Utility Property A: If $P \succ Q$, then $u(P) \geq u(Q)$.

Utility Property B: $u([P, Q]_r) = ru(P) + (1 - r)u(Q)$.

Property A, for any prospects P and Q between P_0 and P_1, follows from the fact that mixtures of P_0 and P_1 are ordered according to the proportion of P_1 in the mixture; thus, if $P = [P_1, P_0]_p$ and $Q = [P_1, P_0]_q$, and $P \succ Q$, then $p > q$. But $u(P) = p$ and $u(Q) = q$, which yields Property A. To obtain Property B, for these P and Q, observe that

$$[P, Q]_r = [[P_1, P_0]_p, [P_1, P_0]_q]_r = [P_1, P_0]_{pr + q(1-r)},$$

which implies that the utility in $[P, Q]_r$ is

$$u([PQ]_r) = pr + q(1 - r) = ru(P) + (1-r)u(Q).$$

Property B can be expressed in terms of expectation: When faced with a mixed prospect $[P, Q]_r$, the utility is a random variable with possible values $u(P)$ and $u(Q)$ and corresponding probabilities r and $1 - r$; the expected utility is therefore $ru(P) + (1 - r)u(Q)$, which is the utility assigned to the random prospect. *The utility of a random prospect is the expected value of the utility.*

As constructed above, the utility of prospects intermediate to two given prospects P_0 and P_1 is uniquely defined. But any linear function of this utility would also satisfy Utility Properties A and B, and serve just as well as a utility function. Suppose, then, one were to define a function $v(P)$ on prospects between P_0 and P_1 as follows:

$$v(P) = au(P) + b,$$

for $a > 0$. This has the effect of shifting the origin and introducing a scale factor; the utility of P_0 and P_1 in this new scheme would be

$$v(P_0) = b \quad \text{and} \quad v(P_1) = a + b.$$

That $v(P)$ satisfies Property A is easy to see; to obtain Property B it is only necessary to compute, using Property B for $u(P)$:

$$v([P, Q]_r) = au([P, Q]_r) + b$$
$$= a[ru(P) + (1 - r)u(Q)] + b$$
$$= r[au(P) + b] + (1 - r)[au(Q) + b]$$
$$= rv(P) + (1 - r)v(Q).$$

Example 2-4. The diner of Example 2-3 decides after some reflection that his utilities for the prospects of beef, chicken, and fish are fairly represented as follows:

$$v(\text{beef}) = 5, \quad v(\text{chicken}) = 2, \quad v(\text{fish}) = 1.$$

He would then be indifferent to chicken and a mixture of beef and fish, with probability p of beef, provided that

$$v([\text{beef, fish}]_p) = 5p + 1 \cdot (1 - p) = 4p + 1 = v(\text{chicken}) = 2.$$

That is, if $p = \frac{1}{4}$ the mixture has the same utility as does chicken. Notice that these utilities are essentially no different than those in Example 2-3, being obtainable by a linear transformation:

$$v(P) = 4u(P) + 1.$$

The matter of utilities for prospects that are not between two given prospects P_0 and P_1 has been studiously avoided, as has the natural question of whether or not utility depends essentially on the selection of P_0 and P_1. The next section will define utilities for all prospects, given a system of prospects and preference axioms 1–4; these will not depend essentially on the choice of P_0 and P_1 in that starting with a different choice would simply lead to a utility related to the first by linear transformation. The generally defined utility function will satisfy Utility Properties A and B.

2.3 Utility for Arbitrary Prospects*

It remains to define utility for prospects that are not between P_0 and P_1, and to show that the extended function still satisfies Properties A and B for a

---

* This section may be treated as extra for the more mathematically inclined and sophisticated, if the reader is willing to accept the result of Theorem 2 on page 45.

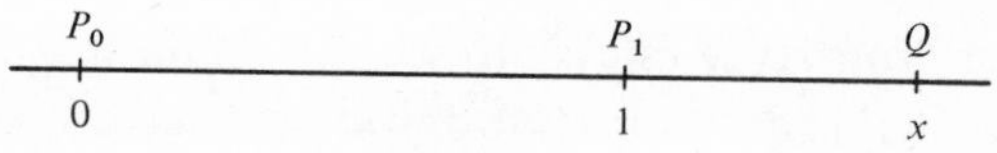

Figure 2–1

utility function. Suppose first that a prospect Q is preferred to P_1: $P_0 \prec P_1$
$\prec Q$. This situation is represented in Figure 2–1, in which P_0 and P_1 are placed
on a scale opposite their utilities, 0 and 1, respectively. The prospect Q is
shown to the right of P_1, being preferred to P_1, and opposite a utility x which
is now to be defined. The definition is to be made so that, in particular,
utility Property B is satisfied. For prospects P_0, P_1, and Q there is a mixture
of Q and P_0 which is as desirable as P_1:

$$P_1 \sim [Q, P_0]_y.$$

But Property B would require

$$u(P_1) = 1 = yu(Q) + (1 - y)u(P_0) = yx + 0$$

so that $x = 1/y$. Thus, the utility of Q must be defined to be $1/y$.
   Similarly, if R is a prospect less desirable than P_0, there is a mixture
$[P_1, R]_z$ just as desirable as P_0 (see Figure 2–2). Then, if utility Property B
is to hold, and if x denotes $u(R)$, one has

$$u(Q) = 0 = zu(P_1) + (1 - z)u(R) = z \cdot 1 + (1 - z)x,$$

from which $u(R)$, or x, must be defined as $-z/(1 - z)$.
   It should now be reasonable to expect that the extended utility function
satisfies Properties A and B (for all prospects P, Q). A formal proof will be
given next, but this may be omitted if the reader wishes to jump directly to
the statement of Theorem 2.
   To show that the extended utility function (now defined and finite for *all*
prospects) satisfies Utility Properties A and B one proceeds as follows. Let P
and Q be any prospects for which it is desired to establish A and B, and let
P_0^* and P_1^* be the least desirable and most desirable, respectively, among the

```
      R                    P₀                          P₁
  ----+--------------------+---------------------------+----
      x                    0                           1
```

Figure 2–2

prospects P_0, P_1, P, and Q. Although the utility $u(\cdot)$ was defined in terms of the given P_0 and P_1, it could have been defined by starting with P_0^* and P_1^*—resulting in a function $u^*(\cdot)$ which is defined for all prospects between P_0^* and P_1^* and obeys Properties A and B for such prospects. Let R be any such prospect that is preferred to P_1. Then, by definition of $u(R)$, P_1 is the mixture

$$P_1 = [R, P_0]_{1/u(R)},$$

so that

$$u^*(P_1) = \frac{1}{u(R)} u^*(R) + \left(1 - \frac{1}{u(R)}\right) u^*(P_0),$$

or (upon solving for $u^*(R)$)

$$u^*(R) = [u^*(P_1) - u^*(P_0)]u(R) + u^*(P_0).$$

Similarly, if R were a prospect (between P_0^* and P_1^*) less desirable than P_0, one would have, by definition of $u(R)$

$$P_0 = [P_1, R]_{u(R)/(u(R) - 1)}$$

whence

$$u^*(P_0) = \frac{u(R)}{u(R) - 1} u^*(P_1) + \frac{-1}{u(R) - 1} u^*(R).$$

Solving this for $u^*(R)$ again yields

$$u^*(R) = [u^*(P_1) - u^*(P_0)]u(R) + u^*(P_0),$$

so in either case, $R \succ P_1$ or $R \prec P_0$:

$$u(R) = \alpha u^*(R) + \beta,$$

where α and β are constants (involving $u^*(P_0)$ and $u^*(P_1)$), and where u^* satisfies Properties A and B. Moreover, if $P_0 \precsim R \precsim P_1$, where $R = [P_1, P_0]_r$, then

$$u^*(R) = r u^*(P_1) + (1 - r) u^*(P_0)$$
$$= r[u^*(P_1) - u^*(P_0)] + u^*(P_0)$$
$$= u(R)[u^*(P_1) - u^*(P_0)] + u^*(P_0),$$

which is again the same linear relation between $u(R)$ and $u^*(R)$. This being the case, it follows that for any P and Q between P_0^* and P_1^*,

$$
\begin{aligned}
u([P, Q]_x) &= \alpha u^*([P, Q]_x) + \beta \\
&= \alpha[xu^*(P) + (1 - x)u^*(Q)] + \beta x + \beta(1 - x) \\
&= xu(P) + (1 - x)u(Q),
\end{aligned}
$$

which is Property B for the extended $u(\cdot)$. Also, if $P \prec Q$,

$$
u(P) = \alpha u^*(P) + \beta < \alpha u^*(Q) + \beta = u(Q),
$$

which is Property A for the extended $u(\cdot)$.

The utility function, now defined for all prospects, appears to be dependent on the prospects P_0 and P_1 chosen arbitrarily to be assigned utilities 0 and 1, respectively. Although it is true that a different function would be obtained if a different pair of prospects were used, this new function is related to the old by a linear transformation (such as relates, for example, degrees Fahrenheit and degrees Centigrade). Thus, utility is unique up to a linear transformation. To see this, consider a function $v(P)$ defined according to the above scheme but starting with Q_0 and Q_1 (with $Q_0 \prec Q_1$), and suppose (to take a specific case) that

$$
P_0 \prec P_1 \prec Q_0 \prec Q_1.
$$

Let y and z be defined by the following equivalences

$$
P_1 \sim [Q_0, P_0]_y \sim [Q_1, P_0]_z,
$$

so that

$$
u(Q_0) = \frac{1}{y} \quad \text{and} \quad u(Q_1) = \frac{1}{z}.
$$

Now consider any prospect P; for definiteness, let P be between P_0 and P_1:

$$
P_0 \prec P \prec P_1 \prec Q_0 \prec Q_1.
$$

Let p and w be defined by the equivalences

$$
P \sim [P_1, P_0]_p, \qquad Q_0 \sim [Q_1, P]_w,
$$

so that

$$u(P) = p, \quad \text{and} \quad v(P) = \frac{-w}{1 - w}.$$

Then (applying Property B),

$$\frac{1}{y} = u(Q_0) = wu(Q_1) + (1 - w)u(P)$$

$$= \frac{w}{z} + (1 - w)p,$$

whence (solving for w and substituting in $v(P)$)

$$v(P) = \frac{-w}{1 - w} = \frac{p - \dfrac{1}{y}}{\dfrac{1}{z} - \dfrac{1}{y}} = \frac{u(P) - u(Q_0)}{u(Q_1) - u(Q_0)}.$$

Thus, $v(P)$ is a linear function of $u(P)$, so constructed that $v(Q_0) = 0$ and $v(Q_1) = 1$. (Other cases are handled similarly.)

In summary, there has thus been established the following theorem.

THEOREM 2   *If Axioms 1 to 4 are accepted, there follows the existence of a finite number $u(P)$ associated with each prospect P satisfying the properties*

$$A: \quad P \succ Q \text{ implies } u(P) > u(Q),$$

$$B: \quad u([P, Q]_r) = ru(P) + (1 - r)u(Q).$$

Property B for utility functions can be strengthened to apply to mixtures of a countably infinite number of prospects, provided one assumes the stronger Axiom 3′. First it will be shown that with this stronger assumption utility is a *bounded* function:

THEOREM 3   *If Axioms 1 to 4 and 3′ are assumed, the utility function is bounded. That is, for some constant B,*

$$|u(P)| \leq B, \quad \text{for all } P.$$

This is proved by assuming that $u(P)$ is not bounded and obtaining a contradiction. Let P_1 be a prospect whose utility is $u(P_1) = 1$. Let P_2 be such that $u(P_2) \geq 2$, (which exists if $u(P)$ is *not* bounded). Similarly define $P_3, P_4, \ldots$ so that

$$u(P_n) \geq 2^{n-1}.$$

Then $P_n \succ P_1$ (for $n = 2, 3, \ldots$) and so, given a probability vector $(\alpha_1, \alpha_2, \alpha_3, \ldots)$,

$$R_n \equiv [P_{n+1}, P_{n+2}, \ldots]_{(\alpha_{n+1}, \alpha_{n+2}, \ldots)} \succ [P_1, P_1, \ldots]_{(\alpha_{n+1}, \ldots)} = P_1.$$

This in turn means that $u(R_n) \succ u(P_1) = 1$. Now

$$P \equiv [P_1, P_2, \ldots]_{(\alpha_1, \alpha_2, \ldots)} = [P_1, \ldots, P_n, R_n]_{(\alpha_1, \ldots, \alpha_n, q_n)},$$

where

$$q_n = 1 - \alpha_1 - \cdots - \alpha_n \to 0, \quad \text{as } n \to \infty.$$

Thus,

$$u(P) = \alpha_1 u(P_1) + \cdots + \alpha_n u(P_n) + q_n u(R_n).$$

If one takes $\alpha_n = 2^{-n}$,

$$u(P) \geq \frac{1}{2} \cdot 1 + \frac{1}{2^2} \cdot 2 + \cdots + \frac{1}{2^n} \cdot 2^{n-1} + u(R_n) \cdot \frac{1}{2^{n-1}}$$

$$\geq \frac{n}{2} + \frac{1}{2^{n-1}}.$$

Since $u(P)$ exceeds any arbitrary number $n/2$, it is not a finite number—a contradiction. Hence, Theorem 3 is proved.

THEOREM 4 *If Axioms 1 to 4 and 3' are assumed, the utility of a mixture of a countably infinite number of prospects is the expected value of the utility of those prospects*:

$$u([P_1, P_2, \ldots]_{(\alpha_1, \alpha_2, \ldots)}) = \alpha_1 u(P_1) + \alpha_2 u(P_2) + \cdots.$$

With the same notation as in the proof above, one has in the same way

$$u(P) = \alpha_1 u(P_1) + \cdots + \alpha_n u(P_n) + q_n u(R_n).$$

But then,

$$u(P) - \sum_{1}^{n} u(P_j)\alpha_j = q_n u(R_n) \to 0,$$

the approach to zero a consequence of $q_n \to 0$ and the fact (Theorem 3) that $u(R_n)$ is bounded. Hence the asserted result holds.

Problems

2–7 Show that $P \sim Q$ if and only if $u(P) = u(Q)$. (That is, two prospects are equally desirable if and only if they have the same utility.)

2–8 Referring to Example 2–3, and again assuming that the mixture [beef, fish]$_{\frac{1}{4}}$ is as desirable as chicken,
   (a) determine the utility of chicken if $u(\text{beef}) = 1$, $u(\text{fish}) = 0$.
   (b) determine the utility of fish if $u(\text{chicken}) = 0$, $u(\text{beef}) = 1$.
   (c) determine the utility of beef if $u(\text{fish}) = 0$, $u(\text{chicken}) = 1$.

2–9 If $u(P) = 0$, $u(Q) = 1$, and $u(R) = 2$, determine the utility of the mixture $[P, Q, R]_{(\frac{1}{4}, \frac{1}{4}, \frac{1}{2})}$, that is, of facing P with probability $\frac{1}{4}$, Q with probability $\frac{1}{4}$, and R with probability $\frac{1}{2}$.

2–10 A man is convinced that he is allergic to fish, and becomes excruciatingly ill after eating it. Suppose that he assigns utilities as follows: $u(\text{beef}) = 1$, $u(\text{chicken}) = 0$, and $u(\text{fish}) = -100$.
   (a) Is there a p less than 1 such that the mixture [fish, beef]$_p$ is preferred to chicken?
   (b) Suppose instead the man decides that there is no mixture of fish and beef with a positive probability of getting fish that would be better than chicken. Show that his utility for fish could not be a finite number.

2–11 A man is deliriously happy eating filet mignon, but can take or leave fish and chicken, with a slight preference to chicken. Suppose his utilities are $u(\text{fish}) = 0$, $u(\text{chicken}) = a$, and $u(\text{beef}) = 1$.
   (a) If $a = .01$, determine a mixture of fish and beef over which chicken is preferred.
   (b) Show that if even the slightest chance of getting beef in a mixture of beef and fish is preferred over chicken, then a must be 0.

2–12 Employees A and B each rate two-week vacations with pay. B comes to A with the proposition that they "toss" (perhaps a biased coin) for the vacations, with the winner getting four weeks and the loser none. The reason for B's proposition is that he desperately wants to take a trip for which two weeks is insufficient time. On the other hand, A very much wants some vacation, but is only mildly excited over having the extra time. After some introspection, A decides that if the probability p of his winning the toss is as high as $\frac{7}{8}$, then he will be indifferent to the status quo (no bet) and the chance of getting four weeks. If $u_A(P)$ denotes his utility of the prospect P, and if

u_A(status quo) = 1, and u_A(no vacation) = 0, what does this imply about his utility for getting a four-week rather than a two-week vacation? Can you construct utilities $u_B(P)$ for B so that tossing as proposed is preferred by B to the status quo, even with $p = \frac{7}{8}$?

2.4 Utility for Money

In a good many practical situations, particularly in business, prospects are expressible in terms of amounts of money. These amounts are measured as numbers, of dollars (or cents or pounds or francs). In such cases one might be tempted to treat the number of dollars (say) as utility, or as proportional to utility: $u(M) = M$, or $u(M) = kM$. Even discounting the possibility that such a utility function overlooks other aspects of prospects (considerations such as ethics or humanitarianism), this scale of values is not usually a totally adequate basis in terms of which to analyze decision problems involving money.

For one thing, the function $u(M) = M$ is not a bounded function of M, at least if M is allowed to range over all real numbers. The example of the "St. Petersburg Paradox" illustrates the difficulty:

Example 2–5.   You are offered, for a fee, the following random prospect. You will be given \$$2^N$ if in repeated tosses of a coin the first heads does not appear until the Nth toss. What entry fee would you be willing to pay?

If money is utility, (that is, $u(M) = M$), you should be willing to pay any fee up to the expected value of the payoff, because your utility would not be decreased by so doing. It can be shown that the probability of obtaining heads for the first time on the Nth toss is $\frac{1}{2}^N$, and accepting this one obtains as the expected payoff:

$$E(\text{Payoff}) = \sum_1^\infty 2^N \cdot \frac{1}{2^N} = 1 + 1 + 1 + \cdots = \infty.$$

(That is, the sum is not a finite number; for it would take only finitely many of the 1's to obtain a sum *larger* than any given number.) Despite the infinite expected payoff, it is found that people generally will not pay even a large but finite entry fee for the proposed game. (For instance, ask yourself whether *you* would pay \$50 for the privilege of playing the game.)

On the other hand, if it is assumed that one's utility function is

$$u(M) = \begin{cases} 2^M & \text{if } M \le 20, \\ 2^{20} = 1{,}048{,}576 & \text{if } M > 20, \end{cases}$$

the expected utility of the payoff is

$$E[u(\text{Payoff})] = \sum_{1}^{20} 2^N \cdot \frac{1}{2^N} + \sum_{21}^{\infty} (2^{20}) \frac{1}{2^N} = 20 + \left(\frac{1}{2} + \frac{1}{4} + \cdots\right) = 21.$$

The game then has the same utility as $21.

Another aspect of the paradox is that no one could in fact offer the game honestly—no one has 2^{40} to pay out in the event of 39 tails in a row before the first heads, for example. On the other hand, if a gambling house with a capital of $1,048,576 agrees to pay out the entire amount if N is 20 or more, the expected payoff is $21, as the computation above also shows.

Even without the paradox arising from permitting one's capital M to have any finite value, as in the example above, most people's utility for money is not strictly linear, although it may be approximately linear over a restricted range of values of M. For instance, a total capital of a few cents is almost as bad as no capital at all, so that the utility in one or two pennies is essentially 0. On the other hand, having two billion dollars is not much more attractive than having one billion dollars—certainly not twice as attractive! Utility seems to taper off as the amount of capital reaches these heights. Figure 2–3 shows a utility function $u(M)$ plotted against M that is something like most people's utility functions for money.

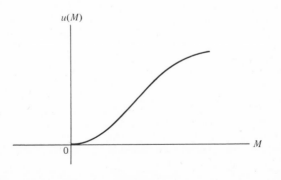

Figure 2–3

The function shown in Figure 2–3 is an increasing function of M, corresponding to the assumption that the greater the monetary value of a prospect, the greater its desirability. It is unusual to encounter a situation in which a greater amount of capital is "worth" less than a smaller amount, for one could bury or give away the excess amount and so achieve the utility of the smaller amount.

The monotonic nature of the curve representing utility for money would show that if one is offered a favorable chance prospect involving money repeatedly, he should accept the offer. That is, if there is a net monetary gain each time, his monetary assets increase—and therefore his utility increases. An example will help to point this up.

Example 2–6. A man has $4 and is offered the prospect [$10, $0]$_{\frac{1}{2}}$. That is, a coin is to be tossed, and if he wins he gets $6 more; if he loses, he loses the $4 he has. The expected monetary status, if he takes the prospect, is $5, or an increase of $1. However, his action is not to be based on expected monetary gain, but on expected utility. Suppose, then, that his utility for money at this point is as shown in Figure 2–4; thus, $u(0) = 0$, $u(4) = 6$, and $u(10) = 10$ In this case,

$$u(\text{Bet}) = \frac{1}{2} u(0) + \frac{1}{2} u(10) = 5,$$

which is less than the utility of not betting: $u(4) = 6$. So not betting is preferred to betting, even though the bet is favorable in terms of money. Suppose, however, that the bet is offered repeatedly, in an indefinitely long sequence of trials. In such a sequence, the relative frequency of heads tends to stabilize and to get and remain close to $\frac{1}{2}$; but in this case there is actually

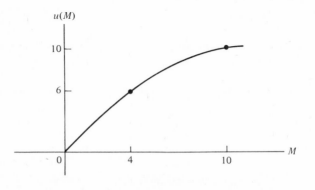

Figure 2–4

a net positive gain in money, which means a net increase in utility—if utility is an increasing function of money. It pays to accept such a sequence of random prospects.

Thus, it is evident in the example above that expected utility is the appropriate guide for action in a *single* experiment, rather than expected money gain, but that in a long sequence of experiments the expected money gain is relevant. This may seem to contradict the notion that even expected utility is an expected value, and should be related to a long sequence of trials. However, the appropriate long sequence in that case would have to be an imagined succession of lifetimes, with rebirth or renewal (after each one) so that the same point in life can again be reached. (Equivalently, one could imagine a large number of people with identical utility functions faced with the same single experiment.) In this case the "expected value" of utility does have the usual interpretation in terms of long-run average. But the successively offered bets in a single lifetime do not really constitute a sequence of identical decision problems; for, the monetary status changes after each toss, and so a different portion of the utility curve would govern each time.

In dealing with a given problem it is often convenient to focus attention on the small portion of the curve representing the function $u(M)$, or one's utility for money, that is significant for the given problem at hand. In so doing it is natural to label the money axis in terms of the amount of money to be lost or gained, rather than in terms of total assets. But it must be kept in mind that $u(M)$, if M denotes an increase or decrease from an initial status M_0, is really $u(M + M_0)$. Thus, a person's utility function may seem to be different in different situations simply because he is operating around different points on the overall utility curve. If his utility for money is as shown in Figure 2–3, then clearly it is possible for him to have (locally) a utility for gain or loss that is concave down in some instances, and concave up in others, as shown in

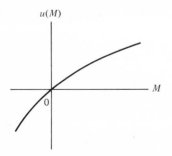

Figure 2–5 (a)

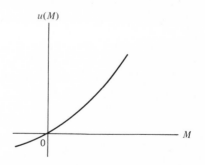

Figure 2–5 (b)

Figures 2–5(a) and 2–5(b). Figure 2–5(b) would be appropriate if he has an initial capital near zero in Figure 2–3, and Figure 2–5(a) would be appropriate for a large initial capital.

It has already been observed that the utility scale is only uniquely determined up to a linear transformation, so it is permissible to label any point on the utility axis (such as $u(M_0)$) as 0, and to use an arbitrary unit on that axis as one unit of utility (sometimes called one *utile*).

Example 2–7. A contractor has the opportunity to bid either on job A or on job B. It will cost him \$2,500 to prepare the bid for job A, and he estimates a probability .6 that he will get the job, which will net him a profit of \$25,000 if the weather is good or \$15,000 if the weather is bad. It will cost him \$5,000 to prepare the bid for job B, and he estimates a probability .5 that he will get the job, which will net him a profit of \$35,000 if the weather is good and \$25,000 if it is bad. The probability of good weather is set at .8. Which bid should he prepare if his utility for money (relative to his present capital) is given by curve I in Figure 2–6?

The utility of bidding on job A is computed as the following average

$$u(b_A) = u(-\$2,500) \times .4 + u(\text{job A}) \times .6.$$

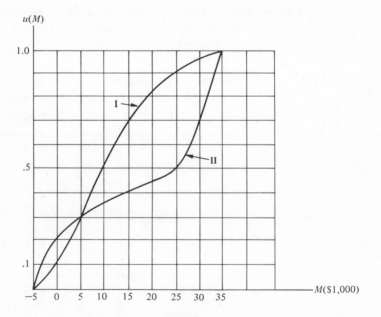

Figure 2–6

The utility of job A, in turn, is an average of the utilities under the two types of weather, so that

$$u(b_A) = .05 \times .4 + .6 \times [u(\$25,000) \times .8 + u(\$15,000) \times .2]$$
$$= .02 + .6 \times (.9 \times .8 + .7 \times .2) = .536.$$

Similarly, the utility of bidding on job B is

$$u(b_B) = u(-\$5,000) \times .5 + .5 \times [u(\$35,000) \times .8 + u(\$25,000) \times .2]$$
$$= 0 + .5 \times (1.0 \times .8 + .9 \times .2) = .490.$$

Bidding on job A has the greater utility and is therefore preferred.

Problems

2–13 A man needs \$6.00 to buy a ticket to a certain ball game, but he has only \$3.00. He wants to see the game badly. Are the numbers of dollars good representatives of his utility? Devise a graph that would better indicate his utility as a function of how much money he has at the time. In terms of this utility scale, determine his utility in tossing a coin for his \$3.00, double or nothing. Is his utility improved in playing this game—that is, should he play it?

2–14 Determine the expected reward in the St. Petersburg game
   (a) if the house (which offers the game) will pay out at most \$1,024 (that is, 2^N if $2^N \le 1,024$, otherwise just \$1,024).
   (b) if the reward $2^{N/2}$ is offered if the first heads occurs on the Nth trial.
   (c) if the reward is $\$N$. [Here you will need to write the sum as

$$\left(\frac{1}{2} + \frac{1}{4} + \frac{1}{8} + \cdots\right) + \left(\frac{1}{4} + \frac{1}{8} + \cdots\right) + \left(\frac{1}{8} + \frac{1}{16} + \cdots\right) + \cdots$$

and add together the sums in the parentheses.]

2–15 You are asked to choose between keeping \$5 (your entire capital) and the random prospect of \$0 or $\$N$ according to the toss of a coin. Assuming $u(0) = 0$, express $u(N)$ in terms of $u(5)$ if you choose N so that these prospects are equally desirable. Suppose next you choose M so that you are indifferent to the prospect of keeping your current capital of \$5 and the random prospect of losing the \$5 with probability 5/6 and gaining $\$(M - 5)$ with probability $\frac{1}{6}$. Determine $u(M)$, again in terms of $u(5)$. Assign values to M and N on the assumption that your \$5 represents your entertainment budget when alone in a strange city over a weekend, and so determine corresponding points on your utility for money in that context.

2–16 Determine the preferred bid in Example 2–7, if utility is given by curve II in Figure 2–6 (instead of by curve I, as in that example).

2.5 Bets, Fair and Unfair

A *bet* is a random or mixed prospect of the type encountered in Example 2–5 of the preceding section: One starts with an initial capital M_0 and according to the outcome of an experiment of chance ends up either with M_L, an amount less than M_0, or with M_W, an amount greater than M_0. In the former case he "loses," his capital being reduced by the amount $y = M_0 - M_L$, and in the latter case he "wins," his capital being increased by the amount $x = M_W - M_0$. It is said that he "puts up" y and his opponent "puts up" x, the winner taking both amounts. (For example, if he wins, he recovers the y he put up and takes an additional x from his opponent, his net gain being x.)

DEFINITION *The* money odds *in such a bet are said to be "y to x" that one wins the bet, or y/x. The* probability odds *in such a bet are said to be "p to $1 - p$" that one wins the bet, or $p/(1 - p)$, where p is the probability that he wins. A bet is said to be a* fair *bet if the probability odds and the money odds are equal.*

A fair bet is "fair" in the sense that if one person is betting against another in a fair bet, neither is favored. For, if the bet is fair, then

$$\frac{y}{x} = \frac{p}{1 - p}, \quad \text{or} \quad y(1 - p) - px = 0.$$

Substitution of $y = M_W - M_0$ and $x = M_0 - M_L$ yields

$$(M_0 - M_L)(1 - p) - (M_W - M_0)p = 0,$$

or

$$pM_W + (1 - p)M_L = M_0.$$

Since the left member of the equation is the expected capital after the bet, a fair bet is one in which the expected capital after the bet is equal to the capital before the bet. Thus, there is no loss nor gain in capital on the part of the one bettor—and therefore none on the part of his opponent. On the other hand, if one player experienced a net expected loss, it would have to come from the other, and the bet would not be "fair."

Example 2–8. Suppose A puts up $40 against $20 put up by B, the winner taking both amounts, after an experiment of chance with two possible outcomes. The money odds are 40/20 or 2 to 1 that A will win. The odds are said to be "2 to 1 in favor of A's winning," and they "favor" A if he has to put up more money than B. For a *fair* bet, the experiment of chance would have to involve a probability that A wins equal to

$$p = P(A \text{ wins}) = \frac{2}{2 + 1} = \frac{2}{3}.$$

Thus, the toss of an ordinary coin, with A winning if heads results, is not a fair bet when the payments are as given. If A has an initial capital of \$100 his final capital will be either \$60 (if he loses) or \$120 (if he wins, with probabilities (for a fair bet) $\frac{1}{3}$ and $\frac{2}{3}$, respectively. The expected final capital is then

$$\$60 \times \frac{1}{3} + \$120 \times \frac{2}{3} = \$100,$$

which is the original capital. Notice that this original capital could have been any amount M, with no change in the bet or its significance, as long as one sticks to amounts of money:

$$(M - 40) \times \frac{1}{3} + (M + 20) \times \frac{2}{3} = M.$$

When utility is measured in terms of money, that is, when $u(M) = kM$, one is indifferent to a fair bet; for, taking the bet and not taking the bet are equally desirable:

$$u(\text{bet}) = pu(M_W) + (1 - p)u(M_L) = k(pM_W + (1 - p)M_L)$$
$$= kM_0 = u(M_0).$$

(The equal desirability follows from the fact that taking the bet has the same *utility* as the initial capital.) Thus, unless some function *other* than $u(M) = kM$ describes utility for money, a fair bet has no particular attraction. It should be pointed out that some people get a "kick" out of the process of betting, which might be considered an attraction in even a fair bet; but, this simply means that there is an additional ingredient to take into account in determining utility (that is, besides the amount of money won) which might make it reasonable to prefer to bet in a fair-betting situation.

To see that one may not be indifferent to a fair bet when the utility of money is not a linear function of money, consider a general utility function $u(M)$, and a fair bet:

$$M_0 = pM_W + (1 - p)M_L.$$

The utility of the bet is

$$U_B = pu(M_W) + (1 - p)u(M_L).$$

These two relations can be combined in the vector equation

$$\binom{M_0}{U_B} = p\binom{M_W}{u(M_W)} + (1 - p)\binom{M_L}{u(M_L)},$$

which is interpreted geometrically to mean that the point (M_0, U_B) is a convex combination of the two points $(M_W, u(M_W))$ and $(M_L, u(M_L))$. Thus, the point (M_0, U_B) lies *on the line segment* joining those two points, as shown in Figure 2–7, drawn for the case of a utility function which makes the given bet unattractive, since U_B is less than $u(M_0)$. Figure 2–8 shows the case of a utility function and fair bet that would be attractive. Notice that if the computations were confined to concave down and concave up portions, respectively, of a utility curve the bets would be correspondingly unattractive

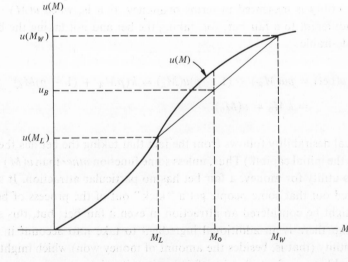

Figure 2–7

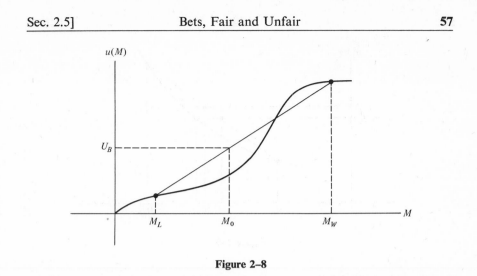

Figure 2–8

and attractive; but observe also that Figure 2–8 illustrates the falsity of the converse. (That is, the utility curve in Figure 2–8 is not concave up over the whole range of M-values in question.)

Just as a fair bet may be actually disadvantageous or advantageous according to the nature of the utility curve, it is also possible that an unfair bet may be advantageous! Consider next, then, a bet that is not fair, biased *against* the person whose interests are of concern and in terms of whose utility the situation is being studied; in such a case the expected capital after the bet is *less* than the initial capital:

$$p'M_W + (1 - p')M_L = M' < M_0,$$

where p' is the probability of winning, and is smaller than the p corresponding to a fair bet for the same amounts of money. The above inequality can be restated in the form

$$\frac{p'}{1 - p'} < \frac{M_0 - M_L}{M_W - M_0} = \frac{y}{x},$$

which says that the money odds are higher than the actual probability odds—so a larger amount must be put up than would be the case in a fair bet. (The last inequality is seen to be equivalent to the one that preceeds it upon cross-multiplying and simplifying.) If U' now denotes the utility in this unfair bet:

$$U' = p'u(M_W) + (1 - p')u(M_L),$$

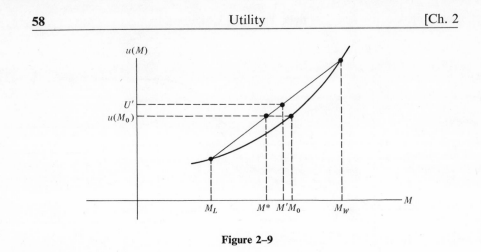

Figure 2–9

then the point (M', U') lies on the line segment joining the points $(M_W, u(M_W))$ and $(M_L, u(M_L))$:

$$\binom{M'}{U'} = p'\binom{M_W}{u(M_W)} + (1 - p')\binom{M_L}{u(M_L)}.$$

This is shown in Figure 2–9, in which is also plotted M_0, the initial capital, which is greater than the expected capital after the bet, M'. Observe that unless the expected capital is *too* much less than the initial capital, the utility of the bet, U', exceeds the utility of the initial capital, $u(M_0)$. In fact, this would be the case so long as M' is not less than M^*, the money co-ordinate of the point where the horizontal line at the height $u(M_0)$ intersects the line segment that determines the bet utilities. Of course, decreasing M' amounts to decreasing p', that is, altering the probability odds, and there is a p^* corresponding to the smallest M^* for which the bet would be worth taking:

$$p^*M_W + (1 - p^*)M_L = M^*$$

or

$$p^* = \frac{M^* - M_L}{M_W - M_L}.$$

Example 2–9. A man has \$6 and puts up \$5 against \$3. With these money odds of 5 to 3, a fair bet would involve a probability $\frac{5}{8}$ of his winning:

$$\frac{5}{8}(\$9) + \frac{3}{8}(\$1) = \$6.$$

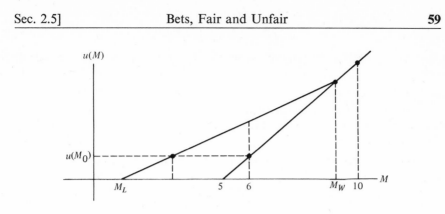

Figure 2–10

With the utility function

$$u(M) = \begin{cases} 0, & M < 5, \\ M - 5, & M \geq 5, \end{cases}$$

the man would surely increase his utility and so be inclined to take a fair bet. However, he would increase his utility so long as the expected final capital exceeds (according to Figure 2–10) the amount $3 = M^*$. A bet with corresponding probability p^* determined by the relation

$$9p^* + (1 - p^*) = 3,$$

or $p^* = \frac{1}{4}$, would be precisely as desirable (in utility) as not betting. And of course any $p > \frac{1}{4}$ would define a bet that is preferred to not betting.

A similar analysis can be applied to a case in which the utility is such that a fair bet is not advantageous, to determine how unfair—biased in one's favor—a bet would have to be to make it advantageous. Figure 2–11 shows a

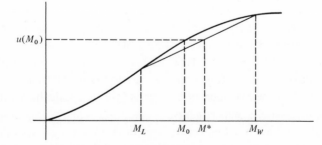

Figure 2–11

utility function for which a fair bet, in which one starts with M_0 and ends up with either M_L or M_W, is not as desirable as not betting. If, however, the probability odds in favor of winning are increased so that the expected final capital is M^*, the prospects of betting and of not betting are equally desirable; moreover, for any expected final capital that is greater than M^* the bet would be preferred, since its utility would be greater than $u(M_0)$, the utility of the initial capital. As above, the critical value of p corresponding to M^* is

$$p^* = \frac{M^* - M_L}{M_W - M_L},$$

and any value of the probability odds larger than this p^* would define a bet that is preferred to not betting.

It should be clear by now that it may be perfectly rational for two people to enter into a bet that is unfair, since it is possible that (with certain types of utility functions) both can increase their utilities.

2.6 Subjective Probability

In Chapter 1 an *experiment of chance* was introduced as a repeatable experiment that (at each trial) results in one of a given set of possible outcomes; the *probability* assigned to each outcome is thought of as an idealization of its relative frequency of occurrence in a long sequence of trials. In the case of a chance or random *variable*, these outcomes are ordinary numbers; more generally they are not necessarily numbers but are characterized by nonnumerical descriptions such as heads and tails, to mention a common example. When the outcomes are thought of as prospects, the experiment which presents one with these prospects according to certain corresponding probabilities has been termed a *random prospect*, or a *mixture* of prospects.

Situations frequently arise, in which one would like to be able to apply methods of decision theory, where the "experiment" that is to produce a particular (but unknown) one of a set of possible prospects is *not* repeatable—except perhaps in the sense of this world's being one of many conceivable worlds that have come to this point of development Thus, the notion of probability needs to be extended or broadened, in its applicability, to events relating to nonrepeatable experiments.

To illustrate the kind of situation we have in mind, consider speculating on the "chances" that a particular man will be elected President of the United States in 1976. A quantification of these "chances" should involve one's beliefs or convictions concerning the occurrence of the event, and should embody the odds at which he is willing to bet that it will occur. It is clear that the matter of chance in this kind of experiment is actually *personal*; the degree of belief of one person will not usually be exactly the same as that of another, and there is no objective basis for saying that the one person is right and the other person wrong.

In the case of the toss of a die, there seems to be a number representing the probability of a six that is *objective*—a property of the die and the tossing mechanism without regard to any person or persons who might be contemplating the experiment. In a sense the number is indisputable, and to some extent it is verifiable by performing the experiment a great many times; and it is agreed on by all. On the other hand, the "probability" that Mr. A will be President in 1976 does not seem to be detachable from the persons who are contemplating the "experiment." Certainly, different people will give different odds, and it would be hard to insist that one person or another is "right."

The term *personal probability*, or alternatively, *subjective probability*, is used to refer to probability that represents a person's degree of belief concerning the occurrence of an event. Although it can be assumed that the subjective probability of a given event exists, it is seldom easy to determine that probability. In principle, the following procedure can be used: Suppose one says to you: "I am going to offer you one of two prospects, and it is up to you to choose the one you prefer. Either I shall give you \$10 in 1976 if a coin I toss now turns up heads (and nothing at all if it falls tails), or I shall give you \$10 in 1976 if Mr. A is elected President then (and nothing at all if he is not elected)." Presumably the toss of the coin has an objective probability model, in which the probability of heads is $\frac{1}{2}$; if you choose the prospect of the \$10 when Mr. A is elected President, it would be said that your subjective probability of his being elected is greater than $\frac{1}{2}$. If you are indifferent between the two prospects, your subjective probability of Mr. A's election is precisely equal to $\frac{1}{2}$. Thus, it ought to be possible, by confronting you with various such choices, using objective experiments with various odds, to find an objective experiment such that you are indifferent to (1) receiving \$10 as the result of a certain event E in that objective experiment and (2) receiving \$10 as the result of Mr. A's election to the Presidency. The objective probability of the event E is then taken to be your subjective probability of Mr. A's election.

With such an approach, one could set up (in principle) a probability model for any given experiment in which subjective probabilities are to be defined. A consistent person would define a model in which the axioms for objective probability models are fulfilled; in the simple case of a random variable with a finite number of possible values, or of a more general experiment of chance with a finite number of outcomes, this consistency would mean that the probabilities assigned to the possible values or outcomes are nonnegative numbers not larger than 1, and that their sum is 1. In particular, in the case of Mr. A's being elected in 1976 or not, the subjective probability of his being elected and the subjective probability of his not being elected should add to 1. It will be assumed that subjective probability models exhibit such consistency, with the realization that in practice, if one were actually to determine subjective probabilities by offering choices between subjective and objective bets, consistency may be hard to achieve.

(One practical difficulty with the approach outlined above for determining subjective probabilities is that a person may, perhaps unconsciously, use his own subjective probability model for the supposedly objective and repeatable experiment, and so compare, say, his *subjective* chances of getting heads with the subjective chances of Mr. A's election in 1976. An attempt to avoid this by using a deterministic experiment for comparison has its own problems. Thus, if one offers you this choice: "I shall either give you $5 in 1976 or give you $10 if Mr. A is elected in 1976, as you wish," your preference of the sure $5 may mean only that you are not a gambling man and not reveal subjective probabilities.)

Although objective probability and subjective probability are different in conception and interpretation, they are not different as mathematical entities, inasmuch as the same basic axioms are assumed to hold for both. Any definitions or theorems concerning objective probabilities apply equally well to subjective probabilities. In particular, the expected value of a random variable, defined earlier for the case of objective probabilities, would be defined in exactly the same way if the probabilities are subjective, namely, as the weighted sum of the possible values, where the weights are the corresponding (subjective) probabilities. Thus, if one can assign subjective probabilities to the various possible levels of demand for his product next year, he can calculate a corresponding expected level of demand for that year.

In most decision problems, both kinds of probabilities are useful. A basic approach to handling a decision problem involves considering the state of nature to be a random prospect; a model for this randomness would ordinarily involve subjective probabilities. On the other hand, the data that are gathered to use as an aid to inference are almost inherently the results of repeated (and therefore repeatable) trials of an experiment; the model for that experiment, which is really the subject of the inference, is then an objective probability model.

Problems

2–17 If A puts up $50 and B puts up $100, what probability of A's winning makes the bet fair?

2–18 Given the utility function for money shown in Figure 2–12, should Mr. A take the bet in Problem 2–17, if his initial capital is
(a) $100?   (b) $200?

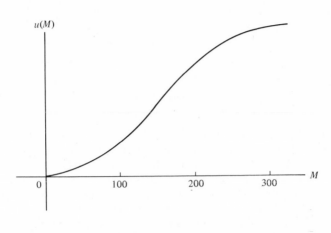

Figure 2–12

2–19 A man pays 25¢ for a $7,500 trip insurance policy. What are the money odds in this bet? Assuming (as in 1968) 0.30 fatalities per 100 million passenger miles* on domestic flights, and assuming an average flight length of 500 miles, what are the probability odds of the bet? Can the man's willingness to take the bet be explained on the basis of utility? How would the odds situation be changed if one takes into account that it costs the insurance company (say) 20¢ to distribute and to process each application?

2–20 Given the utility function of Example 2–9 (given by $u(M) = M - 5$ for $M \geq 5$ and 0 for $M < 5$), is there any bet not worth taking if the initial capital is $5, and the final capital (as before) either $1 or $9?

2–21 Is an unfair bet ever worthwhile if one's utility for money is given by the function $u(M) = 1 - 2^{-M}$?

2–22 Consider the following utility function (see Figure 2–13):

$$u(M) = \begin{cases} M, & \text{if } 0 \leq M \leq 10 \\ 5 + \tfrac{1}{2}M, & \text{if } 10 \leq M \leq 20 \\ 15, & \text{if } M > 20 \end{cases}$$

(a) What is the p for a fair bet with $M_0 = 10$, $M_L = 0$, $M_W = 20$?
(b) Is the fair bet in (a) worth taking?

---

* *Accident Facts*, 1969 Ed., National Safety Council, p. 75.

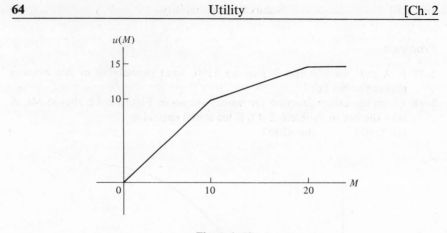

Figure 2–13

(c) How large a probability of winning should a person with the given $u(M)$ have so that he is just indifferent to the bet?

(d) Is any bet with $M_0 = 20$ (and $M_L < 20$) ever worth taking?

2–23 Mr. B owns 500 shares of stock now selling at $8 per share. There is a probability of .2 that in a month the stock will go up to $20 per share, and a probability of .8 that it will go down to $5. Should he sell it if his utility curve is concave down? On his way to the broker, he meets Mr. A, and finds that Mr. A is interested in buying the stock at $8. The reason Mr. A wants to buy the stock is that his debts amount to $10,000 but his cash on hand is only $5,000, and in a month he will be forced to declare bankruptcy. Thus, his utility for any negative net amount is 0. Is it really to Mr. A's advantage to buy the stock?

Chapter 3   No-Data Decision Problems

Decision problems called *statistical* are those in which there are data, or *observations* on the state of nature, hopefully containing information that can be used to make a better decision. Before treating such problems, it will be useful to consider problems of making decisions in the absence of data, not only because these problems are simpler, but also because one approach to handing problems involving data is to convert them to no-data problems.

The ingredients of a no-data problem, then, are the set Θ of states of nature θ, the set $\mathscr{A}$ of available actions a, and a function $l(\theta, a)$ whose value represents the loss incurred when one takes action a and nature is in state θ. These will be referred to, respectively, as the *state space*, the *action space*, and the *loss function*. A theoretical analysis of any decision problem will require knowledge of these ingredients.

The *loss* incurred will be assumed to be measured in negative utility units. A study of the preceding chapter would suggest that in most real situations it is indeed presumptuous to pretend to have an accurate knowledge of the utility of each of the prospects implied by the various pairs (θ, a). Yet, without such knowledge it is unreasonable to judge decision processes, and fortunately it turns out that respectable decision rules are often not so very sensitive to inaccuracies in one's assessment of loss. So it will be assumed, however unrealistic such an assumption may be, that the loss function is known.

In order to keep at the level of "finite" mathematics, the problems to be taken up in this chapter will be those in which both the state space Θ and the action space $\mathscr{A}$ are finite, that is, only finitely many actions are available, and nature is in one of only finitely many possible states.

3.1 The Set of Mixed Actions

Most people at some point have made a decision by tossing a coin—or have at least talked about doing so. Introducing such an extraneous random device turns out to be useful for the purpose of discussing the general theory of making decisions and actually provides decision rules that under some criteria are better than those that use only the given, nonrandom actions. From the rather special device of tossing an ordinary coin, one generalizes to *biased* coins—devices that choose between two actions with probabilities other than $\frac{1}{2}$—and further, to situations in which the actions from which the random device is to select are more than two in number. In general, then, the random device is an experiment of chance having as many possible outcomes as there are actions from which to choose; each outcome is associated with an action, and when a particular outcome is observed, the corresponding action is taken.

Using a random device to select an action from the set of possible actions is called a *randomized* or *mixed* action. Picking a mixed action from among all possible actions amounts to picking a random device from among all random devices that could be used to determine the action actually taken. Picking a random device, in turn (once the set of available actions is settled on), amounts to selecting a set of probabilities for the various actions. This leads to the following

DEFINITION   *A* mixed action, *for a problem with action space consisting of actions* $a_1, a_2, \ldots, a_k$, *is a probability vector* $(p_1, p_2, \ldots, p_k)$, *that is, a sequence of nonnegative numbers* p_i *whose sum is* 1.

To carry out a given mixed action, one constructs an experiment of chance with outcomes (say) $e_1, e_2, \ldots, e_k$ having probabilities $p_1, p_2, \ldots, p_k$, respectively; he then performs this experiment, and if the outcome is e_i, he takes action a_i.

Example 3–1.   In a problem with three available actions, a, b, and c, a probability vector such as $(\frac{1}{3}, \frac{1}{4}, \frac{5}{12})$ defines a mixed action. To carry out this particular mixed action, one could construct a long cylinder with a twelve-sided regular polygon as its cross section, label four of the sides a, three of the sides b, and the remaining five sides c. Rolling the cylinder results in an outcome (say, the side that ends up on top) which selects one of the three actions according to the assigned probabilities. On the other hand, to construct an experiment with probabilities $(1/\sqrt{2}, 1 - 1/\sqrt{2}, 0)$

would not be possible with a discrete object like a cylinder with finitely many sides. What could be done in such a case is to approximate the experiment by substituting one in which the probabilities are $(.707, .293, 0)$, that is, discrete approximations to the given ones.

The original actions $a_1, a_2, \ldots, a_k$ are called *pure actions*, to distinguish them from the mixed actions given by probability vectors. However, a pure action can be achieved by using a *singular* probability vector. Thus, for instance, the action a_2 is equivalent to the probability vector $(0, 1, 0, \ldots, 0)$ that assigns all of the probability mass to action a_2. In this sense the pure actions constitute a *subset* of the set of mixed actions.

In a decision problem with a given loss function, the use of a mixed action makes the loss a *random variable*, for each state of nature. The utility of such a random prospect is computed by taking its *expected value*, according to the properties of utility. Therefore, the consequence of employing a given mixed action when nature is in a given state is measured by the expected value of the loss. In particular, if the loss function is $l(\theta, a)$ and one uses the mixed action $(p_1, p_2, \ldots, p_k)$ to choose among the actions $a_1, \ldots, a_k$, the expected loss is the following weighted sum:

$$l(\theta, a_1)p_1 + l(\theta, a_2)p_2 + \cdots + l(\theta, a_k)p_k.$$

Example 3–2.   Upon entering his building, an instructor with an office on the third floor can either go down one flight of stairs to the basement and ride up in the elevator, or go up one flight to the first floor and ride the rest of the way. (It is assumed that he is not an exercise fanatic and will not walk all the way up unless he has to.) The elevator is either working, a "state of nature" that might be called θ_1, or inoperative, a "state" θ_2. If it is working, going up one flight costs that much energy, and going down (it is assumed) costs no energy. But if the elevator is inoperative, going down one flight means walking up to the third floor from the basement, whereas going up to the first floor means only an additional hike of two floors. With the assumption that loss is proportional to the number of stairs climbed, the loss function is given in the following table of its values:

	θ_1 (working)	θ_2 (out of order)
a_1 (down to basement)	0	6
a_2 (up to first)	1	5

A mixed action is a probability vector of the form $(p, 1 - p)$, where p is on the interval from 0 to 1. If nature is in state θ_1, the loss will be either 0 or 1, according as action a_1 or a_2 is chosen, which in turn will be the case with probabilities p and $1 - p$, respectively. The expected loss is then

$$L_1 \equiv 0 \cdot p + 1 \cdot (1 - p) = 1 - p.$$

Similarly, if nature is in state θ_2, the loss incurred will be 6 or 5, with probabilities p and $1 - p$, respectively; the expected loss is

$$L_2 \equiv 6p + 5(1 - p) = p + 5.$$

These losses (L_1, L_2) are defined by a choice of p, and it might have been more illuminating to write them as functions $L_i(p)$. In any case it should be remembered that picking a mixed strategy (here by selecting p) yields a set of numbers (L_1, L_2), as determined by the loss function.

In a problem with states $\theta_1, \theta_2, \ldots, \theta_m$, there are m L's corresponding to each mixed action. For the case of k actions, these L's are the following expected losses:

$$L_1 = E[l(\theta_1, a)] = l(\theta_1, a_1)p_1 + \cdots + l(\theta_1, a_k)p_k$$
$$L_2 = E[l(\theta_2, a)] = l(\theta_2, a_1)p_1 + \cdots + l(\theta_2, a_k)p_k$$
$$\vdots$$
$$L_m = E[l(\theta_m, a)] = l(\theta_m, a_1)p_1 + \cdots + l(\theta_m, a_k)p_k,$$

defined by the mixed action $(p_1, \ldots, p_k)$. These relations can be written in the following form

$$\begin{pmatrix} L_1 \\ \vdots \\ L_m \end{pmatrix} = p_1 \begin{pmatrix} l(\theta_1, a_1) \\ \vdots \\ l(\theta_m, a_1) \end{pmatrix} + \cdots + p_k \begin{pmatrix} l(\theta_1, a_k) \\ \vdots \\ l(\theta_m, a_k) \end{pmatrix},$$

which suggests the interpretation of the vector of losses $(L_1, \ldots, L_m)$ as a point in m-dimensional space computed as a *convex combination* of the points $(l(\theta_1, a_i), \ldots, l(\theta_m, a_i))$, for $i = 1, \ldots, k$. Indeed, these latter points are precisely the loss vectors defined by the pure actions, and the above relation says that the loss vectors defined by mixed actions are always convex combinations of those defined by the pure actions!

It is seen then that the set of loss points $(L_1, \ldots, L_m)$ defined by all possible mixed actions $(p_1, \ldots, p_k)$ is a convex set in m-dimensional space, namely, the convex set generated by the points defined by the pure actions; indeed, it is a convex polyhedron—a set having a finite number of faces and *extreme points*, or corners. These corners are (or are defined by) pure actions, although some pure actions may be inside the set. The situation is most easily visualized in two dimensions, a case that arises when there are two states of nature, as in the following example.

Example 3–3. Consider a problem with five available actions, two states of nature, and the loss function given in the following table

	a_1	a_2	a_3	a_4	a_5
θ_1	2	4	3	5	3
θ_2	3	0	3	2	5

The pure actions define the loss vectors in the columns of this table, namely, (2, 3), (4, 0), (3, 3), (5, 2), (3, 5), and the mixed actions define the convex set generated by these five points, shown in Figure 3–1. The vertices of the polygon are points defined by pure actions, but one of the pure actions happens to fall inside the set. (This would mean, incidentally, that the same expected losses can be achieved by a mixture of a_1, a_2, a_4, and a_5 as would be incurred by using the pure action a_3.)

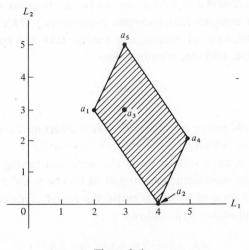

Figure 3–1

It was pointed out in Chapter 1 that a convex combination of a set of points corresponds precisely to the center of gravity of a system of point masses at those points, these masses being proportional to the weights in the convex combination. Thus, the mixed action $(p_1, p_2, \ldots, p_k)$ yields a point $(L_1, \ldots, L_m)$, which is the center of gravity of a system of masses with p_1 units at a_1, p_2 units at a_2, $\ldots$, and p_k units at a_k.

Interpreting the mixed actions as centers of gravity helps to visualize the kinds of mixtures that produce certain points. For instance, if only p_1 and p_2 are positive, with no mass at $a_3, \ldots, a_k$, then the center of gravity (and therefore the point (L_1, L_2) corresponding to that mixture) must lie on the line segment joining a_1 and a_2. If these actions are represented by extreme points, then such a mixture of just these two actions lies on the edge of the convex set of points representing all mixtures. In Example 3–3 above, it is clear from Figure 3–1 that action a_3 results in the same losses as a certain mixture of a_1, a_2, and a_5 or as a mixture involving only a_1, a_4, and a_5, as well as many mixtures of a_1, a_3, a_4, and a_5. On the other hand, it could not be obtained by mixing actions a_2, a_4, and a_5.

3.2 Regret

If one only knew the state of nature, he would immediately know what action to take, namely, the action for which the loss is smallest. (This is an immediate consequence of taking loss to be the negative of what has been called utility, a quantity that measures preferences.) Thus, if it were known that θ_i were the state of nature, one should take the action a for which $l(\theta_i, a)$ is smallest, and this minimum loss

$$m_i = \min_{\mathscr{A}} l(\theta_i, a),$$

is a loss that could not be avoided with even the best decision. But if one takes the action a_j, say, which does *not* produce this minimum, and then discovers that nature is indeed in state θ_i, he would regret not having chosen the action that produces the minimum; the amount of loss he could have saved himself by knowing the state of nature is called the *regret*. This is then defined for each state θ_i and action a_j as follows:

$$r(\theta_i, a_j) = l(\theta_i, a_j) - \min_{\mathscr{A}} l(\theta_i, a).$$

So for each state of nature, one subtracts the minimum loss m_i from the losses involving that state to obtain the regret.

Regret sometimes goes under the name *opportunity loss*. This terminology stems from thinking in terms of gain rather than loss. The gain resulting from taking action a when nature is in state θ is the negative of the loss:

$$-g(\theta, a) = l(\theta, a).$$

Hence, the minimum loss is the negative of the maximum gain:

$$\min_{\mathscr{A}} l(\theta, a) = -\max_{\mathscr{A}} g(\theta, a),$$

and the regret can be expressed in terms of gain as follows:

$$r(\theta_i, a_j) = l(\theta_i, a_j) - \min_{\mathscr{A}} l(\theta_i, a) = \max_{\mathscr{A}} g(\theta_i, a) - g(\theta_i, a_j).$$

This represents the maximum that could have been gained if the state of nature had been known, minus the amount that actually was gained by taking action a_j, and so the name "opportunity" loss.

Example 3–4.   Repeated below is the loss table of Example 3–3, with an additional column giving, for each state of nature, the minimum loss over all of the five actions:

	a_1	a_2	a_3	a_4	a_5	$\min_{\mathscr{A}} l(\theta, a)$
θ_1	2	4	3	5	3	2
θ_2	3	0	3	2	5	0

To obtain the regret table, the minimum in each row is subtracted from the losses in that row:

	a_1	a_2	a_3	a_4	a_5
θ_1	0	2	1	3	1
θ_2	3	0	3	2	5

Notice that there is at least one zero for each state, and the remaining entries in the regret table are positive. Geometrically, the effect is to translate the set of loss points representing the five actions, parallel to the coordinate axes,

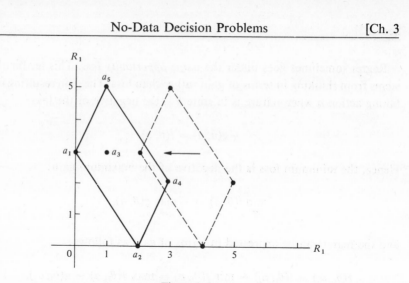

Figure 3–2

so that at least one action is on each axis, and the rest of the points are in the first quadrant (see Figure 3–2).

In Figure 3–2, for Example 3–4, it should be noticed that the whole convex set of mixed actions is shifted along with the five pure actions. This is true generally, and follows because the amount subtracted from each loss is independent of the action a, upon which a probability distribution is imposed in a mixed action:

$$R_i = E[r(\theta_i, a)] = E[l(\theta_i, a)] - \min_{\mathscr{A}} l(\theta_i, a) \equiv L_i - m_i.$$

The question naturally arises as to whether it would make any difference, in studying a decision problem, if one used regret instead of loss. It will emerge in the subsequent discussion that in some cases it does make a difference and in others it does not. The classical treatment of statistical problems, when viewed as problems in decision theory, frequently amounts to assuming a loss function that is already a regret function. This is surely defensible if the method used is one for which replacing actual losses by opportunity losses does not alter the solution. At any rate, the decision maker, or the statistician, if he himself does not incur the loss, would presumably be interested in regrets—the amounts of loss he could not avoid even with the decision that is best when the state of nature is known. His client, however, would suffer the losses, not the regrets (if they are different).

Problems

3–1 Given the losses in Example 3–2, determine the corresponding table of regrets. Sketch the representations of the mixed actions as (L_1, L_2) and again as (R_1, R_2), that is, in terms of expected losses and in terms of expected regrets.

3–2 In Problem 3–1, determine weights for the two possible actions that would result in equal expected regrets under the two states. (Is there any set of probability weights that would produce equal expected losses?)

3–3 Sketch the set of mixed actions, in terms of expected losses, and also in terms of expected regrets, for a problem with the following loss table:

	a_1	a_2	a_3
θ_1	-2	4	3
θ_2	5	1	4

3–4 Determine a mixed action for Problem 3–3 having expected losses $L_1 = 3 = L_2$. (Is this unique? Why?)

3–5 Make a three-dimensional sketch of the points (R_1, R_2, R_3) representing the expected regrets for the various mixed actions in a three-action problem with the following loss table

	a_1	a_2	a_3
θ_1	-1	2	0
θ_2	2	-2	3
θ_3	4	2	1

Determine also a mixture of the three actions with expected regrets $(\frac{4}{5}, 3, \frac{5}{3})$.

3–6 In Example 3–3, determine at least two mixtures of a_1, a_2, a_4, a_5 with the same expected losses as the pure action a_3.

3.3 The Minimax Principle

The fundamental difficulty of decision problems has already emerged, namely, the fact that actions are not usually comparable in a natural way, since an action that is best under one state of nature is likely not to be best under other states of nature. And the state of nature is unknown! Various schemes have been proposed—decision principles that lead to the selection of one or more actions as "best" according to the principle used. None is universally accepted, unfortunately.

What is needed, in any case, is a means of *linearly* ordering the available actions, assigning "values" to each action according to its desirability so that one may choose the action with the greatest value, or greatest desirability.

The *minimax principle* places a value on each action according to the worst that can happen with that action; in a sense one expects the worst and prepares for it. That is, one determines, for each action a, the *maximum loss* over the various possible states of nature:

$$M(a) = \max_{\Theta} l(\theta, a),$$

and this provides an ordering among the possible actions. One takes the action a for which the maximum loss $M(a)$ is a *minimum*; hence, the name *minimax*.

Example 3–5. The loss table for Example 3–3 is repeated below, with an additional row of entries which are the maximum losses for the various actions:

	a_1	a_2	a_3	a_4	a_5
θ_1	2	4	3	5	3
θ_2	3	0	3	2	5
$\max_{\Theta} l(\theta, a)$	3	4	3	5	5

Clearly the smallest maximum loss is 3, achieved for either action a_1 or action a_3. These two actions are minimax actions.

It is interesting to note that the application of the minimax principle to regrets in this problem produces a different solution. The table of regrets, together with a row of maximum regrets for each action is as follows:

	a_1	a_2	a_3	a_4	a_5
θ_1	0	2	1	3	1
θ_2	3	0	3	2	5
$\max_{\Theta} l(\theta, a)$	3	2	3	3	5

The minimum maximum regret is 2, achieved by taking action a_2, which is then the minimax regret action, and is different from the minimax loss action.

That the minimax regret action and the minimax loss action may differ, as in the example above, is clear from a graphical analysis of the process of

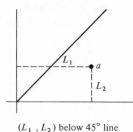

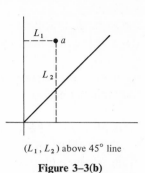

((L_1, L_2)) below 45° line

((L_1, L_2)) above 45° line

Figure 3–3(a)

Figure 3–3(b)

determining the minimax point—which is feasible when there are two states
of nature. For a given action a with losses (L_1, L_2) under (θ_1, θ_2), respectively,
the maximum of these losses is the first coordinate if the point lies below the
bisector of the first quadrant, as seen in Figures 3–3(a) and 3–3(b). And if the
point lies above that bisector, the maximum loss is the second coordinate, L_2.
Thus, if two points lie above the bisector, or 45° line, the lower one has the
smaller maximum; and if two points both lie below it, the left-most point has
the smaller maximum. So the minimax action among the actions all lying
above the 45° line is obtained by moving a horizontal line up until it first
strikes one of the points representing the actions. The minimax action among
the actions all lying below the 45° line is obtained by moving a vertical line to
the right until it first strikes one of the points. For points lying some above and
some below the 45° line, one obtains the minimum maximum by comparing

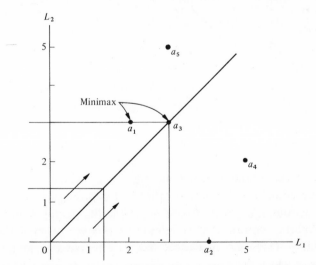

Figure 3–4

the vertical coordinates of those above with the horizontal coordinates of those below the line. This can be accomplished by moving a wedge whose vertex is on the 45° line (defined by $L_1 = L_2$) and whose sides are parallel to the coordinate axes up to the set of actions. The first point encountered gives the minimax action.

Example 3–6. The graphical determination of a minimax action is shown for the problem of Example 3–5 in the accompanying Figures 3–4 and 3–5. Study of these figures, and a little experimentation with other cases, should make it apparent why different solutions can be obtained using regret and loss. It is simply that the minimax process is intimately related with the location of the origin of the coordinate system, and that moving the action points relative to the coordinate system can alter the process of finding the minimax point. Of course, it should be clear that there will be some instances in which the minimax loss action and the minimax regret action will *not* differ.

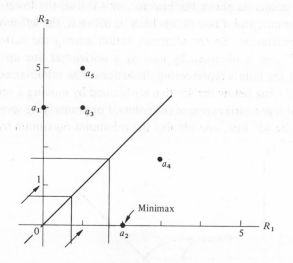

Figure 3–5

To determine the minimax action among the set of all *mixed* actions is generally more complicated, because instead of choosing an action from a finite set of actions one must choose a probability vector from a set of possible probability vectors that is infinite in number (even if the set of actions is finite). There are two cases that can be handled at this point, namely, those in which there are just two states of nature, and those in which there are just two actions.

When there are just two states of nature, a graphical solution to the problem of determining a minimax mixed action can be carried out in precisely the same manner as for pure actions, by representing the mixed actions in terms of (L_1, L_2) or (R_1, R_2) as before, and using the "wedge" technique. This technique will at least locate a point in the plane with the minimum maximum expected loss (or minimum maximum expected regret), and it is then a simple matter, seeing which actions must be involved, to determine a mixture with such minimum maximum expected loss (or regret).

Example 3–7. Continuing with the situation of Example 3–6 and 3–5, Figure 3–6 shows the determination of a point with minimum maximum expected loss, by moving a wedge with vertex on the 45° line up to the action set.

It is clear from the figure that this point lies on the segment joining the points representing a_1 and a_2, and so represents a mixture involving only those two actions. Indeed, the point (x, y) in question is a convex combination of a_1 and a_2:

$$\binom{x}{y} = p\binom{2}{3} + (1 - p)\binom{4}{0}.$$

Moreover, it is the point on that line segment with equal coordinates:

$$2p + 4(1 - p) = x = y = 3p + 0(1 - p),$$

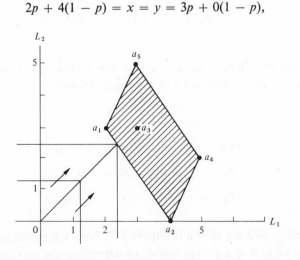

Figure 3–6

and equating these two functions of p yields $p = \frac{4}{5}$. The minimax action therefore puts $\frac{4}{5}$ of the total probability (1) at a_1, $\frac{1}{5}$ at a_2, and none at any other action; it is, thus, the probability vector $(\frac{4}{5}, \frac{1}{5}, 0, 0, 0)$. The minimax loss, that is, the smallest maximum expected loss, is the value obtained by setting $p = \frac{4}{5}$, namely, $3p = \frac{12}{5}$. The point on the graph representing the minimax actions is thus $(\frac{12}{5}, \frac{12}{5})$. Notice that this minimax expected loss is actually *less* that the minimum maximum loss achieved when only pure actions are admitted, namely 3, as determined in Examples 3–5 and 3–6.

Consider next the other situation that can be handled with the elementary techniques at hand, namely, that in which there are just two actions. In such a case the mixed actions are vectors of the form $(p, 1 - p)$, defined by a single variable p. The expected losses under the various states of nature can be computed as functions of p, and from this one can determine (at least graphically) the function $\max_{\theta} E[l(\theta, a)]$. The minimum point of this latter function then defines the minimax action.

Example 3–8. A decision problem with two actions and four states of nature is defined by the following loss table:

	θ_1	θ_2	θ_3	θ_4
a_1	4	2	1	−1
a_2	0	−1	5	2

Imposing the distribution $(p, 1 - p)$ on the action space one computes the expected losses for each state of nature, as follows:

$$\theta_1: \quad 4p + 0(1 - p) = 4p,$$

$$\theta_2: \quad 2p - (1 - p) = 3p - 1,$$

$$\theta_3: \quad p + 5(1 - p) = 5 - 4p,$$

$$\theta_4: \quad -p + 2(1 - p) = 2 - 3p.$$

These functions of p are shown in Figure 3–7. For each mixed action, that is, each choice of p, it is a simple matter to determine the maximum expected loss, which is the ordinate on the highest line at that p. The heavy line is then

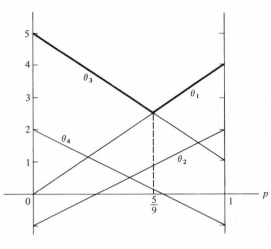

Figure 3–7

a graph of the maximum expected loss as a function of p; its minimum occurs at $p = \frac{5}{8}$, which defines the minimax action: $(\frac{5}{8}, \frac{3}{8})$. The minimum maximum expected loss is the ordinate of the lowest point on the heavy curve, and is $\frac{5}{2}$.

Problems

3–7 The decision problem facing the instructor who could either walk up to the first floor elevator stop or walk down to the ground floor stop was studied in Example 3–2. The loss function given there was

	θ_1	θ_2
a_1	0	6
a_2	1	5

Determine the minimax solutions (pure, mixed, and using loss, regret), (Notice that it does make a difference whether loss or regret is used, and the choice may depend on whether the decision maker has to do the climbing. Observe also the advantage in using a randomized or mixed action in the case of regret.)

3–8 Determine the minimax solutions (pure, mixed, and using loss, regret) for the decision problem with losses as follows:

	a_1	a_2	a_3
θ_1	−2	4	3
θ_2	5	1	4

3–9 Determine the minimax loss and minimax regret pure actions for the decision problem with losses as follows:

	a_1	a_2	a_3
θ_1	-1	2	0
θ_2	2	-2	3
θ_3	4	3	1

3–10 A lot of five articles is to be accepted (action a_1) or rejected (action a_2). The state of nature is characterized by the number M of defective articles among the five; thus, $M = 0, 1, 2, 3, 4,$ or 5. Assuming losses equal to twice the number of defectives in lots that are passed, and equal to the number of good articles in lots that are rejected, determine the minimax mixed action.

3–11 Consider actions a and a^* (among others), and a loss function $l(\theta, a)$ with the property that $l(\theta, a) \leq l(\theta, a^*)$ for all states of nature θ. Show that one can get by without admitting a^* into competition, in the sense that the minimum maximum loss is as small when a^* is included as when a^* is not included. Show further that if the inequality is strict for each θ: $l(\theta, a) < l(\theta, a^*)$, then a^* would never be a part of a minimax action. Construct a situation for the case of two states, aided by graphical sketches, in which the inequalities hold but are not both strict so that a^* can be a part of a minimax solution.

3.4 Bayes Solutions

Using the minimax principle to determine what action to take protects against the *worst* that can possibly happen, for each action, even though the state of nature that produces that worst consequence has—in some sense—only a remote chance of being the actual state. This kind of thinking results in the concept of randomness for the state of nature, which up to this point had been conceived of as *fixed* but unknown. The decision principle that is referred to by the name *Bayes* adopts the stance that whether one wants to consider nature as random or not, it is nevertheless rational to incorporate into the decision making process one's prior hunches, convictions, or information about the state of nature—and how "likely" (whatever that means) the various states of nature are to be governing the situation. This is accomplished by weighting the states in a way that characterizes or summarizes the prior ingredients mentioned and by using this weighting to obtain an ordering of the actions that permits the selection of a "best" action. In this way, if an extremely large loss can occur for a given action when nature is in a state that is felt intuitively by the decision maker to be most unlikely, the role of that extreme loss is minimized by weighting only slightly the state of nature that would produce it.

Example 3–9.   In the problem of deciding whether to go down one flight or up one flight to take the elevator to the third floor (Example 3–2), the loss table was as follows:

	Elevator working (θ_1)	Elevator inoperative (θ_2)
Walk down (a_1)	0	6
Walk up (a_2)	1	5

Perhaps past experience suggests that the elevator works four times out of five. With this prior information, however ill-founded it may happen to be, one can compute weighted averages of the losses, for each action, using weights .8 for θ_1 and .2 for θ_2. The results of these computations, which are just averages with respect to the probability distribution (.8, .2) for (θ_1, θ_2), are given in the following extended table:

	θ_1	θ_2	Expected loss
a_1	0	6	1.2
a_2	1	5	1.8
Prior weights	.8	.2	

The expected loss yields a number for each action in terms of which the actions become ordered; action a_1 has the smaller expected loss, and so is preferred. It is called the *Bayes action*, corresponding to the assumed prior weights.

In a general decision problem, a probability weight $g(\theta)$ is assigned to each state of nature θ, where these assigned weights are nonnegative and add up to 1. Such a set of probabilities or weights is called a *prior distribution* for θ. (The Latin version, *a priori* distribution, is also used.) Given the distribution $g(\theta)$, the loss incurred for a given action a is a random variable, with expected value

$$B(a) = \sum_i g(\theta_i) l(\theta_i, a).$$

This is referred to as the *Bayes loss* corresponding to action *a*. The *Bayes action* is then defined to be the action *a* that minimizes the Bayes loss $B(a)$. That is, the computation of the expected loss according to a given prior distribution provides a means of arranging or ordering the available actions on a scale (namely, $B(a)$) such that the action farthest to the left on that scale is the most desirable, and is to be taken.

When *mixed actions* are considered, one can again define a Bayes loss as the expectation—with respect to a given prior distribution—of the expected loss (with respect to the mixed action): For a mixed action $\mathbf{p} = (p_1, \ldots, p_k)$, which assigns probability p_i to action a_i, the expected loss for a given state θ is

$$E[l(\theta, a)] = \sum_j l(\theta, a_j)p_j,$$

and the Bayes loss is obtained by averaging these (for the various θ's) with respect to $g(\theta)$:

$$B(\mathbf{p}) = \sum_i g(\theta_i)E[l(\theta_i, a)] = \sum_i g(\theta_i)\left\{\sum_j l(\theta_i, a_j)p_j\right\}.$$

Since this Bayes loss is a function of $(p_1, \ldots, p_k)$, or $k - 1$ variables (p_k is determined as soon as $p_1, \ldots, p_{k-1}$ are specified), the problem of determining the minimum Bayes loss is now that of minimizing a function of $k - 1$ variables—generally speaking a nontrivial task.

Some useful insights can be obtained by taking first the special case in which there are just two states of nature. This simple case is amenable to a graphical analysis.

Example 3-10. Given the losses of the elevator problem, as in Example 3-9, and prior probabilities $g(\theta_1) = w$ and $g(\theta_2) = 1 - w$, where $0 \leq w \leq 1$, the expected losses for actions a_1 and a_2 are

$$B(a_1) = 0 \cdot w + 6(1 - w) = 6 - 6w$$
$$B(a_2) = 1 \cdot w + 5(1 - w) = 5 - 4w.$$

The loss table, extended to show these Bayes losses, is as follows:

	θ_1	θ_2	$B(a)$
a_1	0	6	$6 - 6w$
a_2	1	5	$5 - 4w$
$g(\theta)$	w	$1 - w$	

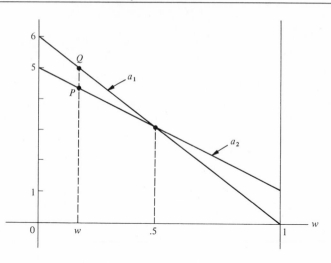

Figure 3–8

The Bayes losses are functions of the single variable w and can be represented graphically, as in Figure 3–8.

For any given w, such as the one shown, the Bayes losses are ordinates on the two lines, that is, of P (for a_2) and of Q (for a_1). Because P is lower than Q the smaller Bayes loss is incurred for a_2, if the prior distribution is defined by the given w. It is then clear that for any w to the left of .5, the value of w for which the Bayes losses are equal, the smaller Bayes loss is incurred by taking action a_2. For any w to the right of .5, the Bayes action is a_1, since this yields the smaller Bayes loss in such cases. When $w = .5$, so that the losses are equal, it does not matter whether one takes action a_1 or action a_2. The reasonableness of these results should be observed. A small w means a small "chance" that the elevator is working and the Bayes solution is the action a_2, to walk up to the first floor to try the elevator. A large w, on the other hand, means that one is pretty sure the elevator will be working; the Bayes action is to walk down one flight to catch it at the ground floor.

In general, the Bayes losses for the various actions will be linear functions of w, in a problem with two states of nature and $g(\theta_1) = w$, $g(\theta_2) = 1 - w$. These functions of w will be represented by straight lines, and for a given value of w the action corresponding to the line whose ordinate at that w is smallest is the Bayes action. The picture will be something like that of Figure 3–9, drawn for a problem with four actions. Examination of that figure shows that for a prior distribution defined by a w in the range $0 \le w < w_1$ the Bayes action is a_1; for $w_1 < w < w_2$ it is a_2; and for $w_2 < w \le 1$ it is a_3.

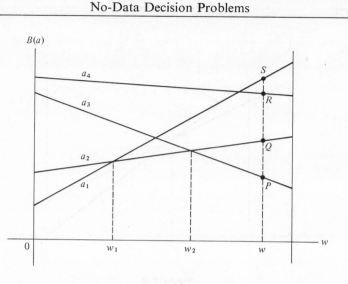

Figure 3–9

If one admits mixed actions, say $(p_1, \ldots, p_k)$ for actions $a_1, \ldots, a_k$, respectively, the expected losses are

$$B(\mathbf{p}) = \sum_i g(\theta_i)\left\{\sum_j l(\theta_i, a_j)p_j\right\} = \sum_j p_j\left\{\sum_i g(\theta_i)l(\theta_i, a_j)\right\}.$$

Thus, the value of $B(\mathbf{p})$ is a convex combination of the values of the Bayes losses for the various pure actions, and so is at least as great as the smallest of those values. This means that there is no gain possible in the use of mixed actions; a pure action can always be found which yields the minimum Bayes loss. In the case of four actions and two states of nature shown in Figure 3–9, the ordinates of the points P, Q, R, and S are the Bayes losses corresponding to the pure actions and to a prior distribution defined by w. The Bayes losses for mixtures of the four actions would be ordinates of points on the line segment $\overline{SP}$, none of which would be any less than the minimum Bayes loss achieved by using a_3.

The determination of a Bayes action, that is, an action that minimizes the Bayes loss, also can be carried out, when there are two states of nature, in the (L_1, L_2) plane, where L_i is the expected loss using a given mixed action when the state of nature is θ_i. This method will be introduced in the following example, but clearly would apply for any number of actions.

Example 3–11.   Given again the elevator problem of the preceding examples, with the loss table as shown, the expected losses for a mixed action $(p, 1 - p)$ are as follows:

$$L_1 = 0 \cdot p + 1 \cdot (1 - p),$$

$$L_2 = 6p + 5(1 - p).$$

	θ_1	θ_2
a_1	0	6
a_2	1	5

The Bayes loss for a prior distribution $(.8, .2)$ is then

$$B(p) = (0.8)L_1 + (0.2)L_2.$$

Any two actions would have the same expected Bayes loss so long as the quantity $.8L_1 + .2L_2$ is the same for both; thus, the set of all points with a given Bayes loss is given by the equation

$$(0.8)L_1 + (0.2)L_2 = K,$$

for some constant K. This is a straight line in the L_1L_2-plane, a line with slope $-.8/.2 = -4$. An action with a greater expected Bayes loss would lie on on a line parallel to this one, but with a bigger value of K, and the larger the K the higher up on the coordinate system is the line $.8L_1 + .2L_2 = K$. (For, the L_2-intercept is $K/.2$, which is proportional to K.) So, to compare two actions, either pure or mixed, one determines which two lines of the family $.8L_1 + .2L_2 = K$ they fall on and chooses the action that lies on the line with the smaller K, which is the one that is lower on the graph. Alternatively, one imagines a line with slope -4 moving up to the set of actions from below all of them; the first action encountered by the moving line is a Bayes action. This is illustrated in Figure 3–10, both for the case of $(.8, .2)$ as the prior distribution and for $(.1, .9)$, the slope in the latter case being $-\frac{1}{9}$.

Observe that as w is decreased from $.8$, so that the slope of the family of pertinent lines is not so extreme, the Bayes action continues to be a_1 until w reaches $.5$, in which case the family of lines would be parallel to the line through a_2 and a_1. In this case, $w = .5$, either a_2 or a_1 is chosen, since they have the same Bayes loss—as would any mixture of these. But then reducing w further yields families of lines with slopes such that a_2 is encountered first in coming up from below. It should not be too surprising that these conclusions are precisely the same as those reached earlier, in Example 3–10.

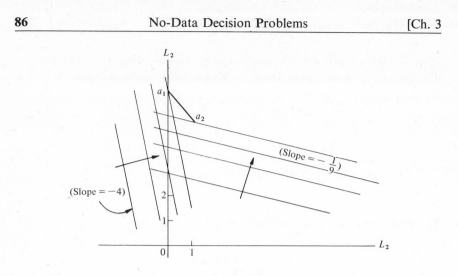

Figure 3–10

One of the byproducts of the geometrical analysis carried out in Example 3–11 above is the fact that if losses had been converted into regrets prior to determining the Bayes action, there would have been no difference in final results. For, what determined those results was in no way linked to the location of the coordinate origin, involving only families of parallel lines. Regrets are obtained by moving the set of points representing the mixed actions, without rotation, so that at least one point lies on each coordinate axis with the rest of them in the first quadrant; so long as the set is not rotated relative to the coordinate system, the points first encountered in moving a line with fixed slope upward to the set are the same with regrets as with losses.

Although this result—that the Bayes actions are the same using regret as using losses—is evident for the problem involving only two states of nature (from the geometry of the problem), it is also true in general. Substitution of

$$r(\theta_i, a_j) = l(\theta_i, a_j) - \min_a l(\theta_i, a)$$

into the expression for expected regret:

$$E[r(\theta, a_j)] = \sum_i r(\theta_i, a_j)g(\theta_i)$$

yields

$$E[r(\theta, a_j)] = \sum_i l(\theta_i, a_j)g(\theta_i) - \sum_i g(\theta_i) \min_a l(\theta_i, a)$$
$$= E[l(\theta, a_j)] - \sum_i g(\theta_i) \min_a l(\theta_i, a).$$

Thus, $E[r(\theta, a_j)]$ differs from $E[l(\theta, a_j)]$ by a term that does not involve a_j. The action that minimizes one must therefore minimize the other.

Example 3–12. Consider the decision problem with the following loss table

	a_1	a_2	a_3
θ_1	2	5	3
θ_2	3	1	5

The regrets are

$$r(\theta_1, a) = l(\theta_1, a) - 2$$
$$r(\theta_2, a) = l(\theta_2, a) - 1.$$

The expected regrets, given prior weights $g(\theta_1)$ and $g(\theta_2)$, are

$$E[r(\theta, a_1)] = 2g(\theta_1) + 3g(\theta_2) - [2g(\theta_1) + g(\theta_2)]$$
$$E[r(\theta, a_2)] = 5g(\theta_1) + g(\theta_2) - [2g(\theta_1) + g(\theta_2)]$$
$$E[r(\theta, a_3)] = 3g(\theta_1) + 5g(\theta_2) - [2g(\theta_1) + g(\theta_2)]$$

so that

$$E[r(\theta, a_i)] = E[l(\theta, a)] - [2g(\theta_1) + g(\theta_2)].$$

The action that minimizes $E[r(\theta, a_i)]$ is the same as the action that minimizes $E[l(\theta, a_i)]$, since these differ by $[2g(\theta_1) + g(\theta_2)]$, which does not involve the action.

Problems

3–12 Use the graphical methods of Examples 3–10 and 3–11 to determine the Bayes solutions corresponding to the prior distribution $g(\theta_1) = w$ and $g(\theta_2) = 1 - w$ for the decision problem with the following loss table

	a_1	a_2	a_3
θ_1	2	0	3
θ_2	-1	4	3

Examine the dependence of the solution on the probability w.

3–13 Determine the Bayes action or actions for prior probabilities (.3, .3, .4) for $(\theta_1, \theta_2, \theta_3)$, respectively, for the decision problem with loss table

	a_1	a_2	a_3
θ_1	-1	2	0
θ_2	2	-2	3
θ_3	4	3	1

(Would your answer be different if you consider *mixed* actions as well? Would it be different if you considered regrets instead of losses? Work out the Bayes regrets and so verify your answer.)

3–14 Determine the Bayes action in the problem of rejecting or accepting a lot of five articles, given in Problem 3–10, assuming prior probabilities $g(0) = .6$, $g(1) = .2, g(2) = g(3) = .1, g(4) = g(5) = 0$.

3–15 Determine a prior distribution for Problem 3–12 above against which the minimax (mixed) action is Bayes. Also plot the graph of $\min_a B(a)$ as a function of w, and determine the largest value of this function. Do you observe any relationship?

3–16 Repeat the analysis called for in Problem 3–15, but for the elevator problem (Example 3–10 and others), using regrets rather than losses.

3–17 Observe in Problem 3–13 that the losses for action a_3 are (for each state) greater than the corresponding losses for action a_1. Observe also that a_3 does not enter into a Bayes solution. Examine this phenomenon and see if you can state (and prove?) a general fact.

3.5 Dominance and Admissibility

Examples have been encountered in which certain of the available actions would never be used because there are others for which losses are always less. Some definitions along this line are as follows.

DEFINITION *An action a^* (pure or mixed) is said to* dominate *an action a if the loss incurred by using action a is always at least as great as that incurred by using a:*

$$l(\theta, a) \geq l(\theta, a^*), \quad \text{for all } \theta.$$

DEFINITION *An action a^* is said to* dominate strictly *an action a if it dominates action a and if, in addition, there is some state of nature for which the loss inequality is strict:*

$$l(\theta, a) > l(\theta, a^*), \quad \text{for some } \theta.$$

DEFINITION   *An action* (*pure or mixed*) *is said to be* admissible *if no other action dominates it strictly.*

The case of two states of nature is useful in that it is possible to gain an appreciation of the significance of these definitions through a graphical representation. In this case an action is represented as a point in the $L_1 L_2$ plane, where L_i is the loss (or expected loss, in the case of a mixed action) incurred when that action is taken and θ_i is the state of nature. Figure 3–11 shows points corresponding to actions a^*, a_1 and a_2, for which losses are such that a^* dominates both a_1 and a_2. In the case of a_1 the losses are greater

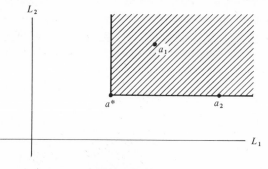

Figure 3–11

than for a^* for both states of nature; in the case of a_2 only the loss for θ_1 is strictly greater than with a^*. Incidentally, the action a^* would strictly dominate every action represented by points in the shaded quadrant (including the boundaries), with the exception of the point a^* itself. (In this kind of representation, an action that dominates action a but does not *strictly* dominate it would be represented by the *same* point as action a, since the losses would be the same.)

If an action a^* dominates an action a there is no need to leave a in the competition for a best action. If the dominance is not strict, then the losses are the same for a as for a^*, and a can be dispensed with; if it is strict, then one may actually do worse by using a than by using a^*. This latter fact was shown in Problem 3–11 in connection with the minimax principle and in Problem 3–17 for Bayes solutions.

A comment on the term *admissibility* should be made. An action that is not admissible is said to be inadmissible, and can be dispensed with because there is an action that does at least as well under all circumstances. On the other hand, an action that is close to the lower left boundary of a set of mixed actions (in the $L_1 L_2$ representation) may not be so bad as the name *inadmissible* would imply. That is, there are degrees of inadmissibility which the terminology ignores. In some statistical problems, for example, there may be solutions that are slightly inadmissible but are preferred for some reason to those that dominate them—because of computability, for instance.

3.6 Bayes Versus Minimax

Again the geometric representation possible when there are just two states of nature is instructive. Because the set of all possible (mixed) actions is represented in the L_1L_2 plane as a convex set, the minimax procedure of moving a wedge with its vertex on the 45° line up until it first strikes the set will always yield as a minimax action one whose representative point is on the left lower portion of the boundary. In Figure 3–12 a convex set is shown together with a number of wedges, as they first strike the set, corresponding to different locations of the 45° line relative to the set.

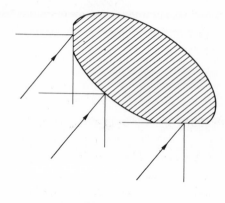

Figure 3–12

In Figure 3–13 is shown a convex set, representing the set of all mixed actions in some decision problem, together with various lines with negative slopes, corresponding to different prior distributions $(w, 1 - w)$. Again the situation is clear: Bayes solutions, obtained by moving a line with negative slope up to the set of mixed actions, will lie only along the lower left portion of the boundary.

Several possible generalities should have occurred to the reader by now, after studying the above figures, namely

(1) Bayes solutions are usually admissible.

(2) A minimax action is a Bayes action.

(3) Admissible actions are Bayes, for some prior distribution.

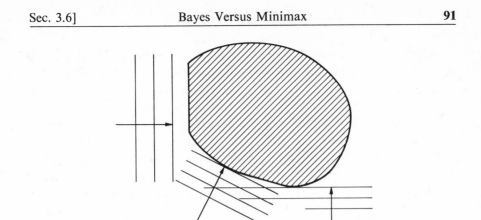

Figure 3–13

With suitable hedging, in the form of restrictions ruling out certain extreme cases for which they are clearly not so, these turn out to be facts—theorems, susceptible of mathematical proof. The exact statements and their formal proofs will not be given here.

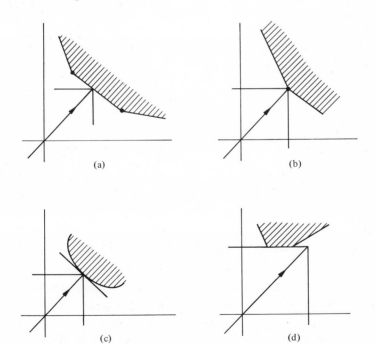

Figure 3–14

That a minimax solution is Bayes for some prior distribution is evident, for the case of two states of nature, from the geometrical representation in the L_1L_2 plane. Figure 3–14 gives four kinds of situations that may arise. In Figure 3–14(a), the minimax action occurs on the boundary of the set of actions, and is a mixture of two pure actions; this action would be Bayes for the prior distribution $(w, 1 - w)$ such that $-w/(1 - w)$ is equal to the slope of the line through the two pure actions involved. In Figure 3–14(b), the minimax action, which is a pure action, would be Bayes for any prior distribution such that $-w/(1 - w)$ is a slope between the slopes of the line segments which meet in that pure action. In Figure 3–14(c) the prior distribution which produces the minimax action as a Bayes action corresponds to the tangent line at $L_1 = L_2$; this kind of set of mixed actions would only occur if there are infinitely many pure actions at the outset. In Figure 3–14(d) the minimax action would be any that yields an (L_1, L_2) on the bottom edge of the action set; these are Bayes for the prior distribution, which assigns probability 1 to θ_2.

Example 3–13. Consider again the decision problem of Example 3–12, with loss table as follows:

	a_1	a_2	a_3
θ_1	2	5	3
θ_2	3	1	5

The Bayes losses are as follows, given prior probabilities $(w, 1 - w)$:

$$B(a_1) = 2w + 3(1 - w) = 3 - w$$

$$B(a_2) = 5w + (1 - w) = 1 + 4w$$

$$B(a_3) = 3w + 5(1 - w) = 5 - 2w.$$

The graphs of these are shown in Figure 3–15. The minimum for a given w is the ordinate of the lowest line, and the highest minimum is at $w = \frac{2}{5}$. That is, of all the prior distributions that Nature might choose, the statistician has the highest minimum Bayes loss (loss incurred by using the Bayes action) for the prior distribution $(\frac{2}{5}, \frac{3}{5})$. (This is said to be a *least favorable* prior distribution.) The minimax mixed action is easily found (by the usual graphical

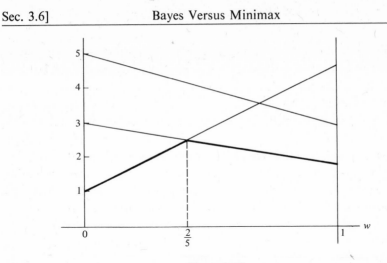

Figure 3–15

procedure) to be $(\frac{4}{5}, \frac{1}{5}, 0)$ with losses $L_1 = L_2 = 13/5$. For (see Figure 3–16), it is the point on the line through $(2, 3)$ and $(5, 1)$ with equal coordinates:

$$\frac{L_1 - 3}{L_1 - 2} = -\frac{2}{3}, \quad \text{or} \quad L_1 = \frac{13}{5}.$$

A prior distribution that would yield this mixed action as a Bayes action is defined by a w such that

$$\frac{-w}{1 - w} = -\frac{2}{3},$$

where $-\frac{2}{3}$ is the slope of the line through $(5, 1)$ and $(2, 3)$. Notice that this w, which is $w = \frac{2}{5}$, is precisely the w of the least favorable distribution determined above.

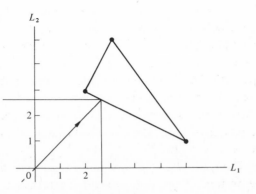

Figure 3–16

The phenomenon of a *least favorable* distribution giving rise to the minimax action as a Bayes action is general, but nontrivial to establish. More will be said of it in the chapter on game theory.

It is not unusual to use a probability model for an experiment which has already taken place, to yield a result that exists—but is unknown. Thus, if someone tosses a coin but covers the coin as it falls so that no one sees the result, one can still usefully treat the outcome as an experiment of chance—even though the outcome is already determined and fixed. In the case of the state of nature, however, one might wonder whether he should consider the state that prevails to be an outcome (albeit unknown) of an experiment of chance. Actually, it is not necessary to adopt this attitude in order to use the Bayes principle for determining an action. Mathematically what one is doing is just postulating a weighting function that provides an ordering among the actions; practically, he is incorporating into that weighting function his personal attitude and hunches about what the unknown state of nature is likely to be. In this sense, if the weight is a probability at all, it is *subjective* or *personal*, as discussed in Section 2.6.

It may be argued that personal factors and considerations *should* play a role in the making of *rational* decisions. Surely, the prior weighting required for a Bayes solution does permit the incorporation of such factors into the problem. Indeed, it requires this incorporation. This in itself may be good, for the pressure to analyze and think through carefully enough to set forth a prior distribution is itself healthful.

Another argument in defense of the Bayes approach is that the solution is often not terribly sensitive to moderate changes in the prior distribution, so that some inaccuracy in its specification is not harmful.

An argument in favor of the Bayes approach is that Bayes solutions are generally admissible, and that reducing the list of all actions to just the set of Bayes actions is often a major accomplishment. That is, if an action is Bayes for *some* prior distribution, it is already rather special.

The minimax approach, on the other hand, is not nearly so easy to defend. As mentioned previously, it is pessimistic, making the assumption that the worst will happen. Although it is frequently admissible, and Bayes for some prior distribution, that distribution is least favorable—the distribution that Nature would choose were she playing a game with the decision maker and trying her best to outwit him. The obvious instance in which a minimax solution is inadmissible is that shown in Figure 3–17, for the case of two states of nature. There are actually many minimax actions, only one of which (the one at the bottom of the vertical side) is admissible. These minimax solutions are also Bayes (for the prior $(1, 0)$); and so this is an example in

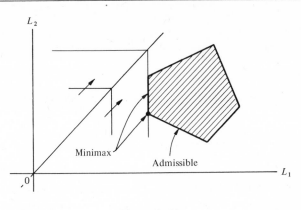

Figure 3–17

which many of the Bayes solutions are not admissible, being dominated by the one at the bottom of the vertical side.

Sometimes a minimax solution can be computed by determining among the Bayes solutions one for which the losses under the various states of nature are equal. That is, if $\mathbf{p}^* = (p_1^*, \ldots, p_k^*)$ is a mixed action that is Bayes with respect to some prior $g(\theta)$ and is such that the (expected) loss function

$$L(\theta, \mathbf{p}^*) = E[l(\theta, a)] = \sum_i l(\theta, a_i) p_i^*$$

is constant in θ, then $\mathbf{p}^*$ is minimax. This is seen as follows: The assumption that $\mathbf{p}^*$ is Bayes for $g(\theta)$ means that for any mixed action $\mathbf{p}$,

$$B(\mathbf{p}^*) = \min_{\mathbf{p}} B(\mathbf{p}) \le B(\mathbf{p}).$$

But since $L(\theta, \mathbf{p}^*)$ is constant, its mean value with respect to the weighting $g(\theta)$ is just that constant value:

$$B(\mathbf{p}^*) = E[L(\theta, \mathbf{p}^*)] = L(\theta, \mathbf{p}^*).$$

On the other hand, since $B(\mathbf{p})$ is the expected value of $L(\theta, \mathbf{p})$, which cannot exceed the maximum value of $L(\theta, \mathbf{p})$:

$$B(\mathbf{p}) \le \max_{\theta} L(\theta, \mathbf{p}),$$

it follows that for any $\mathbf{p}$

$$L(\theta, \mathbf{p}^*) \leq \max_{\theta} L(\theta, \mathbf{p}).$$

But then surely the constant $L(\theta, \mathbf{p}^*)$ cannot exceed the smallest of these maxima

$$L(\theta, \mathbf{p}^*) \leq \min_{\mathbf{p}} \max_{\theta} L(\theta, \mathbf{p}),$$

the right hand member of this inequality being the minimax loss.

Now, since $L(\theta, \mathbf{p}^*)$ is constant in θ, it is equal to its maximum value, which in turn is greater than or equal to the smallest such maximum:

$$L(\theta, \mathbf{p}^*) = \max_{\theta} L(\theta, \mathbf{p}^*) \geq \min_{\mathbf{p}} \max_{\theta} L(\theta, \mathbf{p}).$$

And then because $L(\theta, \mathbf{p}^*)$ is neither less than nor greater than the minimax loss, it must be equal to it—and this means that $\mathbf{p}^*$ is a minimax solution, as was asserted.

This result was previously established for the ease of two states of nature, where it follows easily from the geometrical representation. The losses are equal in that case if $L_1 = L_2$, which characterizes the 45° line in the $L_1 L_2$ plane. The assertion then is that the intersection of the 45° line with the set of Bayes solutions (if they intersect at all) is a point corresponding to a minimax solution. This phenomenon is illustrated in Figures 3–14(a), 3–14(b), and 3–14(c). Figure 3–14(d) illustrates the possibility that the 45° line may not intersect the set of Bayes solutions.

Problems

3–18 Determine the admissible (mixed) actions for the decision problem of Problem 3–12, with loss table

	a_1	a_2	a_3
θ_1	2	0	3
θ_2	−1	4	3

3–19 Determine the prior distribution corresponding to the minimax action for Problem 3–18. Determine also the prior distribution for which the minimum Bayes loss is largest.

3–20 Follow the instructions of Problem 3–19 but for the decision problem of the elevator (see Example 3–11), with loss table

	θ_1	θ_2
a_1	0	6
a_2	1	5

Do it for both losses and for regrets.

3–21 Consider the following loss table

	θ_1	θ_2	θ_3
a_1	3	3	5
a_2	3	3	8

(a) How are a_1 and a_2 related?

(b) Determine any minimax (pure) actions.

(c) Is there a prior distribution for which *both* actions are Bayes?

Chapter 4   Using Data in Making Decisions

By *data* will be meant the results of making one or more observations on some random quantitity that is thought to be intimately related to the state of nature in some decision problem. The availability of such data will generally provide some illumination, so that in the selection of an action one is not completely in the dark concerning the state of nature. It will be seen that the intelligent use of data will define procedures which result in an expected loss that is lower than what would be incurred if the data were not available. However, even the availability of data will not avoid completely the kind of situation encountered in the no-data case, in which there is no clear-cut criterion for rating the various candidate procedures as a basis for choosing one of them as best.

4.1 Data and the State of Nature

To obtain data for use in making decisions one performs an appropriate experiment of chance—one whose *law* is different for the different states of nature. That is, the state of nature determines the generation of the data, and so the probability distribution for the data depends on that state of nature.

The data of a given problem may consist of a single number (value of a random variable), or a sequence of numbers—usually resulting from performing the same experiment repeatedly, or sometimes a result or results that are not numerical. For the general discussion, the name Z will be employed to refer to the data, and in the problems to be considered here Z will denote either a single random variable, or a sequence of random variables:

$(X_1, X_2, \ldots, X_n)$. In any case Z will have certain possible "values," and a probability for each, according to the state of nature. Thus, for each value z of the random quantity Z there is a probability

$$f(z; \theta) = P_\theta(Z = z)$$

assigned to that value z by the state of nature θ. (The notation $P_\theta(E)$ will mean the probability of the event E when the state of nature is θ.) The probability depends both on z and on θ, and so both of these enter into the symbol $f(z; \theta)$. It is important to realize that in order for the data to be of value in making a decision, this dependence of the probability distribution for Z on the state of nature *must be known*. That is, $f(z; \theta)$ is assumed to be given or known.

Example 4–1.   Returning to the situation of Examples 3–9, 3–10, and 3–11, in which the instructor entering the building must choose between going down one flight or up one flight to catch the elevator, suppose that he can see the lights near the buttons for summoning the elevator. Thus, at each floor there is a button and a light; when the button is pushed the light comes on, and goes off again only when the elevator doors open. The *data* here might be summarized simply in the number of lights showing, a quantity Z that takes on one of the values 0, 1, or 2. If $Z = 0$, no one has summoned the elevator; if $Z = 1$, the elevator has been summoned on one floor, and may or may not be in the process of answering the summons; and if $Z = 2$, it has been summoned on both the ground and first floors, and one may suspect that the lights have been on for some time because the elevator is not working. Suppose now that the distribution of probability among the values 0, 1, and 2 is known, for each state of nature, and is as given in the following table:

z	$f(z; \theta_1)$	$f(z; \theta_2)$
0	.6	.1
1	.3	.4
2	.1	.5

Since it has been stated as essential that these probabilities be known, it is natural to wonder where they come from. In this instance, as in most, there are two possible sources. They may come from actual observation—one keeps

track, over a long period in which the elevator is working, of the percentage
of time that 0, 1, and 2 lights are lit, respectively, and also over a period of
time in which the elevator is not working. Or, they may result from some
theoretical considerations; in this case, a mathematical model for the stream
of persons entering the building, and for their use of the elevator, could lead
to the necessary probabilities. (Even in the latter instance, however, some
record of actual goings on would likely to be needed to establish certain
parameters of the model.)

4.2 Decision Functions

A procedure for using data as an aid to decision-making will involve a rule,
or set of instructions, that assigns one of the available actions to each possible
value of the data Z. Thus, when the pertinent experiment is performed and a
value of Z obtained, say $Z = z$, an action has already been assigned by the
rule to that value, and one takes that action. A rule, then, is a *function*:
$a = d(z)$, and is called a *decision function*, or a *statistical decision function*.
With such a function, one is prepared for every contingency (that is, every
conceivable value of Z) with an action to take. This function could be thought
of (and defined by) an instruction card, which one could leave behind for
someone else; this person would obtain the data, look on the card, and take
the action prescribed by the card for the value observed. Different procedures,
or different rules, or different decision functions would then simply be
different instruction cards.

How many rules (distinct instruction cards) are there? If there are just k
available actions ($a_1, a_2, \ldots,$ and a_k), and if the data Z can have one of just m
possible values (say $z_1, z_2, \ldots, z_m$), then there are precisely k^m distinct decision
functions that can be specified. For, in constructing a decision function, one
has k choices of action to assign to the value z_1, k choices of action to assign
to the value z_2, and so on. These choices can then be combined in $k \cdot k \cdots k =
k^m$ ways.

Of the k^m possible decision functions, some are sensible, some are foolish;
some ignore the data, and some will use it wrongly.

Example 4–2. In the elevator problem (see Example 4–1) there are two
actions: a_1 (walk down one flight) and a_2 (walk up one flight). There are three
possible values of the observed Z: 0, 1, and 2. Thus, there are eight (2^3)

distinct decision rules, which can be defined (and arbitrarily labeled) as in the following table:

z	d_1	d_2	d_3	d_4	d_5	d_6	d_7	d_8
0	a_2	a_2	a_2	a_1	a_2	a_1	a_1	a_1
1	a_2	a_2	a_1	a_2	a_1	a_2	a_1	a_1
2	a_2	a_1	a_2	a_2	a_1	a_1	a_2	a_1

Rule d_3, for instance, then, means that action a_2 is to be taken if one observes $Z = 0$ or 2, and a_1 is to be taken if one observes $Z = 1$. Rule d_1 ignores the data in the sense that action a_2 is taken no matter what the value of Z turns out to be. Rule d_8 also ignores the data. Rule d_4 and rule d_5 are *opposite*; surely if one is found to be a good rule, the other must not be so good.

It is possible to *mix* decision rules in much the same way one mixes actions, namely, by using an extraneous random device to choose among the available rules; a mixed decision function is then a probability distribution over the set of pure decision functions, assigning probability p_i (say) to decision function $d_i(z)$. So if there are r decision rules, one rolls an r-sided die, weighted so that the probability of the ith side is p_i, and follows the procedure on instruction card i (that is, $d_i(z)$) if that side turns up.

A mixed decision rule can be defined alternatively by attaching an extraneous experiment of chance to each possible value z_i of the data Z, which selects one of the actions $(a_1, \ldots, a_k)$ according to some probability distribution $(b_1, \ldots, b_k)$. Such a rule is equivalent to a mixture of pure decision functions, when the numbers of actions and possible values of Z are finite, as will be seen in the following example.

Example 4–3. Referring to Example 4–2, consider the mixture of decision rules defined by the probability vector $(.1, .1, .1, .2, .2, .1, .1, .1)$. This would be executed by tossing a 10-sided die with two sides marked d_4, two sides marked d_5, and one side each marked with other rules. Suppose then that the pertinent experiment (the one related to the state of nature) results in $Z = 1$. Then action a_2 would be taken according to instruction cards d_1, d_2, d_4 and d_6, that is, with probability $.1 + .1 + .2 + .1 = .5$. Action a_1 would be taken using cards d_3, d_5, d_7, and d_8, or with probability $.1 + .2 + .1 + .1 = .5$. Similarly if $Z = 0$, action a_2 and action a_1 would each be taken with probability $.5$; and if $Z = 2$, again actions a_2 and a_1 would be taken with equal probabilities. Thus, tossing a fair coin to determine which outcome to take if $Z = 0$, also if $Z = 1$, and also if $Z = 2$, would be equivalent to the given mixed decision rule.

But consider a different mixture of rules: $(0, 0, .1, .3, .6, 0, 0, 0)$. With this procedure, and if $Z = 0$, one would take action a_2 with probability .7; if $Z = 1$, he would take action a_2 with probability .3; and if $Z = 2$, action a_2 with probability .4. Imagine then three "coins," one biased so that $P(\text{heads}) = .7$, one with $P(\text{heads}) = .3$, and one with $P(\text{heads}) = .4$. The procedure of tossing the first of these if $Z = 0$, the second if $Z = 1$, and the third if $Z = 2$, taking a_2 if heads turns up (otherwise a_1), is equivalent to the mixed decision rule obtained by rolling a 10-sided die and using instruction card d_3 if the one side marked d_3 turns up, card d_4 if one of the three sides so marked turns up, and d_5 if one of the six sides so marked turns up.

4.3 The Risk Function

When a given decision function $d(z)$ is used, the loss incurred will depend not only on the state of nature that governs, but also on the value of Z that is observed. Since Z is random, the loss incurred,

$$l(\theta, d(Z)),$$

is a random variable. Because loss is considered to be negative utility, the quantity that should enter in making decisions for a random loss is its expected value:

$$R(\theta, d) = E[l(\theta, d(Z))].$$

This quantity, which as indicated depends on the state of nature θ and on the decision rule d that is used, is called the *risk function*. Assuming a distribution for Z defined by

$$P_\theta(Z = z) = f(z; \theta),$$

the risk function would be calculated as

$$R(\theta, d) = \sum_i l(\theta, d(z_i))f(z_i; \theta),$$

that is, as the weighted average of the various values of the random loss.

Notice that the dependence of risk on the state θ arises because of two facts: the loss for a given action depends on θ, and the probability weights used in computing the expected loss depend on θ.

The decision problem may now be stated as follows. It is up to the decision maker, called a *statistician* when the decision is based on observed results of an experiment of chance, to select a decision rule (pure or mixed) from those available to him, knowing the risk function but in ignorance of the true state of nature. This essential difficulty of the decision problem (not knowing θ), observed in the no-data case, persists; but it will be seen that the availability of data related to the state of nature does permit a better job of decision making, if the data are wisely used. Nevertheless, the problem of selecting a decision rule knowing the risk function is mathematically exactly the same kind of problem as that of selecting an action in the absence of data, knowing the loss function. The methods (minimax, Bayes) used in attacking the no-data problem can be used for the problem with data.

Example 4–4. For the elevator problem, discussed in Examples 4–1, 4–2, and 4–3, the risks are as given in the following table:

	d_1	d_2	d_3	d_4	d_5	d_6	d_7	d_8
θ_1	1	.9	.7	.4	.6	.3	.1	0
θ_2	5	5.5	5.4	5.1	5.9	5.6	5.5	6

The computation will be given for a couple of the entries. For θ_1 and d_5, the risk is a weighted average of 1 and 0, the losses under θ_1:

$$R(\theta_1, d_5) = 0 \cdot P_{\theta_1}(a_1 \text{ is taken using } d_5) + 1 \cdot P_{\theta_1}(a_2 \text{ is taken using } d_5)$$

$$= 0 + P_{\theta_1}(Z = 0) = .6.$$

(The event $Z = 0$, leading to a_2 under d_5, comes from the table in Example 4–2; the probability of .6 of $Z = 0$ under θ_1 comes from the table in Example 4–1.) Similarly,

$$R(\theta_2, d_3) = 6 \cdot P_{\theta_2}(a_1 \text{ is taken using } d_3) + 5 \cdot P_{\theta_2}(a_2 \text{ is taken using } d_3)$$

$$= 6 \cdot P_{\theta_2}(Z = 1) + 5 \cdot P_{\theta_2}(Z = 0 \text{ or } 2)$$

$$= 6 \times .4 + 5 \times .6 = 5.4.$$

Continuing in this way one can easily fill out the table above.

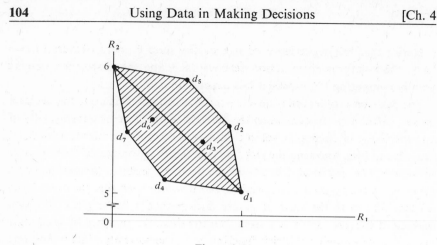

Figure 4–1

The decision rules are representable graphically as before, where one plots now (R_1, R_2), with $R_i = R(\theta_i, d)$, for each rule d. The plot is given in Figure 4–1, which shows in addition to the pure decision rules the set of mixtures of the pure rules, as the convex set generated by them.

Several observations should be made. The pure decision functions d_1 and d_8, which ignore the data, give points (R_1, R_2) which are exactly the same as the corresponding (L_1, L_2) for the no-data problem. The straight line joining d_1 and d_8 would consist of mixtures that are exactly equivalent (as regards risk) to mixtures of the pure actions a_2 and a_1, respectively, in the absence of data. The data then provide risk points which clearly dominate these no-data points; in particular, d_4, d_6, and d_7 are all better, and indeed d_4 and d_7 are admissible. On the other hand, there are several rules (d_2, d_3, and d_5) which are worse than rules that make no use of the data, and which therefore make awfully poor use of the data. So an intelligent use of data can improve the losses (expected losses, really) under all states of nature, and using the data foolishly can deteriorate the loss situation.

The phenomenon observed in the example above is typical; the availability of data permits a reduction of losses if the data are wisely used and if the set of (R_1, R_2) points representing the various procedures is pulled in toward the zero regret point, where decisions are as perfect as they could be. But it should be emphasized that for this to happen the data must have some connection with the state of nature! For, if the distribution of Z is independent of θ:

$$P_\theta(Z = z) = f(z; \theta) = k(z),$$

then the risks for a given rule $d(z)$ are

$$R_i = E[l(\theta_i, d(Z))] = \sum_j l(\theta_i, d(z_j))k(z_j) \quad \text{for } i = 1, \ldots, s.$$

In vector form this becomes

$$\begin{pmatrix} R_1 \\ \vdots \\ R_s \end{pmatrix} = \sum_j k(z_j) \begin{pmatrix} l(\theta_1, d(z_j)) \\ \vdots \\ l(\theta_s, d(z_j)) \end{pmatrix},$$

which is a convex combination of the points $(L_1, \ldots, L_s)$, where

$$L_i = l(\theta_i, d(z_j)),$$

corresponding to the m actions $d(z_1), \ldots, d(z_m)$. These losses can be achieved by the mixture $(k(z_1), \ldots, k(z_m))$ of *pure* actions $d(z_1), \ldots, d(z_m)$, and so the data do not extend the convex set of loss points to risk points that are any better.

Example 4–5. Suppose that in the problem of Example 4–4 one has data Z with values 0, 1, 2 and probabilities as follows:

z	0	1	2
$f(z; \theta_1)$	.2	.3	.5
$f(z; \theta_2)$	.2	.3	.5

Risks are calculated as in the preceding example; for d_3 one obtains

$$R(\theta_1, d_3) = 0 \times .3 + 1 \times .7$$
$$R(\theta_2, d_3) = 6 \times .3 + 5 \times .7$$

or

$$\begin{pmatrix} R_1 \\ R_2 \end{pmatrix} = .3 \begin{pmatrix} 0 \\ 6 \end{pmatrix} + .7 \begin{pmatrix} 1 \\ 5 \end{pmatrix}.$$

This is a convex combination of pure actions a_1 and a_2. Similarly, for *each* decision rule, the (R_1, R_2) is a convex combination of the points corresponding to the pure actions a_1 and a_2. The results that are possible using the given data, then, are the same as with no data.

Problems

4–1 Repeat the computations of risk for the problem of Example 4–4, but using instead the following probability distributions of Z:

z	0	1	2
$f(z; \theta_1)$	0	.1	.9
$f(z; \theta_2)$	.8	.2	0

Compare the plot of the points (R_1, R_2) in this case with that of Example 4–4, noting the effect of a tighter relationship of the data to θ, that allows greater discrimination.

4–2 This refers back to the situation of Problems 3–10 and 3–14: A lot of five articles is to be accepted (a_1) or rejected (a_2), the unknown state of nature being characterized by the number M of defective articles among the five. The loss assumed is $2M$ if a lot is passed, and $5 - M$ if a lot is rejected. One article is drawn from the lot at random and tested, being either good (z_1) or defective (z_2). Assume, unrealistically but to make things simple, that the article tested is replaced in the lot.
(a) Determine the probability function $f(z; M) = P_M(Z = z)$.
(b) Determine the decision functions, and make up a table of risk function values.

4–3 The decision functions studied in Problem 4–2 are to be applied in the following revised situation: The article tested is assumed destroyed, so that only the four remaining articles are passed. The loss, for lots that are passed, is 10 units for each defective in the passed lot, minus 20. (That is, the articles are sold for 5 units each, with a "double your money back" guarantee.) For lots that are rejected the loss is 5 units, representing the cost of junking the lot. Assume that decision functions d_1 and d_4, which in Problem 4–2 ignore the data, call for rejection or acceptance without going to the bother of carrying out the testing process, and that the entire lot of 5 would be for sale in this case.

4–4 In a problem with three states of nature, suppose that among the values of Z are three with the probabilities

$$f(z_1; \theta_1) = f(z_2; \theta_2) = f(z_3; \theta_3) = 1.$$

(The other probabilities can be figured from these!) Suppose further that the regret function is such that $r(\theta_1, a_1) = r(\theta_2, a_2) = r(\theta_3, a_3) = 0$. Determine a decision rule for which the risk function is zero for all three states of nature. [The observation Z is as strongly related to the state of nature as one could hope for.]

4–5 A decision problem is defined by the following tables giving losses and the distributions of data Z under the various states:

	a_1	a_2	a_3
θ_1	2	0	5
θ_2	-1	4	3

	z_1	z_2	z_3
$f(z \mid \theta_1)$	.2	.3	.5
$f(z \mid \theta_2)$	.6	.3	.1

(a) How many decision functions are there? If dominance is used to eliminate actions that will not be used in good decisions, how many?

(b) Determine the risk table for the reduced problem (after elimination of unhelpful actions).

4.4 Selecting a Decision Function

The concepts of dominance and admissibility are extended in the obvious way to decision functions, by defining them in terms of the risk function. That is, a decision function d^* *dominates* a decision function d if and only if

$$R(\theta, d^*) \le R(\theta, d), \quad \text{for all } \theta.$$

The dominance is said to be *strict* if the inequality is strict for at least one state of nature. A decision function is *admissible* if it is not dominated strictly by any other decision function.

A decision function that involves an inadmissible action will be inadmissible. For, if a is not admissible, it is dominated by some action a^*:

$$l(\theta_0, a^*) < l(\theta_0, a), \quad \text{for some } \theta_0.$$

If $d(z)$ assigns the action a to some possible value z_j of positive probability under θ_0, one can define the new rule $d^*(z)$ to be identical with $d(z)$ except that $d^*(z_j) = a^*$, and then

$$R(\theta_0, d^*) = \sum_j l(\theta_0, d^*(z_i))f(z_i; \theta_0)$$

$$< \sum_j l(\theta_0, d(z_i))f(z_i; \theta_0) = R(\theta_0, d).$$

(The inequality follows because the losses in the sums are identical except for the term where $i = j$, in which case $d*$ calls for $a*$ instead of a, yielding a smaller loss.) For states other than θ_0 the inequalities $<$ are replaced by $\leq$, and the strict dominance of d by $d*$ follows.

The selection of a decision function, with the knowledge of the risk function but with the state of nature unknown, is exactly the same problem—mathematically—as the selection of an action, knowing the loss function but not θ. The risk in the present situation plays the role of the loss function in the no-data problem, and the decision function plays the role of the pure action. The selection of a decision function is more complicated because the list of decision functions is larger, usually, than the list of actions, and because the risk function must first be calculated from the given losses. (However, it has already been seen that the effective use of data can reduce losses.)

As in the no-data case, then, it is necessary to devise a scheme of preferences so that in this ordering one can select the most desirable decision rule. The minimax principle again provides a numerical measure of decision rules, namely, the maximum risk over the various states of nature:

$$M(d) = \max_{\theta} R(\theta, d).$$

The minimax decision function is the d that minimizes this maximum risk. It is not always simple to determine, but in the case of two states of nature, the graphical procedure introduced in Chapter 3 for the no-data problem can be employed.

Another scheme for ordering procedures is that of assigning prior probability weights $g(\theta)$ to the various states of nature, and determining the average risk over these states:

$$B(d) = E[R(\theta, d)] = \sum_{j} R(\theta_j, d)g(\theta_j).$$

This is called the *Bayes risk*. The preferred decision rule is the decision function d which minimizes this Bayes risk; it would be called the *Bayes decision function*, corresponding to the given prior distribution. Thus, there is a family of Bayes decision functions, corresponding to the various possible prior distributions for the state of nature.

As in the no-data case, it can make a difference—at least, if one is going to consider a minimax approach—whether one uses regrets or losses. In considering this difference, it should be noted first that there are two ways to introduce the idea of regret—by applying it to the initial loss function, and by applying it to the risk, or expected loss. Not surprisingly, these result in the same thing, as will now be shown. The regret function was defined as

$$r(\theta, a_i) = l(\theta, a_i) - \min_a l(\theta, a),$$

so for each z,

$$r(\theta, d(z)) = l(\theta, d(z)) - \min_a l(\theta, a);$$

and the expected regret is then

$$E[r(\theta, d(Z))] = E[l(\theta, d(Z))] - \min_a l(\theta, a).$$

Now, for any decision rule d,

$$l(\theta, d(z)) \geq \min_a l(\theta, a), \quad \text{for all } z,$$

so that

$$E[l(\theta, d(Z))] \geq \min_a l(\theta, a)$$

and

$$\min_d E[l(\theta, d(Z))] = \min_d R(\theta, d) \geq \min_a l(\theta, a).$$

But if a^* is the action that gives the minimum $l(\theta, a)$, and one considers the decision rule $d^*(z) \equiv a^*$, then

$$\min_d R(\theta, d) \leq R(\theta, d^*) = E[l(\theta, a^*)] = l(\theta, a^*) = \min_a l(\theta, a).$$

Thus, since the minimum regret over all rules d is neither larger nor smaller than the minimum loss over all actions a, these must be equal. Therefore, the expected regret is the same as the "regretized" risk:

$$E[r(\theta, d(Z))] = R(\theta, d) - \min_d R(\theta, d).$$

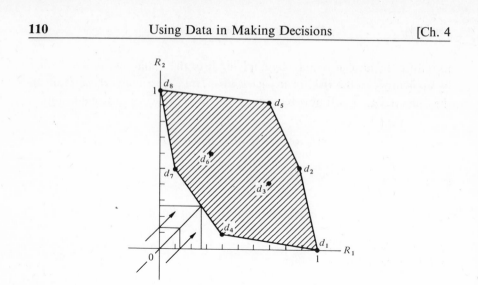

Figure 4–2

Example 4–6. The following table of expected regrets is obtained by regretizing the risks in the table of Example 4–4, that is, by subtracting the minimum value in each row from all of the entries in that row. Shown also are the maximum risks (expected regrets) $M(d)$ for each d, and the Bayes risk (expected regret) $B(d)$ corresponding to prior probabilities $g(\theta_1) = .8$ and $g(\theta_2) = .2$. The minimax pure decision rule is thus d_4, which minimizes

$g(\theta)$	θ	d_1	d_2	d_3	d_4	d_5	d_6	d_7	d_8
.8	θ_1	1	.9	.7	.4	.6	.3	.1	0
.2	θ_2	0	.5	.4	.1	.9	.6	.5	1
	$M(d)$:	1	.9	.7	.4	.9	.6	.5	1
	$B(d)$:	.8	.82	.64	.34	.66	.36	.18	.2

$M(d)$. The Bayes rule for the given prior distribution on θ is d_7, which minimizes $B(d)$. These may also be determined graphically, from the plot of Figure 4–2. From the graph it is evident that the minimax mixed decision rule is a mixture of d_7 and d_4, namely, $(0, 0, 0, p, 0, 0, 1 - p, 0)$, where

$$\binom{x}{x} = p\binom{.4}{.1} + (1 - p)\binom{.1}{.5}$$

or

$$.4p + .1 - .1p = .1p + .5 - .5p,$$

which yields $p = \frac{4}{7}$. Then minimum maximum expected risk is

$$.4\left(\frac{4}{7}\right) + .1 - .1\left(\frac{4}{7}\right) = \frac{19}{70}$$

Notice that for mixed actions and no data, the minimum maximum expected loss would be .5 (obtained by moving the usual wedge up to meet the line joining $(0, 1)$ and $(1, 0)$, which happens at $(.5, .5)$). Thus, the data has provided a reduction in the amount $.5 - \frac{19}{70}$, or $\frac{16}{70}$, in the minimum maximum expected loss. This may be thought of as the *value* of the experiment that provided Z, with respect to the minimax approach. (This is a *value* in the sense that one should not "spend" more than this value to obtain the data Z.)

The value of the data in a Bayes approach is also obtained by comparing the minimum Bayes loss without data, which would be .2, for the prior distribution $(.8, .2)$ used above, with the minimum Bayes expected regret, which (from the table above) is seen to be .18. The experiment that produces Z is worth .02 in the given circumstances. (Notice from the figure that a line with slope -4 through d_7 is not much farther down in the family of lines than the line with the same slope through d_8, which is equivalent to the no-data action a_1. On the other hand, if the prior $(.5, .5)$ has been used, the advantage to be had with the data is more pronounced.)

Problems

4-6 Determine the value of the data in Problem 4–1, as compared with that in Example 4–6, (a) in the case of Bayes solutions with $g(\theta_1) = .8$ and $g(\theta_2) = .2$; and (b) in the case of minimax regret strategies.

4-7 Referring to the acceptance sampling situation of Problem 4–2, use the prior probabilities $g(0) = .6$, $g(1) = .2$, $g(2) = g(3) = .1$ (as in Problem 3–14) to determine a corresponding Bayes pure decision rule. Also determine the minimum Bayes loss with and without the data, to determine the value of the data.

4-8 Determine the value of the data in Problem 4–2 when using a minimax procedure.

4-9 Determine the value of the experiment producing the data Z in Problem 4–5, (a) if the Bayes rule corresponding to the prior $(\frac{1}{2}, \frac{1}{2})$ for (θ_1, θ_2) is used; (b) if the minimax rule is used.

4.5 Conditional Probability

The Bayes approach to selecting a "best" decision involves the assumption of a probability distribution for the state of nature, which means (mathematically) that nature is being considered as a random variable. (If the state of nature is not described by a number, one might question the use of the word *variable*, if he insists that variables are numbers. One could then call nature a random "thing," but there is really nothing to prevent naming it a "variable.") Thus, when data are available, there are *two* random variables in the picture, the data Z and the state of nature Θ. (A capital theta is now used for the state of nature, to serve as a reminder that it is being considered as a random variable.) In such a case the distribution of probability is characterized by a *joint probability function*:

$$f(z_i, \theta_j) = P(Z = z_i \text{ and } \Theta = \theta_j).$$

Such a function of two variables, each of which assumes finitely many values, can be exhibited in a two-way table of values; with the distinct values of one variable at the side and the distinct values of the other variable at the top of the table, the entries opposite pairs of distinct values then being the probabilities of those pairs, respectively.

Even though there are two random variables present, one may still have interest in just one of them, and ask questions concerning probabilities for that one. Such questions can be answered from the probability function for that one, which is readily obtained from the joint probability function. Thus, the event $Z = z_i$ is made up of the various pairs $(z_i, \theta_1), (z_i, \theta_2), \ldots, (z_i, \theta_m)$, and its probability is the sum of the probabilities of those pairs:

$$P(Z = z_i) = P(Z = z_i \text{ and } \Theta = \theta_1) + \cdots + P(Z = z_i \text{ and } \Theta = \theta_m)$$

$$= f(z_i, \theta_1) + \cdots + f(z_i, \theta_m)$$

$$= \sum_j f(z_i, \theta_j).$$

This sum is just the sum of the entries in the two-way table of probabilities that are in the row (or column, depending on the layout) opposite z_i. Such sums are usually computed and written in the margin of the table opposite the values z_i, and so are called "marginal probabilities" for Z. Marginal probabilities for Θ are obtained by summing the probabilities in the columns (or the rows, depending on the layout) opposite the θ_j and are written in the corresponding margin.

Example 4–7.   Consider the random variables X and Y whose joint probability distribution is defined by the following table of probabilities

Y \\ X	x_1	x_2	x_3	
y_1	.2	0	.1	.3
y_2	.1	.3	.3	.7
	.3	.3	.4	

Shown also are the marginal totals, which give the distributions of X and Y separately. Thus, X is a random variable with three possible values, x_1, x_2, and x_3, which are assumed with probabilities .3, .3, and .4 respectively. Similarly, $P(Y = y_1) = .3$, and $P(Y = y_2) = .7$. It is to be noted that these same marginal totals could have been achieved with different joint probabilities in the body of the table. Thus, the joint probabilities carry information about the way X and Y are related, information that is not contained in the (marginal) distributions for X and Y when each is considered by itself.

When two random variables are related, through their joint distribution, information about the value of one may affect how one should bet on the other one—and hence, would affect the appropriate probability model for that other variable. For instance, in Example 4–7 above, if it were known that $X = x_2$, then it would be foolish to bet on $Y = y_1$, since the probability of the simultaneous occurrence of $X = x_2$ and $Y = y_1$ is zero. The information that one of a pair of random variables has a certain value eliminates the combinations in which other values occur, and in long-run proportions one must use as a base only the smaller or reduced set of possibilities. This notion will be explained first by example and then given a formal definition.

Example 4–8.   One interpretation of the probability table in the preceding example, which is repeated below, is that in a long series of trials the combination $(X = x_1, Y = y_1)$ occurs about $\frac{2}{10}$ of the time, the combination $(X = x_1, Y = y_2)$ about $\frac{1}{10}$ of the time, the combination $(X = x_2, Y = y_2)$ about $\frac{3}{10}$ of the time, and so on. Now if one considers only those combinations in which $X = x_1$, which in total occur about $\frac{3}{10}$ of the time, $\frac{1}{3}$ of them (or .1/.3) involve $Y = y_2$ and the rest (.2/.3) involve $Y = y_1$. This is the basis for defining the *conditional probability* of $Y = y_2$, given that $X = x_1$, to be $\frac{1}{3}$. It is written with a vertical bar before the condition (which corresponds to knowing somehow that x_1 must occur or has occurred), and is computed as follows:

$$p(y_1 \mid x_1) \equiv P(Y = y_1 \mid X = x_1) = \frac{.2}{.3} = \frac{P(X = x_1 \text{ and } Y = y_1)}{P(Y = y_1)}.$$

In this way one defines a new distribution for Y, shown in the table below along with the given table of joint probabilities, and with tables showing the conditional distributions for Y that would apply if $X = x_2$, and if $X = x_3$.

Y \ X	x_1	x_2	x_3	
y_1	.2	0	.1	.3
y_2	.1	.3	.3	.7
	.3	.3	.4	

y	y_1	y_2
$p(y \mid x_1)$	$\frac{2}{3}$	$\frac{1}{3}$

y	y_1	y_2
$p(y \mid x_2)$	0	1

y	y_1	y_2
$p(y \mid x_3)$	$\frac{1}{4}$	$\frac{3}{4}$

Conditional distributions for X are also defined for each value of Y, in analogous fashion. Thus, if Y is known to have the value y_1, then x_2 cannot occur as a value for X, and x_1 is twice as likely as x_3. The tables are as follows:

x	x_1	x_2	x_3
$p(x \mid y_1)$	$\frac{2}{3}$	0	$\frac{1}{3}$

y	x_1	x_2	x_3
$p(x \mid y_2)$	$\frac{1}{7}$	$\frac{3}{7}$	$\frac{3}{7}$

More generally, if E and F are any two events (conditions that may or may not be satisfied when an experiment of chance is performed, which characterize corresponding sets of outcomes), the conditional probability of E given F is defined as follows

$$P(E \mid F) \equiv \frac{P(E \text{ and } F)}{P(F)}.$$

Example 4–10. Consider random variables Z with possible values z_1 and z_2, and Θ with possible values θ_1, θ_2, and θ_3. Suppose that the probability distribution of Z given Θ is given, according to the following table

z	$p(z \mid \theta_1)$	$p(z \mid \theta_2)$	$p(z \mid \theta_3)$
z_1	$\dfrac{2}{3}$	0	$\dfrac{1}{4}$
z_2	$\dfrac{1}{3}$	1	$\dfrac{3}{4}$

Suppose further that the marginal distribution for Θ is given by $g(\theta) = P(\Theta = \theta)$:

θ	θ_1	θ_2	θ_3
$g(\theta)$	.3	.3	.4

If Z represents data in a decision problem, and Θ the state of nature, the assumption is that the distribution of the data is known for each state of nature, defined by $f(z \mid \theta)$, and that the prior distribution for Θ is also known, defined by $g(\theta)$. From these one can construct the joint distribution, which would be characterized by the probabilities

$$p(z, \theta) = P(Z = z \text{ and } \Theta = \theta)$$
$$= p(z \mid \theta)g(\theta).$$

Performing the indicated multiplications yields the table for $p(z, \theta)$

	θ_1	θ_2	θ_3
z_1	.2	0	.1
z_2	.1	.3	.3

Problems

4–10 Problem 4–1 gave the following distributions for Z

z	0	1	2
$f(z \mid \theta_1)$	0	.1	.9
$f(z \mid \theta_2)$	.8	.2	0

Problem 4–6 introduced the prior probabilities $g(\theta_1) = .8$ and $g(\theta_2) = .2$. Determine the corresponding joint distribution of Z and Θ, and then the unconditional or marginal probabilities for Z.

4–11 In the acceptance sampling situation of Problems 4–2 and 4–7, conditional probabilities for the data Z given the state M were as follows:

$$f(z \mid m) \equiv P(Z = z \mid M = m) = \begin{cases} \dfrac{m}{5}, & \text{if } Z = 1 \text{ (defective)} \\[2mm] 1 - \dfrac{m}{5}, & \text{if } Z = 0 \text{ (good)}. \end{cases}$$

Using prior probabilities $g(0) = .6$, $g(1) = .2$, $g(2) = g(3) = .1$, construct the table of joint probabilities for (Z, M), and from this calculate conditional probabilities $h(m \mid z)$ for the state M given the data $Z = z$.

4–12 If the prior probabilities point strongly towards one state of nature, say $g(\theta_m) = 1$ and $g(\theta) = 0$ for any other θ, what then is the absolute probability $f(z) = P(Z = z)$ given the distributions

$$f(z \mid \theta) = P(Z = z \mid \Theta = \theta)?$$

4–13 Machines A and B turn out, respectively, 10 and 90 percent of the total production of a certain type of article. Suppose that the probability that machine A turns out a defective article is .01 and that machine B turns out a defective article is .05. What is the probability that an article taken at random from a day's production was made by machine A, given that it is found to be defective?

4.6 The Posterior Distribution

As in Example 4–10, but more generally, let Z represent data with possible values $z_1, \ldots, z_k$ and let Θ denote the state of nature, with possible "values" $\theta_1, \ldots, \theta_m$. Assume further that the distributions of Z under the various states of nature are given:

$$f(z_i \mid \theta_j) = P(Z = z_i \mid \Theta = \theta_j),$$

as well as the prior probabilities for Θ:

$$g(\theta_j) = P(\Theta = \theta_j).$$

From these one can construct the joint probabilities $p(z_i, \theta_j)$:

$$p(z_i, \theta_j) = f(z_i \mid \theta_j)g(\theta_j),$$

and the marginal probabilities for Z:

$$p(z_i) = \sum_j f(z_i \mid \theta_j) g(\theta_j).$$

(Notice that in effect this absolute probability for $Z = z_i$ is an average of the conditional probabilities of z_i with respect to the prior distribution.) And then, finally, the conditional probabilities for Θ given $Z = z_i$ are

$$h(\theta_j \mid z_i) = \frac{p(z_i, \theta_j)}{p(z_i)} = \frac{f(z_i \mid \theta_j) g(\theta_j)}{\sum_j f(z_r \mid \theta_j) g(\theta_j)}.$$

This relation is essentially Bayes' theorem again. The function $h(\theta_j \mid z_i)$ so obtained is called the *posterior* probability function for Θ, and the probability distribution it defines, the *posterior distribution* corresponding to the given prior, $g(\theta)$.

Example 4–11. Consider again with the specific situation of Example 4–10, in which the distributions of Z under the three states of nature, and the prior probabilities for nature, were as in the following table; added to the table are the computations of $p(z_i)$ as weighted averages of the $f(z_i \mid \theta_j)$:

z	$f(z \mid \theta_1)$	$f(z \mid \theta_2)$	$f(z \mid \theta_3)$	$p(z)$
z_1	$\dfrac{2}{3}$	0	$\dfrac{1}{4}$	$.3 \times \dfrac{2}{3} + .3 \times 0 + .4 \times \dfrac{1}{4} = .3$
z_2	$\dfrac{1}{3}$	1	$\dfrac{3}{4}$	$.3 \times \dfrac{1}{3} + .3 \times 1 + .4 \times \dfrac{3}{4} = .7$
$g(\theta):$	$.3$	$.3$	$.4$	

The posterior probabilities are now easily read as the ratios of the terms in the sums which yield $p(z)$ to the sum; for instance

$$h(\theta_1 \mid z_1) = \frac{f(z_1 \mid \theta_1) g(\theta_1)}{p(z_1)} = \frac{.3 \times \dfrac{2}{3}}{.3} = \frac{2}{3}.$$

and

$$h(\theta_3 \mid z_2) = \frac{f(z_2 \mid \theta_3) g(\theta_3)}{p(z_2)} = \frac{.4 \times \dfrac{3}{4}}{.7} = \frac{3}{7}.$$

Thus, if $Z = z_1$ is observed, the probabilities change from the prior probabilities $(.3, .3, .4)$ to the posterior: $(\frac{2}{3}, 0, \frac{1}{3})$. If $Z = z_2$ is observed, the probabilities change from (.3, .3, .4) to the posterior probabilities ($\frac{1}{7}, \frac{3}{7}, \frac{3}{7}$). In this way the data are used to "educate" one's initial hunches or convictions about nature, according to the strength of the relationship between the data and nature. Intuitively, the occurrence of z_1, say, and the fact that z_1 has a greater probability of occurrence under θ_1 than under θ_3 suggest that θ_1 is somewhat more credible after the data are gathered than before; and the credibility for θ_2 in this case goes way down to 0, since if θ_2 were really governing, the value $Z = z_1$ (which has been observed) has zero probability of occurring.

Certain facts are worth specific mention. One is that when the distribution of the data Z is unrelated to the state of nature (that is, is the same for all states), then the posterior probabilities are equal to the prior probabilities. Thus, if $f(z_i \mid \theta) \equiv k(z_i)$,

$$h(\theta \mid z_i) = \frac{f(z_i \mid \theta)g(\theta)}{k(z_i)} = g(\theta).$$

So the observation Z does *not* alter the odds on the various states of nature from what they were before the observation.

Another point is that if a prior conviction is sufficiently strong, observations will not alter it. Thus, if $g(\theta^*) = 1$ and $g(\theta) = 0$ for any other θ, then

$$k(z) = \sum_i f(z \mid \theta_i)g(\theta_i) = f(z \mid \theta^*);$$

and then provided $f(z \mid \theta^*) \neq 0$,

$$h(\theta \mid z) = \frac{f(z \mid \theta)g(\theta)}{f(z \mid \theta^*)} = \begin{cases} 1, & \text{if } 0 = \theta^*, \\ 0, & \text{for any other } \theta. \end{cases}$$

Of course, if an observation occurs which has probability 0 under θ^*, h is undefined; practically speaking, someone has made a mistake somewhere—if nowhere else, then in picking the prior distribution.

4.7 Successive Observations

If an observation can alter prior odds to posterior odds, it would seem that further observations, applied to the first posterior distribution as though it were a prior, should result in yet a new posterior distribution. It is of interest to know that if a posterior distribution is used as a prior distribution with new data, the resulting posterior distribution is the same as if one had waited until all the data were at hand to use with the original prior distribution for a final posterior distribution.

Suppose then that two observations are made, (X, Y), with probability function

$$f(x, y \mid \theta) \equiv P(X = x, Y = y \mid \Theta = \theta).$$

Expressing conditional probabilities using the defining formulas in terms of joint probabilities, it is readily seen that

$$P(X = x, Y = y \mid \Theta) = \theta = P(X = x \mid \Theta = \theta)P(Y = y \mid X = x \text{ and } \Theta = \theta),$$

which is written (in common but somewhat confusing notation)

$$f(x, y \mid \theta) = f(x \mid \theta)f(y \mid x, \theta).$$

The posterior probabilities for θ give $X = x$, and given a prior $g(\theta)$ are

$$h_1(\theta \mid x) = \frac{f(x \mid \theta)g(\theta)}{\sum f(x \mid \theta_i)g(\theta_i)} = \frac{f(x \mid \theta)g(\theta)}{k(x)}.$$

Using this as a prior probability for $\Theta = \theta$ together with the new observation $Y = y$ yields the posterior probability

$$h_2(\theta \mid x, y) = \frac{f(y \mid x, \theta)h_1(\theta \mid x)}{\sum f(y \mid x, \theta_j)h_1(\theta_j \mid x)}$$

$$= \frac{f(y \mid x, \theta)f(x \mid \theta)g(\theta)/k(x)}{\sum f(y \mid x, \theta_j)f(x \mid \theta_j)g(\theta_j)/k(x)}$$

$$= \frac{f(x, y \mid \theta)g(\theta)}{\sum f(x, y \mid \theta_j)g(\theta_j)}.$$

This is precisely the posterior probability that would be computed based on data (X, Y) and the prior $g(\theta)$.

Problems

4–14 Determine the posterior probabilities for the number M of defective articles in a lot of five, based on the observation Z ($= 0$ for good, 1 for defective) resulting from testing one article, with $f(z \mid M) = M/5$ if $z = 1$, and $1 - M/5$ if $z = 0$, assuming equal prior probabilities for the various values of M. (See Problem 4–10.)

4–15 In Example 4–5, the observation Z was assumed to have the same distribution under θ_1 as under θ_2:

z	0	1	2
$f(z \mid \theta_1)$	.2	.3	.5
$f(z \mid \theta_2)$	.2	.3	.5

Obtain the posterior probabilities for Θ, given $Z = 0$, assuming prior probabilities $g(\theta_1) = w$, $g(\theta_2) = 1 - w$. (Can you write the results for $Z = 1$ and $Z = 2$ without further calculation?)

4–16 You have even prior odds that a coin your friend is about to toss is a fair coin, against the possibility that it has two heads. He tosses it, and it lands heads. What are your revised odds? He tosses it again with the same result; what are your new odds? Compare the latter with the posterior odds obtained by applying equal prior odds to the two possible probabilities for the observed phenomenon of heads on two successive tosses, which are as follows:

Data	Probability, if coin fair	Probability, if coin 2-headed
2 heads	$\frac{1}{4}$	1

4–17 Show that if $f(z^* \mid \theta_1)$ is positive for $\theta = \theta_1$ and 0 for any other state, then the posterior distribution given $Z = z^*$ puts all the probability at θ_1, so long as $g(\theta_1) \neq 0$.

4–18 The observation Z in the elevator problem (see Example 4–1) was assumed to have distribution as follows

z	$f(z \mid \theta_1)$	$f(z \mid \theta_2)$
0	.6	.1
1	.3	.4
2	.1	.5

In Problem 4–1, an observation—let it now be called Y—was assumed to have these distributions

y	$f(y \mid \theta_1)$	$f(y \mid \theta_2)$
0	.0	.8
1	.1	.2
2	.9	0

Given the prior distribution $g(\theta_1) = .7$, $g(\theta_2) = .3$, determine the posterior probabilities given the value of Y and also given the value of Z. (Observe the extent to which the observation alters the odds on Θ in each case. Notice also the result of Problem 4–17 coming into play.)

4.8 Bayes Actions From Posterior Probabilities

The Bayes decision rule for a given problem, corresponding to a certain prior distribution, was found in Section 4.4 by applying the Bayes principle to the risk table—weighting the various states of nature and choosing the decision function $d(\cdot)$ so as to minimize the Bayes risk, $B(d)$. This function of d is the expected value of the risk

$$B(d) = \sum_i R(\theta_i, d)g(\theta_i).$$

It will be shown here, by manipulation of this formula, that the minimization can be accomplished in a somewhat different fashion, with less work, in terms of the posterior distribution.

The first step is the introduction of the expression for $R(\theta, d)$ as it is computed from the loss function:

$$R(\theta, d) = \sum_j l(\theta, d(z_j))f(z_j \mid \theta).$$

Substitution of this into $B(d)$ yields

$$B(d) = \sum_i \sum_j \{l(\theta_i, d(z_j))f(z_j \mid \theta_i)\}g(\theta_i).$$

Now, according to Bayes' theorem, the product $f(z_j \mid \theta_i)g(\theta_i)$ can be replaced by the product of the conditional probability in which the condition is the value of Z, and the marginal or unconditional probability of $Z = z_j$:

$$f(z_j \mid \theta_i)g(\theta_i) = h(\theta_i \mid z_j)p(z_j).$$

(In this formula, the marginal probability of $Z = z_j$, called here $p(z_j)$, is calculated by summing the joint probabilities for (Θ, Z) over θ:

$$p(z_j) = \sum_i P(\Theta = \theta_i, Z = z_j)$$

$$= \sum_i f(z_j \mid \theta_i) g(\theta_i).$$

This calculation would be performed in determining the posterior probabilities but is not relevant in the present manipulation.)

Now, the indicated double summation, first on the index j and then on i, is just a systematic way of adding up all of the terms in a finite rectangular array of terms; it can be calculated equally well by summing first on i and then on j:

$$B(d) = \sum_j \left\{ \sum_i l(\theta_i, d(z_j)) f(z_j \mid \theta_i) g(\theta_i) \right\}$$

$$= \sum_j \left\{ \sum_i l(\theta_i, d(z_j)) h(\theta_i \mid z_j) \right\} p(z_j),$$

the last expression being obtained by making the substitution from Bayes' theorem, as given above. The quantity in braces depends on the observed value z_i and on the action assigned to z_i by the decision function used:

$$L_h(d, z_j) = \sum_i l(\theta_i, d(z_j)) h(\theta_i \mid z_j).$$

It is the average of the losses $l(\theta, d(z_j))$ with respect to the *posterior* probability weights; it will be referred to as the *expected posterior loss*. Now since $B(d)$ is a weighted sum of expected posterior losses with nonnegative weights:

$$B(d) = \sum_j L_h(d, z_j) p(z_j),$$

it will be as small as possible if L_h is made as small as possible. So if (for the observed z_i) $d(z_i)$ is taken to be the action that minimizes the expected posterior loss L_h, the resulting rule is one that minimizes the Bayes risk and is a Bayes procedure.

Example 4–12. Consider again the elevator problem with losses as follows:

	θ_1	θ_2
a_1	0	6
a_2	1	5

Suppose that an observation Z is to be made, with distributions under the two states of nature as follows:

z	$f(z \mid \theta_1)$	$f(z \mid \theta_2)$
0	.6	.1
1	.3	.4
2	.1	.5

Suppose further that the one faced with this problem has summarized his feelings, hunches, and possibly some past experience, in the posterior probabilities $g(\theta_1) = .7$ and $g(\theta_2) = .3$. That is, he is willing to bet with odds 7 to 3 that the elevator will be operating. The question is, then, what is the Bayes action if he enters the building and observes (say) the light showing on both the first and ground floors: $Z = 2$? The marginal probability of $Z = 2$ is the weighted average of the conditional probabilities:

$$p(2) = f(2 \mid \theta_1)g(\theta_1) + f(2 \mid \theta_2)g(\theta_2)$$

$$= .1 \times .7 + .5 \times .3 = .22.$$

The posterior probabilities for nature are (given $Z = 2$)

$$h(\theta_1 \mid 2) = \frac{.07}{.22} = \frac{7}{22},$$

$$h(\theta_2 \mid 2) = \frac{.15}{.22} = \frac{15}{22}.$$

Applying these as weights in the original loss table, one obtains the expected posterior losses:

$$\text{Action } a_1: \quad 0 \times \frac{7}{22} + 6 \times \frac{15}{22} = \frac{90}{22},$$

$$\text{Action } a_2: \quad 1 \times \frac{7}{22} + 5 \times \frac{15}{22} = \frac{82}{22}.$$

Since the expected posterior loss for action a_2 is smaller, this is the Bayes action for the observation $Z = 2$.

One can also compute the Bayes action for the other values of Z. For $Z = 1$,

$$p(1) = .3 \times .7 + .4 \times .3 = .33; \qquad h(\theta_1 \mid 1) = \frac{21}{33}, \qquad h(\theta_2 \mid 1) = \frac{12}{33},$$

and the expected posterior losses are

$$a_1: \quad 0 \times \frac{7}{11} + 6 \times \frac{4}{11} = \frac{24}{11},$$

$$a_2: \quad 1 \times \frac{7}{11} + 5 \times \frac{4}{11} = \frac{27}{11},$$

so the Bayes action is a_2. Similarly, the posterior probabilities given $Z = 0$ are $\frac{14}{15}$ and $\frac{1}{15}$, and the Bayes action is a_1. The complete Bayes decision function is then defined by the rule

$$\text{if } Z = 0, \quad \text{take } a_1,$$

$$\text{if } Z = 1, \quad \text{take } a_1,$$

$$\text{if } Z = 2, \quad \text{take } a_2.$$

That is, walk down and catch the elevator on the "ground" floor if either no light or one light is showing, but walk up to the first and try it there if both lights are showing. This happens to be the rule labeled $d_7(z)$ in Example 4–2, easily seen to be the Bayes rule by applying the prior weights .7 and .3 to the risk table of Example 4–4.

Apart from illustrating that the Bayes decision function can indeed be determined by assigning to the value z_i the action that minimizes the expected posterior risk given that z_i, the example above points up vividly the following fact: To obtain the Bayes action given a particular value for Z, it is not necessary to go through the computation of the whole decision rule; it is necessary only to "cross the bridge" actually encountered. Neither is it necessary to construct the whole table of risks; this is usually a big task, since the number of decision functions is of a higher order than the number of actions.

Mathematically, the present approach is a simple process of minimizing a function of the actions, namely, the expected posterior loss, by selecting one of those actions; the earlier approach is a more complicated process of minimizing a function of the decision rules, over all possible decision rules. So, even if it is desired to obtain the Bayes rule in complete detail, the present approach is simpler; and if one is facing an actual decision problem with a given value of the data Z, only the Bayes action corresponding to *that* value of Z need be determined.

The earlier approach incorporates the data into the loss function to obtain the risk function, the original prior then being used on those risks to determine the Bayes rule. The present approach incorporates the data into the prior distribution to obtain the posterior distribution, which is used as a new, or educated "prior" distribution on the original losses. The results are equivalent.

Problems

4–19 The posterior probabilities for M, the number of defective articles in a lot of five, based on the observation Z with probabilities

$$\begin{cases} f(1 \mid M) = \dfrac{M}{5} \\[2mm] f(0 \mid M) = 1 - \dfrac{M}{5} \end{cases}$$

and assuming prior probabilities $g(0) = .6$, $g(1) = .2$, $g(2) = g(3) = .1$, were found in Problem 4–11 to be as follows:

M	$h(M \mid 1)$	$h(M \mid 0)$
0	0	$\dfrac{30}{43}$
1	$\dfrac{2}{7}$	$\dfrac{8}{43}$
2	$\dfrac{2}{7}$	$\dfrac{3}{43}$
3	$\dfrac{3}{7}$	$\dfrac{2}{43}$
4	0	0
5	0	0

Use these together with the original loss table

	0	1	2	3	4	5
pass	0	2	4	6	8	10
reject	5	4	3	2	1	0

to determine the Bayes rule for the given prior distribution. Compare with result of the earlier determination in Problem 4–7.

4–20 Determine (using the method of Section 4.7) the Bayes rule corresponding to prior probabilities $g(\theta_1) = .7$, $g(\theta_2) = .3$ for each of the observations Y and Z as given in Problem 4–18. (The regrets are 0 for walking up (a_2) to the first floor when the elevator is not working (θ_2) and for walking down (a_1) to catch it when it is working (θ_1), and 1 for taking the wrong action.)

4–21 Suppose (referring to Problem 4–20) that *both* observations Y and Z are available and that they are *independent*, which means that their joint distribution is obtained by multiplying probabilities of the marginal values, to yield these tables:

$f(y, z \mid \theta_1)$:

		Y			
		0	1	2	
	0	0	.06	.54	.6
Z	1	0	.03	.27	.3
	2	0	.01	.09	.1
		0	.1	.9	

$f(y, z \mid \theta_2)$:

		Y			
		0	1	2	
	0	.08	.02	0	.1
Z	1	.32	.08	0	.4
	2	.40	.10	0	.5
		.8	.2	0	

Again assume prior probabilities $g(\theta_1) = .7$, $g(\theta_2) = .3$. **(a)** Calculate the absolute probability that $(Y, Z) = (1, 2)$ and from this the posterior probabilities for (θ_1, θ_2) given $Y = 1$ and $Z = 2$. **(b)** Determine the Bayes action given $Y = 1$ and $Z = 2$. **(c)** Calculate posterior probabilities for θ_1 and θ_2 given $Z = 2$, using as prior probabilities the posterior probabilities given $Y = 1$. Compare the results with those obtained in **(a)**, that is, with the posterior probabilities given $Y = 1$ and $Z = 2$.

4–22 In Problem 4–19 determine the *smallest* Bayes risk by means of the formula

$$B(d) = \sum_j L_h(d, z_j) p(z_j),$$

in which d is the Bayes rule. (Compare with the result in Problem 4–7.)

4.9 Sufficiency*

It is common practice for statisticians, when confronted with a mass of data, to compute some simple measure from the data and then to base

---

* This section may be omitted without loss of continuity.

statistical procedures on the simpler quantity. Computing such simpler measures is called *reducing* the data; the measures themselves are called *statistics*.

Example 4–13.   Ten measurements of viscosity were made, with results as follows (in units which are irrelevant, for the present purposes):

$$32.0, \ 33.9, \ 31.3, \ 31.0, \ 32.0, \ 35.0, \ 35.5, \ 31.6, \ 31.8, \ 29.9.$$

Some statistics that might be computed from these observations, for a variety of purposes, are the following

Sample mean: $\bar{X} = \frac{1}{10} \sum X_i = 32.4$.

Sample variance: $S_x^2 = \frac{1}{10} \sum (X_i - \bar{X})^2 = 2.936$.

Sample range: $R =$ largest obs. $-$ smallest obs. $= 35.5 - 29.9 = 5.6$.

Sample median: $M =$ middle obs. (when arranged in order) $= 31.9$.

Mid-range: Average of largest and smallest obs. $= 32.7$.

These are all single numbers, whereas the reduction is not always so drastic; for example, the list of numbers in numerical order is a reduction, called the *order statistic*:

$$29.9, \ 31.0, \ 31.3, \ 31.6, \ 31.8, \ 32.0, \ 32.0, \ 33.9, \ 35.0, \ 35.5.$$

Notice that all of the single numbers can be computed from this order statistic (in which the original order of observations is lost) and so can be thought of as further reductions. Intermediate reductions might consist of pairs (or n-tuples) of single numbers, such as the pair $(\bar{X}, S_x^2)$, or the pair (M, R), or the pair $(\sum X_i, \sum X_i^2)$. (It might be noticed that the last of these pairs can be computed from the first, and conversely, so that in a sense they are equivalent reductions of the original data.)

A question arises naturally: How much reduction of the data is possible without losing such information as the sample may contain concerning the particular statistical problem at hand? The notion of "sufficiency" seems to permit answering such a question.

DEFINITION   *A statistic $T = t(X_1, \ldots, X_n)$ is said to be* sufficient *for a problem involving the set Θ of states of nature if the conditional distribution of the sample $Z = (X_1, \ldots, X_n)$ given the value of T is the same for all states in Θ.*

Example 4–14.   An urn contains eight balls, M numbered 1 and $8 - M$ numbered 0. Three balls are selected, one at a time, at random and without replacement. Let X_i be the number on the ith ball drawn, so that the sample can be expressed as $Z = (X_1, X_2, X_3)$. The probabilities for Z are computed fairly easily; for instance

$$P(0\ 1\ 1) = P(\text{1st ball is 0, second is 1, and third is 1})$$

$$= \frac{8 - M}{8} \cdot \frac{M}{7} \cdot \frac{M - 1}{6},$$

where the $(M - 1)/6$, for example, is the conditional probability that the third ball is 1, given that the first was 0 and the second 1. In similar fashion one can calculate probabilities for all eight values of Z. These are given in the following table, together with the value of the statistic $T = X_1 + X_2 + X_3$, which is the number of 1's among the three balls drawn.

Z	$P(Z = z)$	T
1 1 1	$\dfrac{M}{8}\dfrac{M-1}{7}\dfrac{M-2}{6}$	3
1 1 0	$\dfrac{M}{8}\dfrac{M-1}{7}\dfrac{8-M}{6}$	2
1 0 1	$\dfrac{M}{8}\dfrac{8-M}{7}\dfrac{M-1}{6}$	2
0 1 1	$\dfrac{8-M}{8}\dfrac{M}{7}\dfrac{M-1}{6}$	2
1 0 0	$\dfrac{M}{8}\dfrac{8-M}{7}\dfrac{7-M}{6}$	1
0 1 0	$\dfrac{8-M}{8}\dfrac{M}{7}\dfrac{7-M}{6}$	1
0 0 1	$\dfrac{8-M}{8}\dfrac{7-M}{7}\dfrac{M}{6}$	1
0 0 0	$\dfrac{8-M}{8}\dfrac{7-M}{7}\dfrac{6-M}{6}$	0

The probabilities for T can easily be computed from this, and are as follows.

t	$P(T = t)$
0	$\dfrac{M(M - 1)(M - 2)}{336}$
1	$3 \cdot \dfrac{M(M - 1)(8 - M)}{336}$
2	$3 \cdot \dfrac{M(8 - M)(7 - M)}{336}$
3	$\dfrac{(8 - M)(7 - M)(6 - M)}{336}$

And then by the division

$$P(Z = z \mid T = t) = \frac{P(Z = z \text{ and } T = t)}{P(T = t)}$$

one can obtain the conditional probabilities for Z, given the various possible values of T.

z	$P(Z = z \mid T = 3)$	$P(Z = z \mid T = 2)$	$P(Z = z \mid T = 1)$	$P(Z = z \mid T = 0)$
1 1 1	1	0	0	0
1 1 0	0	$\dfrac{1}{3}$	0	0
1 0 1	0	$\dfrac{1}{3}$	0	0
0 1 1	0	$\dfrac{1}{3}$	0	0
1 0 0	0	0	$\dfrac{1}{3}$	0
0 1 0	0	0	$\dfrac{1}{3}$	0
0 0 1	0	0	$\dfrac{1}{3}$	0
0 0 0	0	0	0	1

The thing to be observed is that these conditional distributions do not involve the parameter M that indexes the state of nature! The statistic T, the number of 1's drawn among the three in the sample, is sufficient for the family of distributions indexed by M.

Data Z can be thought of as having been generated in one of two ways: (a) directly, by performing the experiment whose model is given by $f_Z(z \mid \theta)$, or (b) indirectly, by first performing the experiment defined by $f_T(t \mid \theta)$ to obtain $T = t_i$; and then performing the experiment defined by the conditional distribution of Z, given $T = t_i$. The distribution of Z is the same in either case:

$$P(Z = z \mid \theta) = P(Z = z \mid T = t_i)P(T = t_i \mid \theta), \qquad \text{for } t_i = t(z).$$

(This is simply the multiplication rule for conditional probability given in Section 4.5.)

The reason for performing an experiment whose distribution depends on θ is to learn about θ, and if the distribution does *not* depend on θ there is no point to performing the experiment—no information about θ is obtained by so doing. This shows, intuitively, why nothing is lost if the data Z is reduced to a sufficient statistic $T = t(Z)$. For, if the experiment that produces the particular value of Z given $T = t$ does not depend on θ, there is nothing to be learned by performing it; one may as well be content with the knowledge of the value of T.

More precisely, the set of decision procedures depending only on the value of the sufficient statistic T is what is termed *essentially complete*: Given any procedure at all, there is one which depends only on the value of T for which the risk function is the same. This is seen as follows.

Let $d(Z)$ be any procedure, and define a procedure $\delta(T)$ in terms of d: Observe $T = t$, and then in the distribution of Z given $T = t$ observe $Z = z^*$; then take the action $d(z^*)$. Even if $d(Z)$ is a nonrandomized procedure, $\delta(T)$ is generally randomized, since the action taken, given $T = t$, depends on z^*, and z^* came about by performing the experiment $Z \mid T = t$. Thus, for given θ and $T = t$, the loss is random and what is relevant is the expected loss,

$$L(\theta, \delta(t)) = E(l(\theta, d(Z)) \mid T = t)$$

$$= \sum_{t(z_i) = t} l(\theta, d(z_i))P(Z = z_i \mid T = t).$$

The risk function using $\delta(T)$ is then

$$R(\theta, \delta) = E[l(\theta, \delta(T))]$$

$$= \sum_{t_j} l(\theta, \delta(t_j))P(T = t_j \mid \theta)$$

$$= \sum_{t_j} \sum_{t(z_i)=t_j} l(\theta, d(z_i))P(Z = z_i \mid T = t_j)P(T = t_j \mid \theta)$$

$$= \sum_{t_j} \sum_{t(z_i)=t_j} l(\theta, d(z_i))P(Z = z_i \mid \theta).$$

This sum is really a sum over all values of Z, since the inner sum extends over all z's for which $t(z) = t_j$, and then the outer sum puts together the results over these nonoverlapping but exhaustive sets defined by the T-values. Thus,

$$R(\theta, \delta) = \sum_{z_i} l(\theta, d(z_i))P(Z = z_i \mid \theta) = R(\theta, d).$$

Example 4–15. Consider a problem with actions $\{a_1, a_2\}$, loss function $l(p, a)$, and data Z which consists of two independent observations on the population with distribution:

x	0	1
$P(X = x)$	$1 - p$	p

The *values* of Z are pairs (x_1, x_2), as shown in the following table, along with the values of $T = X_1 + X_2$, and conditional probabilities for Z given T.

z	$P(Z = z \mid p)$	T	$P(Z = z \mid T = 0)$	$P(Z = z \mid T = 1)$	$P(Z = z \mid T = 2)$
0 0	$(1 - p)^2$	0	1	0	0
0 1	$p(1 - p)$	1	0	$\dfrac{1}{2}$	0
1 0	$p(1 - p)$	1	0	$\dfrac{1}{2}$	0
1 1	p^2	2	0	0	1

Notice that $P(Z = z \mid T = t)$ does not depend on p, so T is sufficient. Now consider the particular decision rule $d(z)$ defined as follows

$$d(Z) = \begin{cases} a_2 & \text{if } Z = (0\ 0) \text{ or } (0\ 1), \\ a_1 & \text{if } Z = (1\ 0) \text{ or } (1\ 1). \end{cases}$$

Define $\delta(T)$ as follows: If $T = t$, pick a value z of Z according to the conditional distribution of Z given $T = t$, and take action $d(z)$. Thus,

if $T = 0$, pick $Z = (0, 0)$, and take action a_2,

if $T = 2$, pick $Z = (1, 1)$, and take action a_1,

if $T = 1$, pick $\begin{cases} Z = (0, 1) \text{ with probability } \tfrac{1}{2}, \text{ and take } a_2, \\ Z = (1, 0) \text{ with probability } \tfrac{1}{2}, \text{ and take } a_1. \end{cases}$

In other words $\delta(T)$ is the following rule: if $T = 0$, take a_2; if $T = 2$, take a_1; and if $T = 1$, toss a fair coin to choose between a_1 and a_2. The risk function for $\delta(T)$ is

$$\begin{aligned} R(p, \delta) &= l(p, a_1)p^2 + [\tfrac{1}{2}l(p, a_1) + \tfrac{1}{2}l(p, a_2)]2p(1 - p) + l(p, a_2)(1 - p)^2 \\ &= l(p, a_2)[(1 - p)^2 + p(1 - p)] + l(p, a_1)[p^2 + p(1 - p)] \\ &= R(p, d). \end{aligned}$$

The risk using δ is the same as the risk using d.

Data can be reduced in steps; for instance, the order statistic is a reduction of the original data, and the sample mean is a further reduction. Again, the square of the sample mean is still a further reduction. The question is, if a statistic is sufficient, can it be reduced without losing sufficiency? If it cannot, then it is said to be *minimal sufficient*. To achieve the simplest, good procedures it is desirable to reduce the data to a minimal sufficient statistic.

There are methods of determining a minimal sufficient statistic for a given problem, but perhaps it will suffice here to give some important examples.

1.   If $Z = (X_1, \ldots, X_n)$ is a random sample, then the order statistic is sufficient for any set of states of nature.

2. If Z is a random sample of observations from a 0–1 population (as in Example 4–15, just above) then the number of 1's in the sample is minimal sufficient.

3. If Z is a random selection (no replacement) from a collection of objects of two types, in unknown proportion, then the number of objects of one type is minimal sufficient.

4. If $Z(X_1, \ldots, X_n)$ is a random sample from a normal population (see Chapter 6) then the pair $(\bar{X}, S_x^2)$ is minimal sufficient, as is also the pair $(\sum X_i, \sum X_i^2)$.

Chapter 5   Testing and Estimation

The subject of "statistics" deals with the making of inferences or drawing of conclusions about the state of nature on the basis of data. A primary goal of statistical decision theory is to provide a theoretical framework for the treatment of statistical problems as decision problems. It assumes that making an inference or drawing a conclusion can be thought of as deciding or as selecting an action from a set of available actions. Moreover, it assumes that the consequences of the various actions can be assessed. The fact that only a minority of practicing statisticians would agree to these assumptions suggests that it is not a clear-cut situation. The point of view here is that the treatment of statistical problems as problems of decision theory gives useful insights into the problems and motivates a worthwhile scrutiny of their statements.

Two of the standard or "classical" problems of statistical inference are those of *estimation* and the *testing of hypotheses*. As decision problems these can be characterized in terms of the action spaces: an estimation problem is a decision problem in which the action space is essentially the same as the space of states of nature, and a problem in the testing of hypotheses is one in which the action space has just two elements.

5.1 The Estimation Problem

The problem of estimation is to *guess* the state of nature—and to announce this guess. The *action* is then the announcing of one's guess, whether this be to immediate colleagues or to the scientific world through publication in a journal. The estimation is statistical when the guess is formulated after perusing and digesting data whose distribution is related to the state of nature; the guess thus becomes an *educated guess*.

Since it would not make sense to announce a state of nature that is not among the states of nature admitted in a given problem, the set of available actions is equivalent to the set of states of nature: $A = \Theta$, and it is this feature of the decision problem that makes it one of *estimation*. Usually, in such problems, the states of nature are characterized by a parameter, that is, a numerical variable whose various values define the various states of nature, and it is said that one is engaged in estimating the parameter. This parameter is often restricted to some interval of real values, such as $0 \leq \theta \leq 1$, or $\theta > 0$, but is sometimes the set of all real numbers: $-\infty < \theta < \infty$. Occasionally it is restricted to a finite set of values, such as a set of integers.

The losses involved in the making of an announcement of an estimated value of a parameter θ are usually very difficult to assess. Even discounting the unknown losses incurred by unknown consumers of the estimate, there are losses to the statistician himself—even if it is only his reputation that suffers. In a general discussion one can really only consider regret, and one reasonable requirement of a regret function is that it yields zero regret when the announced value of θ is the actual value of θ, that is, when there is no error. If the announced value is T and the actual value is θ, the *error* would be $T - \theta$; and regret is often considered to be a function of this error—one that is zero when the error is zero, and that increases as the absolute error increases. Thus, the regret function is of the form

$$r(\theta, T) = h(T - \theta),$$

where $h(0) = 0$ and

$$h(a) \leq h(b) \quad \text{if } \theta < a < b \text{ or if } b < a < \theta.$$

Two functions that immediately suggest themselves and that have the desired property are

$$h_1(u) = c|u|, \quad \text{and} \quad h_2(u) = cu^2.$$

These are shown, along with a less specific $h(u)$ having the desired properties, in Figure 5–1. If it is now recalled that utility is supposed to be the basis of assessing losses, and that utility is supposed to be a bounded function of prospects, one may immediately object to both h_1 and h_2, since these functions are not bounded. However, $h_2(u)$ in particular has a special appeal in its

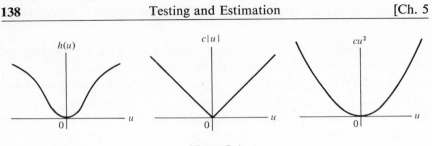

Figure 5–1

mathematical simplicity. Moreover, many functions such as the $h(u)$ shown behave near $u = 0$ like a quadratic, and it is this behavior that seems to be crucial in estimation. And to top it off, almost all of classical estimation theory is based on the notion that the success of an estimator is measured by the square of the error—large errors being emphasized, and small ones minimized, in the squaring process. Whether these remarks justify it or not, the remaining discussion of estimation will usually assume losses as defined by this regret function

$$r(\theta, T) = (T - \theta)^2,$$

which will be referred to in words as *quadratic regret* or *quadratic loss*.

The minimax principle is not very useful if one assumes a quadratic regret function, since the maximum loss for any action, that is, any estimated value, is infinite, and the minimum maximum is infinite. Because of this the minimax principle will not be considered further here in connection with estimation.

A Bayes estimate can be made if one is willing (and able) to postulate a prior weighting on the possible values of θ, or the possible states of nature. The Bayes estimate would be that T which minimizes the average loss with respect to the prior weighting; if this weighting is defined by a probability $g(\theta)$ for θ, the average loss is

$$
\begin{aligned}
E_g[(\theta - T)^2] &= \sum_i (\theta_i - T)^2 g(\theta_i) \\
&= \sum_i \theta_i^2 g(\theta_i) - 2T \sum_i \theta_i g(\theta_i) + T^2 \sum_i g(\theta_i) \\
&= E_g(\theta^2) - 2T E_g(\theta) + T^2 \\
&= T^2 - 2T E_g(\theta) + [E_g(\theta)]^2 + E_g(\theta^2) - [E_g(\theta)]^2 \\
&= [T - E_g(\theta)]^2 + [E_g(\theta^2) - (E_g\theta)^2].
\end{aligned}
$$

(Once this expression was seen to be a quadratic in T, the remaining steps were standard in the process of *completing the square*.) Since the first of the bracketed terms is the only one that contains T and is nonnegative, it is clear that the smallest value of the average loss will be achieved by the announcement that T is $E_g(\theta)$; this is the Bayes estimate of θ corresponding to the prior distribution $g(\theta)$:

$$\text{Bayes estimate} = E_g(\theta) = \sum_i \theta_i g(\theta_i).$$

This is just the center of gravity of the prior distribution.

Because the center of gravity or balance point of a discrete distribution of masses may be at a point where there is no mass, the minimizing T may not be one of the states of nature. The value $T = E_g(\theta)$ may not be one of the states of nature—not one of the available actions. In such cases the T that does minimize the expected loss would be near $E_g(\theta)$; indeed, it is the state nearest to $E_g(\theta)$, since the risk is smallest when the distance $|T - E_g(\theta)|$ is smallest.

Example 5–1. A lot of 10 articles includes an unknown number M of defective articles, where then M is a "population parameter" having one of the values $M = 0, 1, \ldots, 10$. One possible prior distribution, sometimes used when one is in utter ignorance of the conditions that might have produced the prevailing state of nature, is that which assigns probability or weight $\frac{1}{11}$ to each of the eleven possible values of M. This "uniform" distribution of probability, being symmetrical, would balance at the central value, namely $M = 5$. Thus, $M = 5$ would be the Bayes estimate, in the absence of data and assuming the uniform prior weighting. On the other hand, the process by which the articles are made may be sufficiently intimately known so that one has a very strong conviction that more than two defectives in a lot is "practically impossible." Perhaps he summarizes his beliefs about M (as would be implied by how he would bet) by assigning these weights:

$$g(0) = .5, \quad g(1) = .3, \quad g(2) = .2, \quad g(3) = \cdots = g(10) = 0.$$

The mean value of M would be the following weighted sum:

$$0 \times .5 + 1 \times .3 + 2 \times .2 + 0 = .7 = E_g(M).$$

Of course, $\frac{7}{10}$ of an article is not a realistic value of M to announce. The expected loss, when T is the announced value, would be

$$E_g[(T - M)^2] = T^2 - 2TE_g(\theta) + E_g(\theta^2)$$

$$= T^2 - 1.4T + 0^2 \times .5 + 1^2 \times .3 + 2^2 \times .2$$

$$= T^2 - 1.4T + 1.1.$$

The value of this for $T = 0$ is 1.1, for $T = 1$ it is .7, for $T = 2$ it is 2.3, for $T = 3$ it is 5.9, and so on. The smallest expected loss is clearly achieved for the announced value $T = 1$, which would be the Bayes estimate. (Notice that it is indeed the closest permissible value of M to the expected value of θ under g, namely, the closest integer to $E_g(\theta) = .7$.)

Problems

5–1 Referring to Example 5–1, in which the state of nature is the value of M, the number of defectives in a lot of ten articles, determine the Bayes estimate (without data) corresponding to a prior distribution defined by the probabilities $g(M) = (10 - M)/55$, $M = 0, 1, \ldots, 10$.

5–2 Referring again to Example 5–1, suppose that the loss function is

$$r(M, T) = |T - M|.$$

Assuming a prior that assigns equal probabilities to the states $M = 0, 1, \ldots, 10$, determine the expected loss for $T = 3, 4$, and 5. From these computations infer the value of T that minimizes the expected loss. Notice that the result is the same as the expected value of M, that is, the same as the Bayes estimate assuming a quadratic loss. To show that this is not always the case, determine the T that minimizes the expected loss, using the absolute difference as loss, when the prior probabilities are $g(0) = .6$, $g(1) = .3$, and $g(2) = .1$.

5.2 Continuous Distributions

The concept of a discrete random variable, and corresponding discrete distribution of probability among its possible values, is not adequate to handle a random variable whose value is not restricted to a finite, discrete set of numbers, but which can take on any value, say, in an interval. What is needed is the notion of a continuous random variable, or a continuous distribution of probability, analogous to a continuous distribution of mass.

Such distributions are smeared out over a continuum of points, with no mass *at* a point, but with nonzero amounts of mass assigned to intervals.

Since the weighting at individual points in a continuous distribution is zero, one cannot define or characterize the weighting by just giving the probabilities of individual values. A useful way of defining a continuous distribution is by means of a density function, a nonnegative function the area under whose graph is used to define mass or probability. The total area under the graph and above the horizontal axis is taken to be the total weight, or mass, or probability. In the case of a mass distribution, this total mass can be infinite (in the mathematical model) if it extends over an infinite interval; but in most practical problems it is finite. In the case of a probability model, the total probability is 1, since probability is a relative measure, corresponding to a proportion of the whole. Thus, a probability density function has a graph such that the area under the graph (and above the horizontal axis) is 1. The probability of an interval is then defined to be the area under the graph above that interval. This probability is the probability assigned to the event that the random variable in question takes on a value in that interval. Figure 5–2 shows a typical density function, and a shaded area representing $P(a < X < b)$, for some interval (a, b).

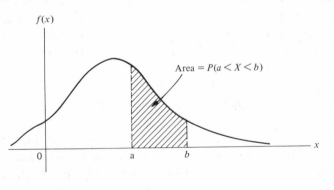

Figure 5–2

Example 5–2. In a certain trial, the outcome will be *success* or *failure*. (For example, a missile is about to be launched, and the launching will either succeed or not.) The probability p that the outcome will be *success* is unknown, except that it is a number on the interval $0 \leq p \leq 1$. But it can be *any* number on this interval, and so if a probability model is assumed for the value of p (in which model p then becomes a random variable), the model will have to be based on the infinite set of real numbers in the interval $0 \leq p \leq 1$. Probability can be defined in terms of density function, $f_p(x)$—a nonnegative

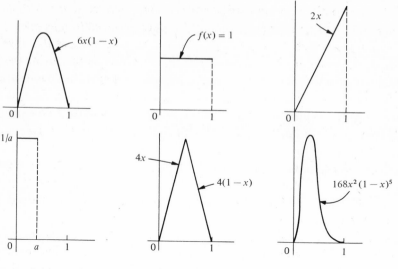

Figure 5–3

function such that the area under its graph over the interval $(0, 1)$ is 1. Several such functions are shown in Figure 5–3. These happen to be defined by nice algebraic formulas, at least in sections, but of course the really appropriate model may or may not be so simply specifiable. In some of the instances shown, probability can be calculated geometrically for a given interval. For example, if the density is

$$f_p(x) = 2x, \quad \text{for } 0 \le x \le 1,$$

the probability of an interval (a, b) is the probability of the trapezoid defined by the graph of $2x$, the horizontal or x-axis, and the ordinates at a and b (which are, respectively, $2a$ and $2b$), as shown in Figure 5–4. The area of the trapezoid is the average of the lengths of the parallel sides, which would be $(a + b)/2$, times the length of the interval, $b - a$:

$$P(a < p < b) = \frac{1}{2}(b + a)(b - a) = \frac{1}{2}(b^2 - a^2).$$

The concept of expectation, or expected value, can be extended to random variables having continuous distributions; this can be done by approximating a continuous random variable by a discrete one, which is the commonly used idea of *rounding off*. Suppose, then, that a random variable X has a continuous distribution such that all of the probability is assigned to the finite

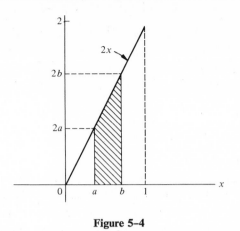

Figure 5–4

interval $A \le x \le B$. Let this interval be divided into n equal parts, each of width $h = (B - A)/n$. Let x_i denote the left endpoint of the ith subinterval, counting from left to right, and round off all values of X in that ith subinterval to x_i, for $i = 1, 2, \ldots, n$. The rounded-off values $x_1, \ldots, x_n$ are values of a new random variable X^*, which is discrete because it can take on one of only n values. The probability that X^* takes on the value, say, x_3, is the probability that X takes on a value that would be rounded off to x_3:

$$P(X^* = x_3) = P(x_3 < X < x_3 + h) \doteq f(x_3)h.$$

This last approximation is that of approximating the area under $f(x)$ above the third subinterval by the area of a rectangle of height $f(x_3)$ and base h (see Figure 5–5). The expected value of X^* is, as for any discrete variable, the weighted sum of its values, where the weights are the corresponding probabilities:

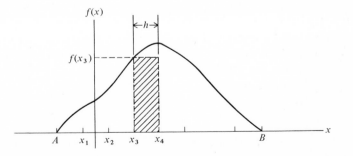

Figure 5–5

$$E(X^*) = \sum_i x_i f(x_i)h.$$

The limit of such sums, as n is allowed to become infinite, is taken to be the expected value of X:

$$E(X) = \lim_{n \to \infty} E(X^*).$$

As one might anticipate, from the rather complex definition of the expected value of a continuous random variable, it is often not easy to compute. Techniques of calculus can be employed when the density function is suitably well behaved, but in general one could only employ numerical techniques to determine an approximation to the limiting value.

Example 5–3. Consider the uniform density for p, defined by

$$f_p(x) = 1, \quad \text{for } 0 < x < 1.$$

The expected value of p can be calculated as follows. Division of the interval $(0, 1)$ into n equal subintervals of length $1/n$, and rounding off the values of p on the interval $(i/n, (i + 1)/n)$ to i/n, results in an approximating X^* with expected value

$$E(X^*) = \sum_{i=0}^{n-1} \frac{i}{n} \cdot 1 \cdot \frac{1}{n} = \frac{1}{n^2} [0 + 1 + 2 + \cdots + n - 1]$$

$$= \frac{1}{n^2} \frac{n(n-1)}{2} = \frac{1}{2} - \frac{1}{2n}.$$

As n becomes infinite, $1/(2n)$ approaches 0, and so the expected value of X is the remaining term, $\frac{1}{2}$. This result should not seem surprising if one interprets the distribution as a distribution of mass. A uniform mass distribution on the interval $(0, 1)$ is like, say, a thin piece of chalk of total weight 1, and of length 1. The balance point is obviously half-way from one end to the other if the density is in fact uniform.

Computations of the expected value of continuous distributions are generally not so simple as that carried out in Example 5–3, and the techniques for obtaining such expectations will not be developed here. However, the reader's intuition will be called upon to convince himself that *if a probability distribution is symmetrical about some value, X = k, then the expected value is that center of symmetry*: $E(X) = k$. This is intuitively evident for distributions of mass, with the analogue of the expected value being the balance point, and can be proved mathematically for probability distributions. Another fact, not so obvious, is useful for certain distributions on the interval $0 \le x \le 1$, namely, those having densities of the form

$$f(x) = (\text{const.})x^r(1 - x)^s, \qquad 0 \le x \le 1.$$

A random variable having this density can be shown to have expected value

$$E(X) = \frac{r + 1}{r + s + 2}.$$

Problems

5-3 Let p have the following density:

$$f_p(x) = \begin{cases} 4x, & \text{if } 0 < x < \frac{1}{2}, \\ 4(1 - x), & \text{if } \frac{1}{2} < x < 1, \\ 0, & \text{otherwise.} \end{cases}$$

(This is one of the densities shown in Figure 5–3.) Use your knowledge of geometry to calculate the following: (a) $P(p > \frac{3}{4})$, (b) $P(p < \frac{1}{4})$, (c) $P(|p - \frac{1}{2}| < \frac{1}{6})$.

5-4 A quantity Y has a continuous distribution on the interval $-2 < y < 2$ that is defined by the density function

$$f_Y(y) = \begin{cases} \frac{1}{4}, & \text{if } -2 < y < 2, \\ 0, & \text{otherwise.} \end{cases}$$

Calculate: (a) $P(Y < 1)$, (b) $P(|Y| > 1)$, (c) $P(-1.7 < Y < .7)$.

5-5 Using the remarks at the end of the section above, determine the expected value for each of the densities shown in Figure 5–3.

5-6 Calculate the expected value of the distribution defined by the probability density function $f(x) = 2x$ for $0 < x < 1$ (which is one of those shown in Figure 5–3). Do this by taking a limit of approximating sums, using the fact that

$$1^2 + 2^2 + \cdots + (n - 1)^2 = \frac{n(2n^2 - 3n + 1)}{6}.$$

5–7 If p is the (unknown) probability of "success" in a trial that results in either "success" or "failure," calculate the (no-data) Bayes estimate of p, assuming a quadratic loss and a prior distribution given by the density (a) $f_p(x) = 2x$, for $0 < x < 1$, (b) $f_p(x) = 168x^2(1 - x)^5$, for $0 < x < 1$. (The densities are 0 outside the given interval.)

5.3 Estimators Using Data

When data are available, a decision function assigns one of the available actions to each possible "value" of the data. In the case of estimating a real-valued parameter θ, the actions are precisely the values of θ, and so a decision function is just an ordinary real-valued function defined on the possible values z of the data Z. (As usual, Z may represent a single random variable X, or a sequence of variables $X_1, X_2, \ldots, X_n$, with a corresponding interpretation of the *value* z.) A function $t(z)$ defined on the data values defines the random quantity

$$T = t(Z),$$

which gives the result of applying the function to the random variable Z. Since the announced value T is now a random variable, the loss is thereby a random quantity—even before considering the possibility of making the state of nature random: $r(\theta, t(Z))$. The risk function is defined then as the expected loss:

$$R(\theta, t) = E[r(\theta, t(Z))].$$

In this case of quadratic regret, this becomes

$$R(\theta, t) = E[(T - \theta)^2]$$
$$= \sum [t(z_i) - \theta]^2 f(z_i \mid \theta),$$

where as before the function $f(z_i \mid \theta)$ is the probability function of Z when θ is the state of nature. A function $t(Z)$ is called an *estimator,* and the risk function depends on the estimator used and on the state of nature.

Example 5–4. A bag contains five beads, M of them white and $5 - M$ black. When two beads are selected randomly from the bag, the number Z of white beads in the selection is a random variable with values and probabilities as given in the following table:

z	$P(Z = z) = f(z \mid M)$
0	$\dfrac{(5 - M)(4 - M)}{20}$
1	$\dfrac{2M(5 - M)}{20}$
2	$\dfrac{M(M - 1)}{20}$

The number of possible decision functions or estimators is $6^3 = 216$, which is the number of distinct ways one can assign one of 6 *actions* (0, 1, 2, 3, 4, 5) to each of three values of Z (0, 1, 2). One of these 216 estimators is the following:

$$T_1 = \begin{cases} 0, & \text{if } Z = 0, \\ 2, & \text{if } Z = 1, \\ 4, & \text{if } Z = 2. \end{cases}$$

The corresponding risk function is

$$R(M, T_1) = E[(T_1 - M)^2]$$
$$= (0 - M)^2 f(0 \mid M) + (2 - M)^2 f(1 \mid M) + (4 - M)^2 f(2 \mid M)$$
$$= \frac{M(6 - M)}{5}.$$

(Stop to think why it is reasonable for this risk to be 0 when $M = 0$.) The graph of this function is shown in Figure 5–6. Another of the 216 possible estimators assigns the value 3 to each value of Z

$$T_2 = 3, \quad \text{for } Z = 0, 1, \text{ or } 2.$$

The risk function for T_2 is

$$R(M, T_2) = E[(3 - M)^2] = (3 - M)^2.$$

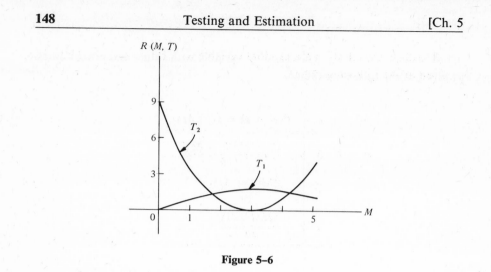

Figure 5–6

This is also shown in Figure 5–6. Notice that if M is really near 3, then T_2 is better than T_1; but if M is closer to 0 or 5, the estimator T_1 is the better of the two.

As in the general decision problem, a variety of techniques can be used to pick a particular estimator. The minimax principle frequently breaks down because the regret being used is not a bounded function, unless the parameter is restricted to a finite interval.

A Bayes estimator would be the function $t(\cdot)$ that minimizes the Bayes risk, which is computed as the average or expected value of the risk function $R(\theta, t)$ with respect to a given prior distribution, say with probability function $g(\theta)$:

$$B(t) = E_g[R(\theta, t)]$$
$$= \sum_j R(\theta_j, t) g(\theta_j).$$

But in Section 4.8 it was seen that, generally, the decision rule that minimizes the Bayes risk can be obtained by applying the posterior probabilities for θ to the original loss function, treating the problem as one with no data. It has already been explained (Section 5.1) that the no-data Bayes estimate, assuming a quadratic loss, is the mean of the prior distribution assumed for the states of nature. Thus, given $Z = z$, the Bayes estimate of θ, with quadratic loss, is the mean of the corresponding *posterior* distribution for θ:

$$E_h[\theta] \equiv \sum \theta_j h(\theta_j \mid z),$$

where $h(\theta \mid z)$ is the posterior probability of θ given $Z = z$ and given a certain prior weighting $g(\theta)$.

Example 5–5.   In a certain small town there are five TV sets, an unknown number M of which are tuned in to a certain program, and it is desired to estimate M on the basis of a sample of two drawn randomly from the five. (This is mathematically the same problem as that in Example 5–4—white beads in that example corresponding to sets tuned in to the program in this problem.) Suppose that of the two selected in the sample, exactly one is tuned in, and the other is not. The probability of this, given M, is (see Example 5–4)

$$f(1 \mid M) = \frac{2M(5 - M)}{20}.$$

If now one assumes a certain prior distribution, say equally likely values of M in the set 0, 1, 2, 3, 4, 5, the absolute probability of one set being tuned in is

$$p(1) = E_g[f(1 \mid M)]$$

$$= \frac{1}{6}\left(0 + \frac{8}{20} + \frac{12}{20} + \frac{12}{20} + \frac{8}{20} + 0\right) = \frac{1}{3}.$$

The posterior probabilities, given $Z = 1$, are then the ratios of the terms in this sum to the value of the sum:

M	0	1	2	3	4	5
$h(M \mid 1)$	0	.2	.3	.3	.2	0

The Bayes estimate, given $Z = 1$ and a prior distribution with equal weights on the possible values of M, is the mean of the posterior distribution, namely, 2.5 (which is the center of symmetry of the distribution, but can also be obtained by summing the products of values and probabilities). Now, 2.5 is not a value possible for M to assume, and one would be apt to announce that the estimate of M is 2 or 3.

If, to take another example, the prior distribution of M is defined by the following table:

M	0	1	2	3	4	5
$g(M)$	.4	.3	.2	.1	0	0

the posterior probabilities are calculated from the absolute probability

$$p(1) = E_g[f(1 \mid M)]$$

$$= 0 + .4 \times \frac{8}{20} + .3 \times \frac{12}{20} + .2 \times \frac{12}{20} + .1 \times \frac{8}{20} + 0 = \frac{1}{2},$$

with the results as follows:

M	0	1	2	3	4	5
$h(M \mid 1)$	0	.32	.36	.24	.08	0

The mean value or expected value of this distribution is

$$E_h(M) = 0 + 1 \times .32 + 2 \times .36 + 3 \times .24 + 4 \times .08 + 0$$

$$= 2.08.$$

One would probably announce the estimated value of M to be 2.

Problems

5–8 Consider the estimator $T_3 = 5$ if $Z = 0$ or 1, and 0 if $Z = 2$, for Example 5–4. Determine the risk function values for $M = 0, 1, \ldots, 5$ and compare them with those shown in Figure 5–6. (Is T_3 admissible?)

5–9 Determine the complete Bayes estimator for Example 5–5, assuming a uniform prior distribution. (That is, supply the estimate to be announced if $Z = 0$ and if $Z = 2$.)

5–10 It is observed that there are just two Democrats in a sample of 3 from a group of M Democrats and $8 - M$ Republicans. Assume the following probability of such an occurrence:

$$f(2 \mid M) = \frac{M(M - 1)(8 - M)}{112}.$$

Determine the Bayes estimate of M if the prior distribution of M is given by $P(M = k) \equiv \frac{1}{4}$, for $k = 0, 1, 2, 3$.

5.4 Maximum Likelihood Estimation

The Bayes estimator in the case of quadratic loss has been seen to be the expected value, or center of gravity, of the posterior distribution. Other loss functions would alter this conclusion. For instance, it turns out that if the loss function is $|T - \theta|$, that is, the absolute error, then the Bayes estimator is the median of the posterior distribution—the value (or values) that divides the θ-axis into two sections of equal probability. The median is another kind of *middle* or *center* of the distribution. Still another measure of centering, for distributions that have a single hump or maximum, is the value at which that maximum occurs, called the *mode* of the distribution. (This is not inconsistent with the everyday notion of the mode as being the most popular fashion.)

When the prior distribution is *uniform*, that is, with equal probabilities for all values of θ, the posterior probabilities given $Z = z$ are proportional to the probabilities $f(z \mid \theta)$ for that z:

$$h(\theta \mid z) = \frac{f(z \mid \theta)g(\theta)}{p(z)} = (\text{const.})f(z \mid \theta).$$

The mode of this posterior distribution is then that value of the parameter θ for which $f(z \mid \theta)$ is largest. As a function of θ, the quantity $f(z \mid \theta)$ is called the *likelihood function*, and the value of θ that maximizes it is called the *maximum likelihood estimate* of θ. Thus, the maximum likelihood estimate is the mode of the posterior distribution of θ when one assumes a uniform prior distribution for θ. Nevertheless, maximum likelihood estimators are often used by those who are violently anti-Bayesian, on the intuitive basis that the state for which an observed result has the highest probability is the "best" guess. Such estimators are frequently good, but are sometimes a bit extreme, and can be actually bad.

Example 5–6. In Example 5–4, the data variable Z was assumed to have probabilities, given M, according to the formula

$$f(z \mid M) = \begin{cases} \dfrac{(20 - 9M + M^2)}{20}, & \text{if } z = 0, \\[2mm] \dfrac{2M(5 - M)}{20}, & \text{if } z = 1, \\[2mm] \dfrac{M(M - 1)}{20}, & \text{if } z = 2. \end{cases}$$

For a given value of Z, say $Z = 1$, the likelihood function is

$$L(M) = f(1 \mid M) = \frac{2M(5 - M)}{20}.$$

As M ranges over the values 0, 1, 2, 3, 4, 5 the maximum value of $L(M)$ is easily computed to be $\frac{12}{20}$, achieved for either $M = 2$ or $M = 3$. These are maximum likelihood estimates of M, given $Z = 1$. Similarly, if $Z = 0$, the value of M that maximizes $(20 - 9M + M^2)/20$ is $M = 0$, and if $Z = 2$, the value of M that maximizes $M(M - 1)/20$ is $M = 5$. The maximum likelihood estimator of M is then the function

$$T = \begin{cases} 0 & \text{if } Z = 0, \\ 2 \text{ or } 3, & \text{if } Z = 1, \\ 5 & \text{if } Z = 2. \end{cases}$$

The appropriateness of the term *extreme* used above to describe the occasional behavior of a maximum likelihood estimator is in evidence here: If $Z = 0$, that is, if the sample contains no white beads, one announces that there are *no* white beads in the bag. (The "extremity" of this position would be more obvious if one were drawing from a bag with 100,000 beads, in which case again the result $Z = 0$ would lead to the announcement of the estimate $M = 0$, which is not a very defensible position.)

5.5 Mean Squared Error—Variance

The expected value of the regret, when the estimator $T = t(Z)$ is employed, called the risk function, is the measure by which estimators are judged:

$$R(\theta, T) = E[r(\theta, t(Z))].$$

If the regret is quadratic, this becomes the *mean squared error*:

$$\begin{aligned} R(\theta, T) &= \sum_i [t(z_i) - \theta]^2 f(z_i \mid \theta) \\ &= \sum_i [t(z_i)]^2 f(z_i \mid \theta) - 2\theta \sum_i t(z_i) f(z_i \mid \theta) + \theta^2 \\ &= E(T^2) - 2\theta E(T) + \theta^2 \\ &= E(T^2) - [E(T)]^2 + (E(T) - \theta)^2. \end{aligned}$$

The mean squared error is a classical measure of quality of an estimator. It has been expressed as the sum of two terms; it is convenient to have the following terminology:

$$\text{Variance of } T = \text{var } T = E(T^2) - [E(T)]^2,$$

$$\text{Bias in } T = b_T(\theta) = E(T) - \theta.$$

Thus, the mean squared error is the sum of the variance and the square of the bias:

$$\text{m.s.e.} = E[(T - \theta)^2] = \text{var } T + [b_T(\theta)]^2.$$

Clearly, if the m.s.e. is to be small, *both* the bias and the variance must be small in magnitude. An estimator is said to be *unbiased* if the bias is zero, in which case the variance of the estimator is the crucial quantity.

The variance of the random variable T can also be expressed as an average squared deviation about its expected value:

$$
\begin{aligned}
E[(T - ET)^2] &= \sum_i [t(z_i) - ET]^2 f(z_i \mid \theta) \\
&= \sum_i [t(z_i)]^2 f(z_i \mid \theta) - 2E(T) \sum_i t(z_i) f(z_i \mid \theta) + (ET)^2 \\
&= E(T^2) - 2E(T)E(T) + [E(T)]^2 \\
&= E(T^2) - [E(T)]^2 = \text{var } T.
\end{aligned}
$$

The variance is actually defined for any random variable (not just estimators that come from data Z), and is a useful parameter of its distribution, characterizing the dispersion or spread of the distribution.

Example 5–7. Consider the maximum likelihood estimator of M, the number among five TV sets in a population that are tuned into a certain program, based on the number Z of sets tuned into a selection of two from the five (see Examples 5–5 and 5–6):

$$
T = \begin{cases} 0 & \text{if } Z = 0, \\ 2 \text{ or } 3, & \text{if } Z = 1, \\ 5 & \text{if } Z = 2. \end{cases}
$$

Taking T_4 to be the estimator in which 2 is used if $Z = 1$, one computes the bias as follows:

$$E(T_4) = 0 \cdot f(0 \mid M) + 2 \cdot f(1 \mid M) + 5 \cdot f(2 \mid M)$$

$$= 2 \cdot \frac{2M(5 - M)}{20} + 5 \cdot \frac{M(M - 1)}{20} = \frac{M(M + 15)}{20},$$

$$b_{T_4}(M) = E(T_4) - M = \frac{M(M - 5)}{20}.$$

The variance of T_4 is the expected square minus the square of the expected value of T_4:

$$E(T_4^2) - [E(T_4)]^2 = 0 + 4 \frac{2M(5 - M)}{20} + 25 \frac{M(M - 1)}{20} - [E(T)]^2$$

$$= \frac{M}{20}(17M + 15) - \left(\frac{M}{20}\right)^2 (M + 15)^2.$$

The mean squared error is then

$$E[(T - M)^2] = \operatorname{var} T_4 + [b_{T_4}(M)]^2 = \frac{M(5 - M)(3 + 2M)}{20}.$$

A similar computation would yield the bias for T_5, the maximum likelihood estimator using the estimate 3 when $Z = 1$, as the negative of the bias in T_4; the mean squared error would be that of T_4 but with M replaced by $5 - M$. Perhaps it would be of interest, in view of the ambiguity when $Z = 1$, to study the *randomized* or *mixed* estimator T_6 defined to be the same as T_4 and T_5 when $Z = 0$ or 2, and to be 2 or 3 according to the toss of a coin when $Z = 1$. The expected value of T_6 is

$$E(T_6) = 0 \cdot f(0 \mid M) + 2 \cdot \frac{1}{2} \cdot f(1 \mid M) + 3 \cdot \frac{1}{2} \cdot f(1 \mid M) + 5 \cdot f(2 \mid M)$$

$$= \frac{5}{2} \frac{2M(5 - M)}{20} + 5 \frac{M(M - 1)}{20} = M.$$

That is, this mixture of T_4 and T_5 is unbiased. The mean squared error is then the variance:

$$\operatorname{var} T_6 = \frac{4 + 9}{2} \frac{2M(5 - M)}{20} + 25 \frac{M(M - 1)}{20} - M^2$$

$$= \frac{8M(5 - M)}{20},$$

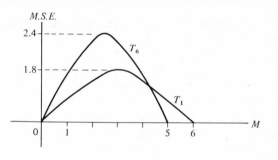

Figure 5–7

which is the average of the mean squared errors for T_4 and T_5, respectively. The graph of the mean squared error for T_6 is shown along with that for T_1 (see Example 5–4) in Figure 5–7.

Problems

5–11 Calculate the variance of the distribution defined by the following table of values and corresponding probabilities:

x	−1	0	1
$f(x)$	.2	.5	.3

5–12 Compute the bias and variance for T_1 defined in Example 5–4, and verify that the variance plus the square of the bias is the mean squared error.

5–13 To estimate, as in Examples 5–5 to 5–7, the number M of TV sets (among 5) tuned to a certain program, two are selected one at a time, at random, but in such a way that the number Y among the two selected that are tuned to the program has the following distribution:

k	$P(Y = k)$
0	$(1 - M/5)^2$
1	$2\dfrac{M}{5}\left(1 - \dfrac{M}{5}\right)$
2	$\left(\dfrac{M}{5}\right)^2$

(This would be the case if the names of the 5 TV owners were put on slips of paper, and two slips were drawn one at a time, the first being replaced and mixed with the rest before the second drawing.) Calculate the mean squared error for the estimator

$$T = \begin{cases} 0, & \text{if } Y = 0, \\ 2 \text{ or } 3, \text{ according to the toss of a fair coin,} & \text{if } Y = 1, \\ 5, & \text{if } Y = 2. \end{cases}$$

5–14 Determine the maximum likelihood estimator of the number of Democrats for the estimation problem of Problem 5–10, that is, assuming that two of sample of three (from the group of M Democrats and $8 - M$ Republicans) are Democrats.

5.5 The Problem of Testing Hypotheses

A decision problem in which there are available just *two actions* is called a problem of *testing hypotheses*. A particular state of nature is called a *simple hypothesis*; the "hypothesis" is that nature is in that state, and it is said to be true if nature *is* in that state. A set of states of nature including more than one state is called a *composite hypothesis*; it is said to be true when any particular hypothesis included in it is the actual state of nature.

The loss function $l(\theta, a)$ can be described by two functions of θ; if the two actions open to the decision maker are A and B, these are

$$a(\theta) = l(\theta, A) \quad \text{and} \quad b(\theta) = l(\theta, B).$$

These losses automatically divide the set of states of nature into two parts:

$H_0 \equiv$ the set of simple hypotheses θ for which $a(\theta) \leq b(\theta)$,

$H_1 \equiv$ the set of simple hypotheses θ for which $a(\theta) > b(\theta)$.

Thus, if (for example) the states of nature are indexed by a real-valued parameter θ, and the losses $a(\theta)$ and $b(\theta)$ are shown in Figure 5–8, the set H_0 consists of all θ to the left of the crossing point, and H_1 consists of the remaining values of θ. Clearly, if H_0 were known to be true, action A would be the preferred action, and it is said that in taking action A one *accepts* H_0. Similarly, taking action B is described as *rejecting* H_0, or *accepting* H_1.

The regret function is obtained by subtracting, for each θ, the smaller of the two losses from the larger, with the result

$$r(\theta, A) = \begin{cases} 0, & \text{if } \theta \text{ is in } H_0 \text{ (i.e., if } H_0 \text{ is true)} \\ a(\theta) - b(\theta), & \text{if } H_1 \text{ is true,} \end{cases}$$

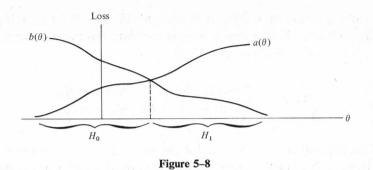

Figure 5–8

and

$$r(\theta, B) = \begin{cases} b(\theta) - a(\theta), & \text{if } H_0 \text{ is true,} \\ 0, & \text{if } H_1 \text{ is true.} \end{cases}$$

In the subsequent discussion it will be assumed that the losses have been already "regretized," and the term *risk* will be used for *expected regret*.

When an observation Z (either a single observation or a sequence of several) is available, a decision rule assigns to each value of Z either the action A or the action B. To carry out such a rule, one obtains a specific value for Z and rejects H_0 (takes action B) if action B has been assigned by the rule to that value of Z, and otherwise accepts H_0. If the number of possible values of Z is finite, as has been frequently assumed, then the number of possible decision rules is finite—equal to 2^K, where K is the number of values of Z. A decision rule is called a *test of H_0 against H_1*. A decision rule or test is characterized by the set of Z-values to which the action A has been assigned, or alternatively by the set of Z-values to which action B has been assigned. The latter is called the *critical region* of the test:

DEFINITION   *The critical region of a test based on a statistic Z is the set of Z-values that call for rejecting H_0, or taking action B.*

This definition may seem arbitrarily unsymmetrical, and so it is; the asymmetry in the language arises from the classical approach to the testing of hypotheses, in which the two hypotheses do not play symmetrical roles as they do in the setting of decision theory. Another carryover from the traditional language is the name *null hypothesis* for H_0 and *alternative hypothesis* for H_1. The test is said to be a test of the null hypothesis H_0 against the alternative H_0.

Suppose that $l(\theta, A) = 0$ for θ in H_0 and $l(\theta, B) = 0$ for θ in H_1, and also that $l(\theta, a) \geq 0$. This loss is a regret function, and the risk, for a given test C, is computed as the expected loss:

$$R(\theta, C) = \begin{cases} b(\theta)P(C \mid \theta), & \text{if } \theta \text{ is in } H_0, \\ a(\theta)[1 - P(C \mid \theta)], & \text{if } \theta \text{ is in } H_1. \end{cases}$$

The function $\pi(\theta) \equiv P(C \mid \theta)$ is called the *power function* of the test C, and knowledge of this function (together with the losses) is sufficient to calculate the risk. In particular, if one could find a critical region C such that $P(C \mid \theta) = 0$ for θ in H_0 and $P(C \mid \theta) = 1$ for θ in H_1, then the risk would be zero; this power function is referred to as *ideal*:

$$\text{Ideal power function} = \begin{cases} 1, & \text{for } \theta \text{ in } H_1, \\ 0, & \text{for } \theta \text{ in } H_0. \end{cases}$$

It will not ordinarily be possible to find a test with the ideal power characteristic if one is restricted (as he is in practice) to data that contain less than complete information about θ.

Example 5–8. Mr. A claims to be able to predict the outcome of the toss of a coin before it is tossed—perhaps not perfectly, but at least with a higher probability of being correct than an ordinary person would have. Mr. B disputes this, and proposes that he conduct an experiment, in which Mr. A is to call the fall of the coin in five independent tosses. The data will be summarized in Z, the number of times (out of five) that Mr. A is correct in his call. An ordinary person (no ESP) would presumably be right about as often as he is wrong in calling out the result; if p denotes his probability of a correct call, he would have $p = \frac{1}{2}$. The hypothesis that Mr. A is not extraordinary is then the hypothesis that for him, $p = \frac{1}{2}$. His claim of being able to predict the fall more often than an ordinary person is an hypothesis p where $p > \frac{1}{2}$. If p is a number assumed to lie on the interval $\frac{1}{2} \leq p \leq 1$, this interval of possible states of nature is made up of $H_0: p = \frac{1}{2}$, and $H_1: p > \frac{1}{2}$. The losses in this situation would be particularly hard to assess. Thus, if p is really $\frac{1}{2}$ and it is concluded from the test that $p > \frac{1}{2}$, this is an error and there would be a loss associated with it (whatever falsely according Mr. A with occult powers would imply). Conversely, if $p > \frac{1}{2}$ but it is concluded from the test that $p = \frac{1}{2}$, then Mr. A is a prophet without honor, a misfortune that surely involves the loss of something.

The test statistic Z can have any of the values 0, 1, 2, 3, 4, 5. Since a test divides this set of values into a critical region and the set complementary to the critical region, the number of tests is the number of subsets of the six values that can be constructed, namely, $2^6 = 64$. Some of these tests are obviously bad, for instance, asserting that H_0 is false (and therefore $p > \frac{1}{2}$) if $Z = 0$ (no successes in five tries). And none of the 64 tests is ideal. The critical region $Z = 4$ or 5 would call for rejecting $p = \frac{1}{2}$ if Mr. A calls the fall correctly at least four out of five times; the intuitive basis for this particular critical region would be the feeling that this large number of successful calls is "significantly" different from what one would expect for a person with $p = \frac{1}{2}$.

5.6 Simple H_0 Versus Simple H_1

When there are just two states of nature, one called H_0 and the other H_1, the loss function of regret type is easily given in a table:

	State of nature	
	H_0	H_1
Action A	0	a
B	b	0

(The earlier function called $a(\theta)$ has just one value, a; and $b(\theta)$ is simply the constant b.) The risk function for the test with critical region C is then

$$R(\theta, C) = \begin{cases} b\alpha, & \text{if } \theta \text{ is } H_0, \\ a\beta, & \text{if } \theta \text{ is } H_1, \end{cases}$$

where α and β are called the *size of the type I error* and the *size of the type II error*, respectively:

$$\alpha = \text{size of type I error} = P(C \mid H_0),$$
$$\beta = \text{size of type II error} = 1 - P(C \mid H_1).$$

Thus, α is the probability of rejecting H_0 when H_0 is true, and β is the probability of accepting H_0 when H_0 is false.

When there are just two states of nature, there are just two distributions for the test statistic Z:

$$f_0(z) \equiv f(z \mid H_0) = P(Z = z \mid H_0),$$
$$f_1(z) \equiv f(z \mid H_1) = P(Z = z \mid H_1).$$

If a prior distribution is assumed for nature, say $g_0 = P(H_0)$ and $g_1 = P(H_1)$, the absolute probability of the value $Z = z$ can be computed as the weighted average of f_0 and f_1:

$$p(z) = g_0 f_0(z) + g_1 f_1(z).$$

The posterior probabilities are then the ratios of the terms in this sum to the value of the sum:

$$h_0 = P(H_0 \mid Z = z) = \frac{g_0 f_0(z)}{p(z)},$$

$$h_1 = P(H_1 \mid Z = z) = \frac{g_1 f_1(z)}{p(z)}.$$

The expected posterior loss can now be computed for each action:

$$\text{Accept } H_0: \quad 0 + ah_1 = \frac{ag_1 f_1(z)}{p(z)},$$

$$\text{Reject } H_0: \quad bh_0 + 0 = \frac{bg_0 f_0(z)}{p(z)}.$$

If the first of these is larger, one should reject H_0; if the second is larger, one should accept H_0. (If they are equal, the action is a matter of indifference.) The critical region is therefore the set of Z-values defined by the rule:

$$\text{Reject } H_0 \text{ if } \quad \frac{f_0(Z)}{f_1(Z)} < \frac{ag_1}{bg_0}.$$

Although one cannot calculate the constant ag_1/bg_0 without knowing the losses a and b and the prior probabilities, it is nevertheless clear that the family of tests, for various values of K, defined by the rule

$$\text{Reject } H_0 \text{ if and only if } \quad \frac{f_0(Z)}{f_1(Z)} < K,$$

includes all Bayes tests, and only Bayes tests. The ratio $\Lambda = f_0/f_1$ is called the *likelihood ratio*, and tests with critical region $\Lambda < K$ are called *likelihood ratio tests*.

Example 5–9. Let the six possible values of a test statistic Z be denoted by $z_1, z_2, \ldots, z_6$; and let the probability of $Z = z$ be $f_0(z)$ under H_0 and $f_1(z)$ under H_1 (both simple), given in the following table:

z	$f_0(z)$	$f_1(z)$	$\Lambda(z)$
z_1	.1	.4	1/4
z_2	.3	.1	3
z_3	.2	.1	2
z_4	0	.2	0
z_5	.1	.2	1/2
z_6	.3	0	∞

The final column gives the value of the ratio $\Lambda = f_0/f_1$ for each possible value of Z. These values of Z can then be ordered according to the size of Λ, which measures (in a sense) the strength of the evidence favoring f_0 over f_1 as describing nature. Ordered in this way, the list of Z-values is as follows:

z	z_4	z_1	z_5	z_3	z_2	z_6
Λ	0	$\frac{1}{4}$	$\frac{1}{2}$	2	3	∞

A likelihood ratio critical region is constructed by putting z's with small values of Λ into it, and z's with larger values of Λ into the acceptance region. This can be accomplished by putting a dividing line in the midst of the Z-values, such that z's to the left have small likelihood ratio values, and to the right, large. For instance, putting the line between z_1 and z_5 defines the test with critical region $C = \{z_4, z_1\}$, that is, calling for rejection of H_0 if $Z = z_4$ or z_1, and acceptance of H_0 if $Z = z_5$, z_3, z_2, or z_6. This particular critical region would be characterized, in terms of Λ, by $\Lambda < \frac{1}{3}$, or by $\Lambda < \frac{2}{5}$, or by $\Lambda < \lambda$, any value between $\frac{1}{4}$ and $\frac{1}{2}$. There are just seven distinct critical regions corresponding to the seven spaces between values of Z or on either end of list. These are given in the following table, with arbitrary numbering.

The error sizes are readily computed for each test; thus, for C_4,

$$\alpha = P(C_4 \mid H_0) = P(Z = z_4, z_1, \text{ or } z_5 \mid H_0)$$

$$= .1 + 0 + .1 = .2,$$

and

$$\beta = 1 - P(C_4 \mid H_1) = P(Z = z_2, z_3, \text{ or } z_6 \mid H_1)$$

$$= .1 + .1 + 0 = .2.$$

C	Values of Z in C	α	β
C_1	$z_4, z_1, z_5, z_3, z_2, z_6$	1	0
C_2	z_4, z_1, z_5, z_3, z_2	.7	0
C_3	z_4, z_1, z_5, z_3	.4	.1
C_4	z_4, z_1, z_5	.2	.2
C_5	z_4, z_1	.1	.4
C_6	z_4	0	.8
C_7	(none)	0	1

For losses $a = b = 1$, the risks under H_0 and H_1 are just α and β, respectively. These are plotted as points in an $R_0 R_1$ plane in Figure 5–9. (The quantity R_i is the risk under H_i.) For other losses a and b the risks would be proportional to α and β, and the graph would be altered only by corresponding scale factors.

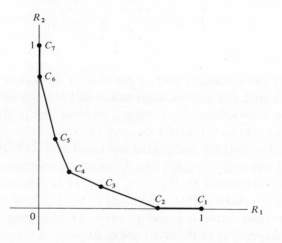

Figure 5–9

There are $2^6 - 7 = 57$ possible tests that are not included in the above list of Bayes tests. These could also be evaluated in terms of error sizes, and the corresponding points plotted in Figure 5–9. Even without actually doing so, however, it is clear that none of these other tests would be represented by a point that is below the broken line shown through the Bayes tests (which would correspond to mixtures of pure Bayes tests, and would also be Bayes). For, if there were such a point, it would certainly imply that there are Bayes tests not included in the list $C_1, \ldots, C_7$ (or mixture thereof); the only reason such a point would not be encountered first, in moving a line with some fixed slope up from the lower left, would be that there is yet another point to the lower left of the broken line of Bayes tests which is Bayes.

The result in the above example is actually quite general. It can be proved that likelihood ratio tests $\Lambda < K$ for simple H_0 against simple H_1 have the property of having the smallest β for a given α, and the smallest α for a given β, provided $0 < K < \infty$. (Figure 5–9 shows that the test C_1, which is defined by $\Lambda \leq \infty$, although Bayes, does not have the smallest α for tests with $\beta = 0$ also, test C_7, which is defined by $\Lambda < 0$, does not have the smallest β for tests with $\alpha = 0$.)

Example 5–10.   In testing the null hypothesis that Mr. A has no occult powers but is rather an ordinary person when it comes to predicting the fall of a coin, suppose there is reason to restrict the possible alternatives to the null hypothesis $p = \frac{1}{2}$ to a single value of p greater than $\frac{1}{2}$, say $p = .7$. Thus, it is desired to test $H_0: p = .5$ against the alternative $H_1: p = .7$. The test statistic to be used is Z, the number of successful predictions in n tries. It will be seen in the next chapter that the probability of k successes in n independent tries is given by the following formula

$$f(k \mid p) = \frac{n(n-1)\cdots(n-k+1)}{k(k-1)\cdots 3 \cdot 2 \cdot 1} p^k (1-p)^{n-k},$$

where p is the probability of a successful prediction. For a given outcome $Z = k$, the likelihood ratio is

$$\Lambda(k) = \frac{f(k \mid .5)}{f(k \mid .7)} = \frac{(.5)^k (.5)^{n-k}}{(.7)^k (.3)^{n-k}} = \left(\frac{5}{3}\right)^n \left(\frac{3}{7}\right)^k.$$

This is a decreasing function of k: the larger the k, the smaller the value of $\Lambda(k)$. Therefore, the critical region $\Lambda < const$ is equivalent to a condition of

Z of the form $Z > const.$ That is, the likelihood ratio tests for $p = .5$ against $p = .7$ call for rejection of $p = .5$ if the number of successes is "inordinately" large, namely, larger than the preassigned constant that defines the critical region. Since Z can only take on the values $0, 1, 2, \ldots, n$, there are precisely $n + 1$ (pure) likelihood ratio tests; and these are Bayes tests, each with respect to some prior distribution and some values of the losses.

To illustrate the computation of α and β, suppose $n = 6$, and consider the critical region $Z > 4$ (which means: reject $p = .5$ if there are more than four successes in six tries). Then

$$\alpha = P(Z > 4 \mid p = .5) = f(5 \mid .5) + f(6 \mid .5)$$

$$= \frac{6 \cdot 5 \cdot 4 \cdot 3 \cdot 2}{5 \cdot 4 \cdot 3 \cdot 2 \cdot 1}(.5)^6 + \frac{6 \cdot 5 \cdot 4 \cdot 3 \cdot 2 \cdot 1}{6 \cdot 5 \cdot 4 \cdot 3 \cdot 2 \cdot 1}(.5)^6$$

$$= \frac{7}{64} \doteq 0.11,$$

and

$$\beta = 1 - P(Z > 4 \mid p = .7)$$

$$= 1 - f(5 \mid .7) - f(6 \mid .7) = 1 - 6(.7)^5(.3)^1 - (.7)^6(.3)^0 \doteq 0.58.$$

Problems

5–15 The elevator problem of Example 4–1, involving two states of nature and two actions, can be thought of as a problem of testing a simple hypothesis (nature is in state θ_1—elevator working) against a simple alternative (nature is in state θ_2—elevator inoperative). If, as in that example, the observation Z has the following distributions under these two states, determine the likelihood ratio tests and the corresponding error sizes:

z	z_1	z_2	z_3
$f(z \mid \theta_1)$	.2	.3	.5
$f(z \mid \theta_2)$	.6	.3	.1

5–16 Let M denote the number of defectives in a lot of five articles and Z the number of defectives in a sample of size one, randomly selected from the lot, so that

$$f(z \mid M) = \begin{cases} \dfrac{M}{5}, & \text{if } z = 1, \\[2mm] 1 - \dfrac{M}{5}, & \text{if } z = 0. \end{cases}$$

Determine the Bayes tests of $M = 1$ against $M = 3$, assuming prior probabilities $g(1) = .3$ and $g(3) = .7$, and losses $b = 5$ in rejecting $M = 1$ when $M = 1$ and $a = 2$ in accepting $M = 1$ when $M = 3$.

5-17 Determine the minimax mixed test for Problem 5-16. For what prior distribution is this a Bayes test?

5-18 Construct all Bayes tests of $p = \frac{1}{2}$ against $p = \frac{3}{4}$ based on the variable Z, where

$$f(z \mid p) = P(Z = z \mid p) = \frac{4!}{z! \, (4 - z)!} \, p^z(1 - z)^{4-z}, \qquad z = 0, 1, 2, 3, 4.$$

Compute α and β for each test and make the usual $\alpha\beta$ plot. Compute also α and β for some of the tests that are not Bayes tests, and observe where the corresponding points fall; are they admissible?

5-19 The following loss function has been used in earlier examples and problems, where M is the number of defectives in a lot of five articles, to be accepted or rejected:

			M			
	0	1	2	3	4	5
Acc. lot	0	2	4	6	8	10
Rej. lot	5	4	3	2	1	0

Construct the corresponding table of regrets, and express the problem as one of testing hypotheses. (That is, define H_0 and H_1 appropriately.)

5.7 Composite Hypotheses

When either H_0 or H_1 is composite, there are more than two states of nature, and the determination of a class of tests that are "good" is not nearly so simple as in the case of a simple H_0 against a simple H_1. As given in Section 5.5, the risk function for a given critical region C is

$$R(\theta, C) = \begin{cases} b(\theta)\pi(\theta), & \text{for } \theta \text{ in } H_0, \\ a(\theta)[1 - \pi(\theta)], & \text{for } \theta \text{ in } H_1, \end{cases}$$

where $a(\theta)$ is the regret if action A (accept H_0) is taken when it should not be, $b(\theta)$ is the regret if action B (reject H_0) is taken when it should not be, and $\pi(\theta)$ is the power function:

$$\pi(\theta) = P(C \mid \theta) = P(\text{reject } H_0 \mid \theta).$$

The determination of a Bayes test for a particular prior distribution is not particularly difficult (in principle, at least) if one uses the approach of applying the posterior distribution to the loss function.

Example 5–11. With the losses assumed in Problem 5–19, the regret table

		M				
	0	1	2	3	4	5
Reject	5	2	0	0	0	0
Accept	0	0	1	4	7	10

defines the problem of testing H_0: $M = 0$ or 1, against H_1: $M = 2, 3, 4$, or 5, where accepting H_0 amounts to accepting the lot (which contains five articles, M of which are defective). An article selected at random is defective ($Z = 1$) with probability $M/5$ and good ($Z = 0$) with probability $1 - M/5$. Assuming equal prior probabilities for $M = 0, 1, 2$, and 3 and zero prior probability for $M = 4$ or 5 yields the following posterior probabilities:

		M				
	0	1	2	3	4	5
$h(M \mid Z = 1)$	0	$\frac{1}{6}$	$\frac{2}{6}$	$\frac{3}{6}$	0	0
$h(M \mid Z = 0)$	$\frac{5}{14}$	$\frac{4}{14}$	$\frac{3}{14}$	$\frac{2}{14}$	0	0

To obtain the Bayes action for $Z = 1$ the posterior probabilities for $Z = 1$ are applied to the regrets in the above table to obtain expected posterior regrets:

$$\text{Accept:} \quad 0 + 1 \times \frac{2}{6} + 4 \times \frac{3}{6} + 0 = \frac{14}{6},$$

$$\text{Reject:} \quad 0 + 2 \times \frac{1}{6} + 0 = \frac{2}{6},$$

the smaller of which is achieved by rejecting H_0 (rejecting the lot). For $Z = 0$, the expected posterior regrets are

$$\text{Accept:} \quad 0 + 1 \times \frac{3}{14} + 4 \times \frac{2}{14} + 0 = \frac{11}{14},$$

$$\text{Reject:} \quad 5 \times \frac{5}{14} + 2 \times \frac{4}{14} + 0 = \frac{33}{14},$$

so that the Bayes action in this case is to accept H_0, or accept the lot.

The power function for this Bayes test (reject H_0 if $Z = 1$ and accept H_0 if $Z = 0$) is

$$\pi(M) = P(Z = 1 \mid M) = \frac{M}{5}.$$

The expected regret for the test is obtained by combining the regrets $a(M)$ and $b(M)$ as given in the table above with the power function. The result is given in the following table, along with expected regrets for each of the other four possible tests. (With just two possible values of Z and two actions there are only four tests.)

		State (M)					
		0	1	2	3	4	5
	$Z = 1$	0	$\frac{2}{5}$	$\frac{3}{5}$	$\frac{8}{5}$	$\frac{7}{5}$	0
C:	$Z = 0$	$\frac{25}{5}$	$\frac{8}{5}$	$\frac{2}{5}$	$\frac{12}{5}$	$\frac{28}{5}$	10
	$Z = 0$ or 1	5	2	0	0	0	0
	empty	0	0	1	4	7	10

It is apparent that no one of these tests dominates any of the others; even the rather unreasonable test with critical region $Z = 0$ is not dominated, having the second smallest risk for the state $M = 2$. The minimax test (pure) is clearly that with critical region $Z = 1$, which has maximum expected regret of 8/5 (the other maxima are 10, 5, and 10). Obtaining the minimax mixed test is not so simple.

The notion of *likelihood ratio* can be extended to the case of composite hypotheses. This is not a decision-theoretic notion, inasmuch as it does not involve the loss function; moreover, the method will not (as in the case of simple null and alternative hypotheses) lead to a class of tests that is readily identified in terms of decision-theoretic concepts. However, no matter how a test is derived or thought up, one can study its performance in terms of the risk function.

The extended or generalized likelihood ratio is based on the intuitive notion that the "best" model, or explanation of a given set of data, is the one in which that set of data is most "likely," that is, has the highest probability. If this is stipulated, then it makes sense to look for the "best" explanation in the models that make up H_0 and compare that with the "best" explanation in H_1, rejecting H_0 if the "best" model in H_1 is "better" than the "best" model in H_0. (Quotes are used repeatedly in this statement to emphasize that the notion of "best" is purely intuitive.) The generalized likelihood ratio statistic is thus defined as

$$\Lambda = \frac{\max_{H_0} L(\theta)}{\max_{H_1} L(\theta)},$$

where $L(\theta)$ is the likelihood function

$$L(\theta) = f(z \mid \theta) = P(Z = z \mid \theta),$$

Z being the random quantity representing the data. Since $L(\theta)$ depends on z, the likelihood ratio is a function of z and defines the test statistic. The test called the *likelihood ratio test* (generalized) is defined by the critical region $\Lambda < (const)$. This is really a class or family of tests, as the constant used as a boundary is varied over the set of positive numbers.

It turns out that one can construct likelihood ratio tests that are worse than tests ignoring the data—in rather special and unusual situations (sometimes called *pathological*); however, likelihood ratio tests are usually quite good in dealing with large samples, and can be good tests for small samples.

Example 5–12. Consider an observation Z obtained to test $H_0: \{\theta_1, \theta_2\}$ against $H_1: \{\theta_3, \theta_4, \theta_5\}$, and related to θ by the following table of probability functions $f(z \mid \theta)$; this same table includes the values of $L(\theta)$ in the rows, for fixed z. Shown also in the table are columns for the maximum of $L(\theta)$ and for θ in H_0, the maximum of $L(\theta)$ for θ in H_1, and the ratio Λ of these maxima:

	H_0		H_1			$\max_{H_0} L(\theta)$	$\max_{H_1} L(\theta)$	Λ
	θ_1	θ_2	θ_3	θ_4	θ_5			
z_1	.1	.1	.2	.7	.6	.1	.7	$\dfrac{1}{7}$
z_2	.5	.8	.2	.1	.3	.8	.3	$\dfrac{8}{3}$
z_3	.4	.1	.6	.2	.1	.4	.6	$\dfrac{4}{6}$

The values of Z in order of increasing Λ are then z_1, z_3, z_2. Four tests of the form $\Lambda < const$ can be constructed, with these critical regions:

$$C_1: \text{ (empty)}$$
$$C_2: \{z_1\}$$
$$C_3: \{z_1, z_3\}$$
$$C_4: \{z_1, z_3, z_2\}.$$

The power functions are readily determined; for instance,

$$\pi_{C_3}(\theta) = P(Z = z_1 \text{ or } z_3 \mid \theta)$$

with values as follows:

θ	θ_1	θ_2	θ_3	θ_4	θ_5
$\pi_{C_3}(\theta)$	.5	.2	.8	.9	.7

So far the losses have not been needed, but to get the risk function from this power function they would have to be specified.

One approach to constructing a test for composite hypotheses, used when nature is identified by a real parameter and the values of θ in H_0 are all to one side of those in H_1:

$$H_0: \theta \leq \theta^* \quad \text{vs.} \quad H_1: \theta > \theta^*,$$

is to introduce a zone of indifference. This is something that is not so much introduced as it is *defined* by the loss function. Often, when pressed, the one who has the problem to be solved by the statistician will confess that if θ is close to θ^*, it really doesn't matter much whether action A or action B is taken. This means that both regrets ($a(\theta)$ and $b(\theta)$) are zero in some interval about θ^*, say from θ' to θ''. With this concession, the statistician will construct a best test for the simple $\theta = \theta'$ against the simple $\theta = \theta''$, and then use this test for the composite situation given. It will usually be a good test.

Example 5–13. Consider again the parameter p introduced in Example 5–10, $0 \leq p \leq 1$, studied with the aid of the statistic Z having probabilities

$$f(k \mid p) = \frac{4!}{k! \, (4 - k)!} p^k (1 - p)^{4-k}, \qquad k = 0, 1, \ldots, 4.$$

To construct a test of $p \leq \frac{1}{3}$ against $p > \frac{1}{3}$, consider values θ' and θ'' such that $\theta' < \frac{1}{3} < \theta''$; in Example 5–10 the Bayes tests for θ' against θ'' were seen to be of the form $Z > const$. Consider then the particular one of these given by the critical region $Z > 2$. The power function of this test is

$$\pi(p) = P(Z > 2 \mid p) = P(Z = 3 \text{ or } 4 \mid p)$$

$$= 4p^3(1 - p) + p^4 = p^3(4 - 3p),$$

which is shown in Figure 5–10. From this and given losses one can compute

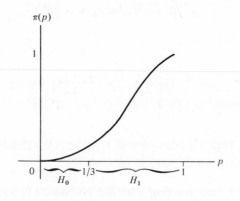

Figure 5–10

the risk function; for instance, if

$$a(p) = \begin{cases} 1, & \text{for } p > 1/2, \\ 0, & \text{for } p < 1/2. \end{cases}$$

and

$$b(p) = \begin{cases} 0, & \text{for } p > 1/4, \\ 2, & \text{for } p < 1/4. \end{cases}$$

then the risk function is

$$R(p, C) = \begin{cases} 2p^3(4 - 3p), & p < 1/4, \\ 1 \cdot [1 - p^3(4 - 3p)], & p > 1/2. \end{cases}$$

This is shown in Figure 5–11.

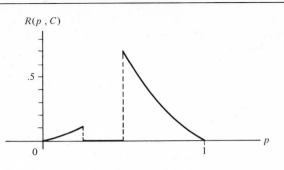

Figure 5–11

Problems

5–20 Assume losses for Example 5–12 according to the following table

	θ_1	θ_2	θ_3	θ_4	θ_5
Action A	0	0	2	2	2
Action B	5	5	0	0	0

From the power function in Example 5–12, determine the risk function for the critical region C_3: $\{z_1, z_3\}$. Determine also the risk function for the test which is the *opposite* of C_3, namely, accept H_0 when Z falls in C_3 and reject otherwise. (Which is better?)

5–21 Sketch the risk function for the test $Z > 2$ in Example 5–13 when the losses are assumed to be

$$a(p) = \begin{cases} 0, & 0 \leq p > \frac{1}{2}, \\ 2p - 1, & \frac{1}{2} \leq p \leq 1, \end{cases}$$

and

$$b(p) = \begin{cases} \frac{1}{2}(1 - 4p), & 0 \leq p < \frac{1}{4}, \\ 0, & \frac{1}{4} \leq p \leq 1. \end{cases}$$

5–22 Referring to Example 5–13, construct the generalized likelihood ratio for testing $p \leq \frac{1}{3}$ against $p > \frac{1}{3}$. (Do this by brute force—examining the likelihood function, perhaps with the aid of a sketch, for each value of Z, to obtain the necessary maxima.) Compare these likelihood ratio tests with the tests given in the example.

5–23 Let Z be an observation that can assume one of four values, with probabilities as shown in the following table. The states of nature are indexed by a parameter θ, H_0 consisting of the single value θ_0 and H_1 defined by the interval $0 < \theta < 1$.

	z_1	z_2	z_3	z_4
$f(z \mid \theta_0)$	1/12	1/12	1/6	2/3
$f(z \mid \theta)$, θ in H_1	$\theta/3$	$(1 - \theta)/3$	1/2	1/6

Determine the likelihood ratio test and show that the critical region $Z = z_3$ dominates it.

5.8 Decision Versus Inference

This chapter has presented the basic statistical problems of estimation and testing hypotheses in a decision theoretic setting, with the goal of clarifying these problems and to some extent "justifying" their classical solutions. Yet, although these two types of problems are precisely those with which most statistics texts concern themselves, it is not altogether clear that they constitute all or even a large part of "statistics." The matter will not be examined in detail, inasmuch as this is a text in decision theory, but perhaps a few things should be said.

In business and industry, actions must be and are taken in the face of uncertainty about nature—actions that may be irreversible and involve huge sums of money. It is in such settings that the application of decision theory seems most natural and profitable. The difficulties of setting prior distributions and determining utilities are there, but if the desire to use decision-theoretic notions forces a study of these things, a useful purpose has been achieved.

The scientist, on the other hand, seeks to broaden and deepen his understanding of the laws that govern his science. He piles experiment on experiment, and essentially never closes the door on new information. The actions he takes can perhaps be expressed only in terms of the possible changes in direction of his research: abandoning one theory, say, and trying another. Decisions are involved, but seldom in the simple way that they arise and are made in industry. A scientist's statistical analysis should be as informative as possible, and he should not be content with such a simple statement as: "The result is significant at the level $\alpha = .05$, and so the theory is discarded." Indeed, he should himself be alert to other scientists' related experiments, not closing the door to possible errors in his own.

In government and politics, statistics are also used to make decisions, but such uses usually reflect the fact that the government is in many ways in business. On the other hand, the statistics with which governments concern themselves are often obtained only to provide for general consumption a description of the way things are concerning the people and the resources of the country.

When the aim of a statistical analysis is that of describing or making inferences about nature, whether this be the population of a country or the

laws governing a physical or social process, it may be that the highly struc-
tured theory of decision making is not so appropriate. Perhaps this is simply
a corollary to the possibility that estimation and the testing of hypotheses are
not really the appropriate problems in such situations.

One view of the Bayesian approach to statistics, motivated by such considerations as these, is that it provides a vehicle for the reduction of data,
transforming problems into no-data problems, the data being used to generate
a posterior distribution. The posterior distribution would then be thought
of as the end result of the analysis, available for anyone to use as he sees fit.
However, the posterior distribution depends upon an assumed prior distribution, and if the analysis is really to be put on display, without a particular
statistician's prior convictions, it is perhaps better done in terms of the
likelihood function. For, with the likelihood function corresponding to the
observed data, anyone is free to construct the posterior in terms of his own
prior distribution, or simply to use the likelihood function as a device for
describing and summarizing what has been observed.

Chapter 6   Normal Distributions

A class of probability models for a continuous random variable that finds widespread application is the class of *normal* distributions. These are defined over the set of all real numbers, $-\infty < x < \infty$, but are also used as useful approximations in instances where the true distribution must be over some smaller interval, such as $x > 0$, or $a < x < b$.

6.1 Normal Densities

The density function of a distribution called *normal* is defined in terms of the number e, the base of the natural logarithm system, a transcendental irrational whose decimal expansion to five places is

$$e = 2.71828\cdots$$

(One of the many characterizations of this number is that it is that value of a such that the graph of the function a^x has a tangent line at $x = 0$ which makes an angle of $45°$ with the horizontal.)

The function e^{-x^2} is clearly a symmetric function of x, having the same value at $x = a$ as at $x = -a$. Geometrically this means that the graph is symmetric about the vertical axis—if the graph paper is folded on the vertical axis, the right-hand portion will fall exactly on the left-hand portion. Because a large negative power of e is very small, the value of e^{-x^2} is very small for either large positive or large negative x's, and tends to 0 as x becomes infinite—either positively or negatively. At $x = 0$, the function has the value

1, which is its largest value. The graph is thus bell-shaped and has points of "inflection" on either side of its maximum, at $x = +1/\sqrt{2}$ and $x = -1/\sqrt{2}$. It is shown in Figure 6–1.

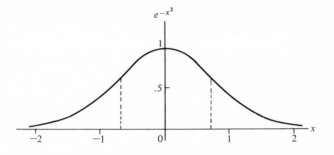

Figure 6–1

For any given constant μ, the graph of $e^{-(x-\mu)^2}$ is congruent to the graph of e^{-x^2}, being shifted horizontally by an amount μ. This is because the function $e^{-(x-\mu)^2}$ has exactly the same values at $x = \mu + a$ and $x = \mu - a$ as has the function e^{-x^2} at $x = a$ and $-a$. The introduction of another parameter into the exponent: $e^{-(x-\mu)^2/2\sigma^2}$, results in a function that differs from e^{-x^2} in the horizontal location of its maximum which occurs at $x = \mu$ instead of $x = 0$, and in its width, being obtained from $e^{-(x-\mu)^2}$ by a change of scale. (Its value at $\mu \pm \sqrt{2}\,\sigma b$ is the same as the value of e^{-x^2} at $\pm b$.) It forms the basis of the general normal density function.

Because the exponent on e will often be at least as complicated as those already encountered, another (common) notation will be employed from here on, namely: $e^x \equiv \exp(x)$. Thus, for example,

$$e^{-(x-\mu)^2/2\sigma^2} = \exp\left[-(x-\mu)^2/2\sigma^2\right].$$

The term "exp" is short for *exponential function*, and can be read: "e to the power."

In order for a function to serve as the density function of a probability distribution the area between its graph and the horizontal axis must be not only finite but equal to 1. Of course, if a function does have a finite area between its graph and the x-axis, multiplication by a constant (the reciprocal of that area) yields a function with area 1 under its graph. This accounts for the constant multiplier in the following general normal density function:

$$f(x;\mu,\sigma^2) = \frac{1}{\sqrt{2\pi}\,\sigma}\exp\left[-\frac{(x-\mu)^2}{2\sigma^2}\right].$$

To summarize the discussion above, the graph of this function is symmetrical about the ordinate at $x = \mu$, it has a maximum at $x = \mu$, it tends to zero as x becomes infinite in either direction, and it has points of inflection (change points in the direction of turning) at $\mu + \sigma$ and at $\mu - \sigma$. The graph is shown in Figure 6–2.

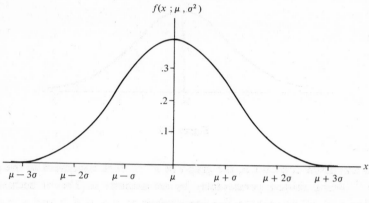

Figure 6–2

It is clear that since μ is a point of symmetry, the mean or expected value of a random variable with the general normal density is μ. It can also be shown that σ^2 is the variance. The positive square root σ is called the *standard deviation*.

The probability of an interval defined by the normal density function is obtained (as with any density function) as the area under the graph over that interval (and above the x-axis). These can only be computed numerically and given in tables. Rather than a table of interval probabilities, it is convenient to have a table of probabilities assigned to semi-infinite intervals of the form $-\infty < x < b$; the probabilities of intervals can be computed from these as differences:

$$P(a < X < b) = P(X < b) - P(X < a).$$

Entering the appropriate table at b and again at a yields the two probabilities whose difference is the probability of the interval from a to b.

Although it might seem at first that it would be necessary to have tables of $P(X < b)$, as a function of b, for each choice of parameters μ and σ^2, it turns out that because these are simply translation and scale parameters one can get by with a single table, constructed for a particular choice of μ and σ. The values $\mu = 0$ and $\sigma = 1$ define the *standard* normal distribution; it is this distribution that is ordinarily tabled, according to the values of $\Phi(z) \equiv P(Z \leq z)$, where Z is a standard normal random variable. Table A–1 on page 278 gives the number of square units of area to the left of the value z under the standard normal density curve, for values of z from -3 to $+3$, at intervals of .01. To use this table for a normal random variable X with mean μ and variance σ^2, for determining the value of $P(X < a)$, it is only necessary to locate a in terms of the number of σ-units to the left or right of μ; that is, one computes

$$z = \frac{a - \mu}{\sigma}$$

and enters the standard normal table at this z.

Example 6–1. It has been found that a useful approximation to the distribution of examination scores on a certain entrance test is provided by the normal distribution with mean 70 and standard deviation 10, that is, variance 100. The probability that a score X picked at random will be less than 95 is then found in the standard normal table as

$$P(X < 95) = \Phi\left(\frac{95 - 70}{10}\right) = \Phi(2.5) = .9938.$$

The probability that it will lie between 50 and 80 is found as a difference:

$$P(50 < X < 80) = P(X < 80) - P(X < 50)$$

$$= \Phi\left(\frac{80 - 70}{10}\right) - \Phi\left(\frac{50 - 70}{10}\right)$$

$$= \Phi(1) - \Phi(-2) = .8413 - .0228 = .8185.$$

6.2 Completing the Square

In dealing with normal density functions it is convenient to have the tool of algebra called *completing the square*. This is based on the expansion

$$(x - A)^2 = x^2 - 2Ax + A^2,$$

and simply involves supplying the constant term when it is missing:

$$x^2 - 2Ax = x^2 - 2Ax + A^2 - A^2 = (x - A)^2 - A^2.$$

More generally, if the term in x^2 has a coefficient other than 1, this can be factored out:

$$ax^2 - 2bx + c = a\left(x^2 - \frac{2b}{a}x\right) + c$$

$$= a\left(x^2 - \frac{2b}{a}x + \frac{b^2}{a^2} - \frac{b^2}{a^2}\right) + c$$

$$= a\left(x - \frac{b}{a}\right)^2 - \frac{b^2}{a} + c.$$

The advantage of this last form is that it shows $x = b/a$ to be a center of symmetry; it also shows the extreme value of the quadratic function to be $c - b^2/a$ for $x = b/a$, which value is a minimum value of the function when $a > 0$ and is a maximum when $a < 0$.

In connection with normal density functions, the quadratic appears in the exponent of e. A normal density is of the form

$$(\text{const}) \exp\left(-ax^2 + 2bx - c\right),$$

and if one encounters it in this general form he can, by completing the square, identify the parameters μ and σ^2, the mean and variance of the distribution. An example will perhaps make this clear.

Example 6–2. Suppose it is known that the function:

$$f(x) = K \exp\left(-3x^2 + 2x\right)$$

is a density function. The exponent can be manipulated as follows

$$-3x^2 + 2x = -3\left(x^2 - \frac{2}{3}x\right)$$

$$= -3\left(x^2 - \frac{2}{3}x + \frac{1}{9} - \frac{1}{9}\right)$$

$$= -3\left(x - \frac{1}{3}\right)^2 + \frac{1}{3},$$

and the density then becomes

$$f(x) = K \exp\left[-3\left(x - \frac{1}{3}\right)^2 + \frac{1}{3}\right] = K' \exp\left[-3\left(x - \frac{1}{3}\right)^2\right],$$

the factor $e^{\frac{1}{2}}$ being incorporated into the K to make K'. In comparing the exponent with the exponent in the general form of the normal density it is clear that $\mu = \frac{1}{3}$, and that

$$-3 = -\frac{1}{2\sigma^2}, \quad \text{or} \quad \sigma^2 = \frac{1}{6}.$$

The function $f(x)$ is then the density of a normal random variable with mean $\frac{1}{3}$ and variance $\frac{1}{6}$. (The constant K' in front has no choice but to be correct, assuming that the function initially given is actually a density.)

6.3 Sampling From a Normal Population

Continuous random variables generally, and normal random variables in particular, are the appropriate mathematical models for measurements on a continuous scale. When measurements are repeated under apparently identical conditions in such a way that the results of one measurement do not affect the model for other measurements, the result is a kind of sample that is known as a *random sample*. Rather than go into the extensive mathematics necessary to derive the result, it will simply be asserted here that the likelihood function for a random sample $(X_1, \ldots, X_n)$ from a continuous population with density $f(x; \theta)$ is given as follows:

$$L(\theta) = f(X_1; \theta) \cdot f(X_2; \theta) \cdots f(X_n; \theta).$$

This product is actually the density function for the random sample point $(X_1, \ldots, X_n)$ in a space of n dimensions.

In the case of a general normal distribution, with the two unspecified parameters μ and σ^2, the likelihood function is

$$L(\mu, \sigma^2) = (2\pi\sigma^2)^{-n/2} \exp \left[-\sum (X_i - \mu)^2/2\sigma^2 \right].$$

If the variance σ^2, say, is given or known, and is hence not a parameter of interest, the relevant likelihood function is the same, but would be denoted simply by $L(\mu)$.

It is not always easy to ensure that an actual physical process of obtaining a sample is such that the above model for random sampling is the correct model. The main things to watch are that the populations being sampled are not changing in some aspect, from one observation to the next, and that some observations do not affect the probabilities for other observations.

One kind of situation in which one is not making a physical or chemical measurement (so that the measuring process itself is not introducing the "randomness") is that in which one is interested in a certain characteristic of an individual, the individual being one of a large population of individuals. If that population is finite, then of course the number of different possible values of the characteristic is finite; but if it is large, one obtains a useful idealization to consider there to be infinitely many possible values—and that the value associated with an individual chosen at random from the population is a continuous random variable. To choose a random sample from such a population, one selects one individual, and then another, and so on, until n individuals are chosen—each time in such a way that he has no knowledge of the disposition of the particular individuals. (One way to do this is to shuffle or thoroughly mix, and then to pick blindly.) In order that he encounter exactly the same population each time, it would appear to be necessary to put back the individual drawn, each time, to mingle with the rest; but if the population size is large in comparison with the number of individuals to be drawn, there is not much practical difference.

Problems

6–1 A random variable X has a standard normal distribution; that is, with mean zero and standard deviation 1. Determine the following from Table A-1:

(a) $P(X < -1)$ (d) $P(|X| < 3)$

(b) $P(X > 3)$ (e) $P(|X| > 2)$

(c) $P(1 < X < 3)$

6–2 A random variable X is normally distributed with mean 50 and variance 25. Determine the following, with the aid of Table A-1:

(a) $P(X > 62)$

(b) $P(|X - 50| < 8)$

(c) $P(|X - 40| > 5)$

6–3 A doorway that is being constructed is to be used by a class of people whose heights are (approximately) normally distributed with mean 5 feet 10 inches and standard deviation 3 inches. How low may the doorway be without causing more than 2 per cent of the people to bump their heads?

6–4 A certain measured pressure is assumed to be a random variable with mean 130 (lbs per square inch) and a standard deviation of 4.

(a) What percentage of a large number of readings will lie below 121.5?

(b) What value is exceeded by 75 per cent of the readings?

(c) What percentage of the readings lie between 121.5 and 134.5?

6–5 If $\Phi(x)$ denotes the area under a standard normal density curve to the left of the abscissa x, show how the symmetry of the density implies that $\Phi(-x) = 1 - \Phi(x)$.

6–6 A density function is proportional to $\exp(-x^2 + 3x)$. Determine the mean and variance.

6–7 A random sample $(X_1, \ldots, X_n)$ is drawn from a normal population with unit variance ($\sigma^2 = 1$). Determine the likelihood ratio corresponding to $\mu_0 = 0$ and $\mu_1 = 2$: $L(0)/L(2)$.

6.4 Posterior Probabilities

When the parameter θ is treated as a continuous random variable, the prior distribution for θ is defined by a density function, $g(\theta)$. The posterior distribution, given data Z, is also defined by a density function, defined (by analogy with the discrete case) to be

$$h(\theta \mid z) = \frac{f(z \mid \theta)g(\theta)}{p(z)},$$

where $f(z \mid \theta)$ is the probability (discrete Z) of $Z = z$ or the density (continuous Z) of Z at $Z = z$, and the denominator $p(z)$ is the unconditional probability or density function, respectively, of Z. This unconditional $p(z)$ is obtained by averaging the conditional $f(z \mid \theta)$ with respect to the weighting given by $g(\theta)$, but for the present purposes it will suffice to know that it is independent of θ, the θ having been averaged out.

Consider now a normal population, and a random sample of size n from this population: $Z = (X_1, X_2, \ldots, X_n)$. The density of Z is what was called in the preceding section the likelihood function, namely

$$f(z \mid \mu, \sigma^2) = (2\pi\sigma^2)^{-n/2} \exp\left[-\sum(x_i - \mu)^2/2\sigma^2\right].$$

The posterior density will now be obtained, in the case of *given* σ^2, for two types of prior distributions.

Consider first the *uniform prior* distribution defined by a constant density over $-\infty < \mu < \infty$. This is not actually a proper probability distribution, since for any nonzero constant density, the area under its graph over the infinite μ-axis would be infinite. However, a useful result is obtained by pushing ahead as though everything were in order. So let $g(\mu) = 1$ for all μ.

The posterior density is then just proportional to $f(z \mid \mu)$ as given above; for the particular case $\sigma^2 = 1$ it is

$$h(\mu \mid z) = (\text{const}) \exp\left[-\sum (x_i - \mu)^2/2\right] = (\text{const}) \exp\left[-\sum (\mu - x_i)^2/2\right]$$

The exponent here, as a function of μ, is a quadratic function. Applying to it the technique of completing the square, one obtains

$$\sum (\mu - x_i)^2 = \sum [\mu^2 - 2\mu x_i + x_i^2]$$

$$= n\mu^2 - 2n\mu\bar{x} + \sum x_i^2$$

$$= n[\mu^2 - 2n\mu\bar{x} + \bar{x}^2] + \sum x_i^2 - n\bar{x}^2$$

$$= n(\mu - \bar{x})^2 + \text{(terms not involving } \mu),$$

where $\bar{x}$ is the symbol for $(x_1 + \cdots + x_n)/n$. Thus, the posterior density is

$$h(\mu \mid z) = (const) \exp\left[-n(\mu - \bar{x})^2/2\right],$$

which is a *normal* density with mean $\bar{x}$ and variance $1/n$. Immediately one has the maximum likelihood estimate of μ, given the observations $X_1, \ldots, X_n$, as their arithmetic average:

$$\bar{X} = \frac{1}{n}(X_1 + \cdots + X_n).$$

And this is the Bayes estimate for a uniform prior on μ, which agrees with the maximum likelihood estimate because the mean of a normal distribution is the same as the mode (point of maximum density).

Consider next a *normal prior* distribution, say with mean m and variance τ^2

$$g(\mu) = \frac{1}{\sqrt{2\pi}\,\tau} \exp[-(x-m)^2/2\tau^2]$$

The posterior density is again proportional to $f(z \mid \mu)g(\mu)$:

$$h(\mu \mid z) = (const)e^{-A/2},$$

where

$$A = \frac{1}{\sigma^2} \sum (x_i - \mu)^2 + \frac{1}{\tau^2} (\mu - m)^2$$

$$= \frac{1}{\sigma^2} [n\mu^2 - 2\mu \sum x_i + \sum x_i^2] + \frac{1}{\tau^2} [\mu^2 - 2m\mu + m^2]$$

$$= \mu^2 \left(\frac{n}{\sigma^2} + \frac{1}{\tau^2}\right) - 2\mu \left(\frac{n\bar{x}}{\sigma^2} + \frac{m}{\tau^2}\right) + \text{(terms not involving } \mu)$$

$$= (\text{const}) \left(\mu - \frac{n\bar{x}\tau^2 + m\sigma^2}{n\tau^2 + \sigma^2}\right)^2 + \text{(terms not involving } \mu).$$

Because, again, this exponent is quadratic with a negative squared term, the density must be normal, and the expected value has been put on display:

$$\frac{n\bar{x}\tau^2 + m\sigma^2}{n\tau^2 + \sigma^2} = \bar{x} + \frac{\sigma^2(m - \bar{x})}{n\tau^2 + \sigma^2}.$$

This posterior mean would be the Bayes estimate of μ for the given prior distribution. In this connection some observations of interest can be made. A small value of τ^2 would mean a narrow prior distribution, centered at m, suggesting a strong conviction that μ is near m; as τ^2 tends to zero, the Bayes estimate of μ tends to m. That is, the posterior mean tends to m; but in fact the variance of the posterior distribution tends to zero, which means that not only is the posterior distribution centered at m, it is also depositing most of the probability very close to m. (This assertion about the variance of the posterior distribution is obtainable from Problem 6–8.) On the other hand, a large value of τ^2 would mean a broad prior distribution, suggesting only vaguely that μ is anywhere near m; it represents weakness of convictions. As τ^2 becomes larger and larger, the mean of the posterior distribution tends to $\bar{x}$, suggesting that the sample carries greater weight in estimating μ than does the prior distribution.

It is noteworthy also that for given σ^2 and τ^2 the mean of the posterior distribution tends to $\bar{x}$ as the sample size becomes infinite. This is as it should be, in the sense that a large amount of data is more reliable than a given prior distribution in providing an estimate of μ. Finally, observe the effect of different values of σ^2: For small σ^2, corresponding to data with low variability, the estimate is near $\bar{x}$; thus, if the data are reliable, trust them. But for large σ^2, or large variability in the observations (with n and τ^2 fixed), the estimate is near m, so that the prior is trusted more than erratic data.

Example 6–3. A certain parameter μ is to be measured; it is assumed that one's prior probability distribution for μ is normal, with mean 18 and standard deviation 2. The measurement error is also assumed to be normal, with mean 0 and standard deviation 3, so that the measurement itself is normal with mean μ and standard deviation 3. A sample of 16 measurements is taken, with the result $\bar{X} = 16.5$. What is the probability that the parameter value is actually between 16 and 17?

This question relates to the distribution of probability on μ, and in particular (since data are at hand) to the posterior distribution. The posterior distribution of μ is normal, with parameters

$$E(\mu) = \frac{n\bar{X}\tau^2 + m\sigma^2}{n\tau^2 + \sigma^2} = \frac{16 \times 4 \times 16.5 + 18 \times 9}{16 \times 4 + 9} = 16.7$$

and

$$\text{var}(\mu) = \left(\frac{n}{\sigma^2} + \frac{1}{\tau^2}\right)^{-1} = \left(\frac{16}{9} + \frac{1}{4}\right)^{-1} = (.703)^2.$$

With these parameters of the posterior distribution one can answer probability questions about μ. In particular, for the question raised:

$$P(16 < \mu < 17) = \Phi\left(\frac{17 - 16.7}{.703}\right) - \Phi\left(\frac{16 - 16.7}{.703}\right)$$

$$= .6653 - .1711 \doteq 0.49.$$

6.5 The Distribution of $\bar{X}$

It was seen in the preceding section that if one obtains the observations $(x_1, x_2, \ldots, x_n)$ as a random sample from a normal population with mean μ and given variance, the arithmetic average of these numbers

$$\bar{x} = \frac{1}{n}(x_1 + \cdots + x_n)$$

is the maximum likelihood estimate of μ, as well as the Bayes estimate when the prior is uniform on $-\infty < \mu < \infty$.

If one thinks of the sampling *process*, which leads to different samples—different sets of numbers $(x_1, \ldots, x_n)$—each time it is employed, the sample observations are naturally considered as random variables, in the sense of what might be observed and with what probabilities. Of course, a given set of numbers such as $(-3.1, 5.2, 3)$ is not a set of random variables, any more than the outcome *tails* in the toss of a coin is a random variable. But just as the outcome of the toss of a coin is random—before it is actually carried out, so the observations comprising a random sample are random variables. And since their arithmetic mean is computed from them, it, too, is a random variable. That is, the sample mean (as $\bar{x}$ is called) varies from sample to sample, even when the same basic sampling process is employed. When thinking of the observations as random we write $(X_1, \ldots, X_n)$, and when thinking of the sample mean as the result of a certain operation carried out on the observations, and so random, we write $\overline{X}$.

If, then, $\overline{X}$ is a random variable, it has a certain distribution of probability —a set of possible values and corresponding probabilities (for individual values, in the discrete case, or for intervals in the continuous case). When the population is normal with mean μ and variance σ^2, the sample mean $\overline{X}$ can be shown to be normal, with mean μ and variance σ^2/n. Thus, just as the individual observations vary, with a distribution centered at μ, so the sample means vary, with a distribution centered at the same point. However, the variability from sample mean to sample mean (if one were to take many samples) is less than the variability from observation to observation; the variance of $\overline{X}$ is smaller by a factor $1/n$. This suggests a greater and greater reliability in $\overline{X}$ as an extimator for μ as the sample size increases. This is certainly not an unexpected phenomenon, if indeed the sample carries information about the population from which it is obtained—the more sampling, the more information, and the less uncertainty.

Example 6–4. A random sample of 25 observations drawn from a normal population with unknown mean μ and variance $\sigma^2 = 4$. What is the probability that the sample mean will fall in the range from $\mu - 1$ to $\mu + 1$?

The distribution of $\overline{X}$ is normal with mean μ and variance $4/25$, which is σ^2/n. Hence,

$$P(\mu - 1 < \overline{X} < \mu + 1) = \Phi\left(\frac{\mu + 1 - \mu}{2/5}\right) - \Phi\left(\frac{\mu - 1 - \mu}{2/5}\right)$$

$$= \Phi(2.5) - \Phi(-2.5) = 0.9876.$$

Problems

6–8   Referring to the derivation of the posterior distribution of μ given a uniform prior distribution, given in the text above, determine the posterior distribution of μ if the population variance is σ^2.

6–9 Determine the Bayes estimate of μ based on a single observation ($n = 1$) in the case when the prior and population distributions have equal widths ($\sigma^2 = \tau^2$).

6–10 Given a population with variance $\sigma^2 = 4$, and a sample of size 25, determine the probability that the population mean lies between $\bar{X} - .4$ and $\bar{X} + .4$, assuming a uniform prior weighting for μ.

6–11 Repeat the computation of Problem 6–10, but for a prior weighting that is normal with mean 10 and $\tau = 1$, given that the sample mean is $\bar{X} = 9$.

6.6 Tests of Hypotheses About μ

Again, for simplicity, assume that the variance of the normal population from which a random sample is drawn is given or known. The remaining parameter μ describes the location or center of the population distribution, and tests of hypotheses about this location will now be considered.

The simplest case is again that of a simple null hypothesis against a simple alternative:

$$H_0: \mu = \mu_0 \quad \text{vs.} \quad H_1: \mu = \mu_1.$$

It was seen in Chapter 5 that the family of Bayes tests is defined by critical regions of the form

$$\Lambda = \frac{L(\mu_0)}{L(\mu_1)} < K',$$

where $L(\mu)$ is the likelihood function corresponding to a given sample. For a random sample of size n this function is

$$L(\mu) = (2\pi\sigma^2)^{-n/2} \exp[- \textstyle\sum(x_i - \mu)^2/2\sigma^2]$$

In the formation of the likelihood ratio Λ the multiplying constants cancel out, and the ratio of the remaining exponential factors can be written as a single exponential, with exponent as follows:

$$-\frac{\sum(x_i - \mu_0)^2}{2\sigma^2} + \frac{\sum(x_i - \mu_1)^2}{2\sigma^2} = \frac{1}{\sigma^2}[\mu_0 \textstyle\sum x_i - n\mu_0^2 - \mu_1 \textstyle\sum x_i + n\mu_1^2]$$

$$= \frac{n(\mu_0 - \mu_1)}{2}\left[\bar{x} - \frac{1}{2}(\mu_0 + \mu_1)\right].$$

The ratio Λ will be less than a constant K' if and only if the exponent is less than $\log K'$ (a constant):

$$\frac{1}{2} n(\mu_0 - \mu_1)\left[\bar{x} - \frac{1}{2}(\mu_0 + \mu_1)\right] < \log K'.$$

If $\mu_0 < \mu_1$, division by $\mu_0 - \mu_1$ reverses the inequality, and the above is equivalent to a condition of the form

$$\bar{x} > K,$$

where K could be determined in terms of K', and the μ's, and n, a determination that is unnecessary to obtain the *class* of best critical regions. Similarly, if $\mu_0 > \mu_1$, the Bayes critical regions would be defined by inequalities of the form $\bar{x} < K$. Thus, in either case, the Bayes rules are of the form: reject the smaller μ if $\bar{X}$ is large, and accept it if $\bar{X}$ is small. These rules have the smallest β for a given α.

For a given value of K, the test which rejects μ_0 and accepts μ_1 if $\bar{X} > K$ has error sizes that are readily computed from Table A–1, using the fact that $\bar{X}$ is normal with mean μ and variance σ^2/n. And as before, the risk can be computed from the error sizes, if losses are given.

Example 6–5. It is desired to test $\mu = 0$ against $\mu = 2$ based on a random sample of size n from a normal population with $\sigma = 1$. The Bayes tests are of the form: reject $\mu = 0$ if $\bar{X} > K$. The error sizes for this test are as follows:

$$\alpha = P(\bar{X} > K \mid \mu = 0) = 1 - \Phi\left(\frac{K - 0}{1/\sqrt{n}}\right)$$

$$\beta = P(\bar{X} < K \mid \mu = 1) = \Phi\left(\frac{K - 1}{1/\sqrt{n}}\right).$$

Given K and the sample size n these are readily computed from Table A–1. Moreover, if it is desired to specify α and β, one can determine a sample size n and a critical value K to achieve these. For instance, if it is desired to have $\alpha = .01$ and $\beta = .05$, then $\sqrt{n}\, K$ must be the point in Table A–1 corresponding to a probability of .99, and $\sqrt{n}\,(K - 1)$ the point corresponding to .05:

$$\sqrt{n}\, K = 2.33$$

$$\sqrt{n}\,(K - 1) = -1.645.$$

Solving these yields $n = 15.8$ and $K = .587$. (Of course, n must be an integer in practice, so one would use $n = 16$, which would yield just slightly smaller error sizes than those specified.)

When there are more than two states of nature, problems of testing hypotheses about the mean of a normal population are ordinarily of one of two types, *one-sided* or *two-sided*:

$$\text{One-sided:} \quad H_0: \mu \leq \mu^* \text{ against } H_1: \mu > \mu^*,$$

$$\text{Two-sided:} \quad H_0: \mu = \mu_0 \text{ against } H_1: \mu \neq \mu_0.$$

The approach to the one-sided case usually taken is that discussed in Example 5–13 and the text preceding it. That is, the composite problem is replaced by a problem with simple H_0 and simple H_1, and the test used for the simpler problem is adapted to the more complicated one. Thus, a one-sided critical region, of the form $\bar{X} < K$ or $\bar{X} > K$, is used for a one-sided hypothesis testing situation. The success of such a test can be measured in terms of the risk function, or equivalently (if losses are known) in terms of the power function.

Example 6–6. To test $\mu \leq \frac{1}{2}$ against $\mu > \frac{1}{2}$ one adopts a critical region of the form $\bar{X} > K$, based on a random sample from the population which is assumed to be normal with, say, variance $\sigma^2 = 1$. The power function of the test is the probability of rejecting H_0 as a function of μ:

$$P(\text{test rejects } H_0 \mid \mu) = P(\bar{X} > K \mid \mu)$$

$$= 1 - \Phi\left(\frac{K - \mu}{1/\sqrt{n}}\right).$$

For the particular test defined by $n = 16$ and $K = .587$ (as in Example 6–5), this becomes

$$\pi(\mu) = 1 - \Phi(2.35 - 4\mu) = \Phi(4\mu - 2.35).$$

This function is readily plotted; a table of values of μ, of $\pi(\mu)$, and of the risk $R(\mu)$ is shown below, the risk being calculated for the case in which the

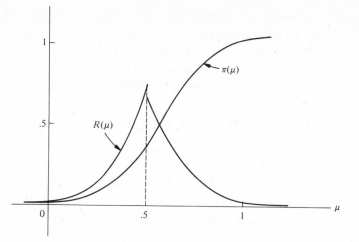

Figure 6–3

losses are zero for correct decisions, 2 for rejecting H_0 when in fact $\mu \leq \frac{1}{2}$, and 1 for accepting H_0 when $\mu > \frac{1}{2}$. The graph of $R(\mu)$ is shown in Figure 6–3.

μ	$4\mu - 2.35$	$\pi(\mu)$	$R(\mu)$
0	−2.35	.0099	.0198
.2	−1.55	.0606	.1212
.4	−.75	.2266	.4532
.5	−.35	.3632	$\begin{cases} .7264 \\ .6368 \end{cases}$
.6	.05	.5199	.4801
.8	.85	.8023	.1977
1.0	1.65	.9505	.0495
1.2	2.45	.9929	.0075

In the case of a two-sided alternative hypothesis, that is, for testing $\mu = \mu_0$ against $\mu \neq \mu_0$, the determination of admissible tests is not an easy matter. The generalized likelihood ratio tests can readily be constructed, however, and turn out to be equivalent to critical regions of the form $|\bar{X} - \mu_0| > K$. That is, one rejects μ_0 if $\bar{X}$ is too far from μ_0, on either side; this is a two-sided critical region for $\bar{X}$. Again, its performance can be studied in terms of the power function.

Example 6–7. Consider the critical region $|\bar{X} - 10| > 1$, for testing $\mu = 10$ against $\mu \neq 10$ in a normal population with variance $\sigma^2 = 4$ using a random sample of size 25. The distribution of $\bar{X}$ is normal with mean μ and variance $4/25 = (2/5)^2$. Thus, the power function of the test is computed (with the aid of Table A–1 for evaluation of normal probabilities) as follows:

$$\pi(\mu) = P(|\bar{X} - 10| > 1 \mid \mu)$$

$$= 1 - P(|\bar{X} - 10| < 1 \mid \mu)$$

$$= 1 - P(9 < \bar{X} < 11 \mid \mu)$$

$$= 1 - \Phi\left(\frac{11 - \mu}{\frac{2}{5}}\right) + \Phi\left(\frac{9 - \mu}{\frac{2}{5}}\right).$$

The graph of this function is given in Figure 6–4. Notice that it is small on H_0 (that is, for $\mu = 10$), and larger for $\mu \neq 10$—the farther from 10 is the alternative, the larger the power.

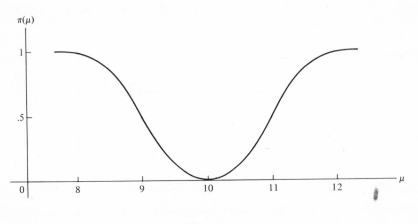

Figure 6–4

6.7 Confidence Intervals and Probability Intervals

The classical notion of a confidence interval is an attempt to furnish an estimate of a population parameter that includes a measure of precision. For the case of the mean of a normal population with given variance the derivation is as follows. Because $\bar{X}$ is normal with mean μ and variance σ^2/n, one can write, for any given *confidence coefficient*, say 0.95,

$$0.95 = P\left(|\bar{X} - \mu| < 2\frac{\sigma}{\sqrt{n}}\right)$$

$$= P\left(|\mu - \bar{X}| < 2\frac{\sigma}{\sqrt{n}}\right)$$

$$= P\left(\bar{X} - 2\frac{\sigma}{\sqrt{n}} < \mu < \bar{X} + 2\frac{\sigma}{\sqrt{n}}\right).$$

(The "2" in this expression comes from Table A–1, given the 0.95 confidence coefficient. The probability is approximately .95 that the variable $\bar{X}$ will differ from its mean μ by more than 2 standard deviations. A different confidence coefficient would require that the 2 be changed accordingly.) The interval from $\bar{X} - 2\sigma/\sqrt{n}$ to $\bar{X} + 2\sigma/\sqrt{n}$ is called a *95 per cent confidence interval* for μ, and has the following interpretation. It is a random interval, depending on the random $\bar{X}$, which in turn depends on the particular sample obtained; different samples would yield different $\bar{X}$'s and different intervals. If one were to sample repeatedly and to compute intervals of this sort, it would turn out that in the long run 95 per cent of such intervals would include the actual mean.

It is not uncommon for a confidence interval statement to be interpreted differently, namely, as though μ were random and the probability that μ falls in the confidence interval obtained were the confidence coefficient. This is *not* the meaning of a confidence interval—but, of course, μ *can* be given a prob- ability distribution, the posterior distribution, in terms of which one can calculate probabilities of intervals.

Example 6–8. Consider a normal population with mean μ and standard deviation 3, as in Example 6–3. And as in that example, suppose that a ran- dom sample of size 16 yields $\bar{X} = 16.5$. The 95.44 per cent confidence interval for μ would be defined by the limits

$$\bar{X} \pm 2\frac{\sigma}{\sqrt{n}} = 16.5 \pm \frac{6}{\sqrt{16}},$$

or the interval from 15 to 18. A different sample would have yielded a different confidence interval, and one has only the "confidence" that he is using a procedure that gives an interval which traps μ on its interior 95 per cent of the time. On the other hand, for a given prior distribution one can calculate the probability of the interval $15 < \mu < 18$. For instance, with the prior of Example 6–3, namely, normal with mean 18 and variance 4, the posterior distribution of μ is normal with mean 16.7 and standard deviation .703. In this distribution,

$$P(15 < \mu < 18) = \Phi\left(\frac{18 - 16.7}{.703}\right) - \Phi\left(\frac{15 - 16.7}{.703}\right)$$

$$= 0.96.$$

But if one were to assume a uniform prior distribution, the posterior would be normal with mean $\bar{X}$ and variance $\sigma^2/n = 9/16$. In this case

$$P(15 < \mu < 18) = \Phi\left(\frac{18 - 16.5}{.75}\right) - \Phi\left(\frac{15 - 16.5}{.75}\right) = .9544.$$

The probability of the confidence interval in *this* posterior distribution, that is, with a uniform prior, turns out to be the same as the confidence coefficient.

Problems

6–12 Determine the critical region for $\bar{X}$ that corresponds to $\Lambda < 1$ in testing $\mu = \mu_0$ against $\mu = \mu_1$ in a normal population with given variance, based on a random sample of size n. Show that this test is minimax, if one assumes equal losses for the two types of error; and determine also a prior distribution against which it is Bayes, with these same equal losses.

6–13 Determine a critical region of the form $\bar{X} > K$ that has power .05 at $\mu = 10$ and power .90 at $\mu = 15$, where $\bar{X}$ is the mean of a random sample of size n from a normal population with mean μ and variance 20. (That is, determine n and K.) Determine also the power function $\pi(\mu)$.

6–14 A population is normal with mean μ and variance 1. In choosing between actions A and B one has these regrets:

$$r(\mu, A) = \begin{cases} 0, & \text{if } |\mu - 10| < 2 \\ 1, & \text{if } |\mu - 10| > 2, \end{cases}$$

$$r(\mu, B) = \begin{cases} 2, & \text{if } |\mu - 10| < .1 \\ 0, & \text{if } |\mu - 10| > .1. \end{cases}$$

This might be considered to be a problem of testing, say, $|\mu - 10| \leq 1$ against $|\mu - 10| > 1$. For the test with critical region $|\bar{X} - 10| > 1$, based on a random sample of four observations, determine the power function, and from this the risk function.

6–15 The following rule is adopted for testing $\mu = 10$ against $\mu \neq 10$ in a normal population with mean μ and known variance $\sigma^2 = 1$: Reject $\mu = 10$ if the 90 per cent confidence interval based on the mean of a random sample of size 16 does not include the value $\mu = 10$; otherwise accept $\mu = 10$. What is the size of the type I error? Determine the power function.

6–16 Referring to Example 6–8, calculate the probability of the interval $15 < \mu < 18$ if the prior distribution of μ is normal with mean 20 and variance 1.

Chapter 7 The Bernoulli Model

In many situations involving the element of randomness the only concern is whether the final result has or does not have a certain specified characteristic. Examples are the following:

(a) A coin is tossed, and the result is either heads or not heads.

(b) A machine stamps out a certain part, which can be classed either as defective or as not defective (that is, good).

(c) A rocket is fired on a certain space mission; it either succeeds in the mission or does not succeed.

(d) A horse is entered in a certain race; he either wins or does not win.

(e) A customer enters an automobile show room; he either does buy a car or does not.

(f) A person is drawn at random from a population of people; the person drawn is either male or not male.

(g) A person is drawn at random from a population; the person drawn is either in favor or not in favor of a certain proposal.

(h) A part is selected from a box of 100 supposedly identical parts; the part selected is either defective or not defective.

In each case it is convenient to adopt a numerical coding, assigning the value 1 to an outcome if it has the characteristic of interest (*success*), and the value 0 if it does not (*failure*). The result is a random variable, say X, with two values (0 and 1), and a distribution defined by giving the value p, which is the probability that the outcome has the characteristic of interest

x	1	0
$f(x)$	0	$1 - p$

This random variable is said to be a *Bernoulli variable*, or to have a *Bernoulli distribution*. In situations **(f)** through **(h)**, where there is an actual population or collection of objects from which objects can be drawn, that population is referred to as a *Bernoulli population*. This same term is used even in the other situations, where there is no actual population; one imagines an (infinite) population with proportion p coded 1 and $1 - p$ coded 0.

7.1 Sampling

To learn more about a Bernoulli population, it is natural to gather "data" by performing the basic experiment over and over, say n times. The result is said to be a *sample*; and with the 0–1 coding defined above, this sample is simply a sequence of 0's and 1's. Thus, the sequence

$$(0, 0, 0, 1, 0, 1, 0)$$

is a sample of size 7, in which just the fourth and sixth trials resulted in outcomes having the characteristic of interest.

One method of sampling is that which is carried out in such a way that information about some of the trials does not alter the betting odds on the other trials. The trials are then said to be *independent*, and for such sequences of trials it can be shown that the probability of a given sequence of outcomes is obtained by multiplying together the probabilities of the individual outcomes. Thus, the sequence $(0, 0, 0, 1, 0, 1, 0)$ has the probability

$$(1 - p)(1 - p)(1 - p)p(1 - p)p(1 - p) = (1 - p)^5 p^2,$$

where for each trial

$$p = P(\text{outcome is 1}), \qquad 1 - p = P(\text{outcome is 0}).$$

In a sequence of n trials, the probability of any given sequence of outcomes of which k are 1's and $n - k$ are 0's is (in similar fashion)

$$p^k (1 - p)^{n-k}.$$

This is the *likelihood function* corresponding to that sequence of outcomes.

Another method of sampling is available when the trials consist of selecting an object from an actual population of objects, recording 1 if the object has a certain characteristic and 0 if it does not. If the object drawn is replaced and thoroughly mixed with the population before the next one is drawn, the situation is exactly as before, in which one conducts independent, identical Bernoulli trials. But if there is *no replacement* of objects drawn, the population changes at each selection. Suppose, for instance, there are 12 objects in the population, of which 6 have and 6 do not have the characteristic in question, and that seven objects are drawn, one at a time, and with no replacement. If the individual drawings are at random, the probability of a 1 is just the ratio of the number of objects remaining coded 1 to the total number of objects remaining at that stage. Thus, the probability of the sequence used above for illustrative purposes is

$$f(0, 0, 0, 1, 0, 1, 0 \mid M = 6) = \frac{6}{12} \frac{5}{11} \frac{4}{10} \frac{6}{9} \frac{3}{8} \frac{5}{7} \frac{2}{6}.$$

(This computation follows the rule derived from the defining formula for conditional probability: $P(E \mid F)P(F) = P(E \text{ and } F)$. Thus, to start out, the probability of 0 on the first and 0 on the second draw is the product of the probability of 0 on the first by the conditional probability of 0 on the second given 0 on the first.) An examination of the structure of this product shows how to obtain the probabilities in general. For, there are as many factors as observations; the factors in the denominator start from the population size and go down by integer steps, and the factors in the numerator can be grouped into those four starting with 6 and going down in steps and those two starting with $12 - 6 = 6$ and going down in steps.

Generally, if there are N objects in the population, of which M are of type 1 and $N - M$ of type 0, and n are drawn, the probability of any particular sequence with k 1's and $n - k$ 0's would be

$P(\text{seq. with } k \text{ 1's})$

$$= \frac{M(M-1)\cdots(M-k+1)(N-M)(N-M-1)\cdots(N-M-n+k+1)}{N(N-1)\cdots(N-n+1)}$$

$$= \frac{(M)_k(N-M)_{n-k}}{(N)_n},$$

where $(r)_s$ means s factors starting with r and going down in steps of 1.

The probability of a particular sequence of 0's and 1's has been seen to depend only on the number of 1's in the sequence, whether the sampling be random sampling (with replacement, if there is a finite population) or sampling without replacement from a finite population. That is, each sequence with a given number of 1's has the same probability. This means that the probability of a given number of 1's is just the number of sequences with that number of 1's times the probability of each sequence. But the number of sequences of n numbers, k of which are 1's and the remaining $n - k$ are 0's, is given by

$$\binom{n}{k} = \frac{(n)_k}{(k)_k} = \frac{n(n - 1)\cdots(n - k + 1)}{k(k - 1)\cdots 3 \cdot 2 \cdot 1}.$$

These are called binomial coefficients, because they appear as coefficients in the expansion of the binomial $(x + y)^n$.

Given that a sequence of 0's and 1's has k 1's, it is of interest to compute the conditional probability for a particular sequence:

$$P(\text{seq.} \mid k \text{ 1's}) = \begin{cases} 0, & \text{if the sequence has not exactly } k \text{ 1's,} \\ \dfrac{P(\text{seq.})}{P(k \text{ 1's})} = \dfrac{1}{\binom{n}{k}}, & \text{if the sequence } has \text{ } k \text{ 1's.} \end{cases}$$

This does not depend on p (or on M, in the finite population case). The significance of this fact is that the number of 1's in a sequence is the information in the sequence relevant to p, whereas the matter of which particular sequence with that number of 1's gave rise to it has nothing to do with p. The conclusion drawn is that the number of 1's is *sufficient*; it suffices to base decisions on this quantity computed from the sample. If Y denotes the number of 1's, then for an observed value of Y the likelihood function is just $\binom{n}{k}$ times the likelihood function when the sequence itself is observed.

Example 7.1   A population of 100 TV watchers consists of M who are and $100 - M$ who are not watching a particular program. A sample of 10 is drawn. If the sampling is done with replacement and mixing, so that the 10 observations are independent and identically distributed, then the probability that 4 are watching the program is

$$P(Y = 4) = \binom{10}{4}p^4(1 - p)^6,$$

where $p = M/100$ is the probability that one person drawn at random is found to be watching the program. The probability of the *particular* sequence of responses: $(0, 0, 0, 1, 0, 1, 1, 0, 1, 0)$ is $p^4(1 - p)^6$; but its probability given that $Y = 4$ is

$$\frac{1}{\binom{10}{4}} = \frac{4 \cdot 3 \cdot 2 \cdot 1}{10 \cdot 9 \cdot 8 \cdot 7} = \frac{1}{210}.$$

(That is, all 210 sequences with four 1's and six 0's are equally likely to have been the one leading to the observation $Y = 4$.)

If the sampling is done without replacement, but in such a way that all remaining persons are equally likely to be obtained at a given drawing, the probability of four 1's, that is, four people watching the program, is

$$\binom{10}{4} \frac{(M)_4 (100 - M)_6}{(100)_{10}}.$$

The probability of a particular sequence with four 1's is just the second factor, but the probability of a particular sequence *given* that it has four 1's is again $1/210$.

7.2 The Binomial Distribution

Let Y denote the number of successes in n independent Bernoulli trials in which the probability of success at each trial is p. Then, according to the preceding section

$$P(Y = k \mid p) = \binom{n}{k} p^k (1 - p)^{n-k}, \quad \text{for } k = 0, 1, 2, \ldots, n.$$

This random variable Y is said to have a *binomial distribution*. It will be given without proof (and can be verified easily by direct computation in simple cases) that the expected value and variance are as follows

$$E(Y) = np, \quad \text{var } Y = np(1 - p).$$

Values of the binomial probabilities, as defined by this formula, are given in Table A–2 for values of n up to 10 and for certain selected values of p. It will be noted that only values of p not larger than $\frac{1}{2}$ are given; this is because the case of, say, $p = .8$ can be handled by interchanging the roles of success and failure. The probability of 3 successes with $p = .8$ would be equal to the probability of $n - 3$ successes with $p = .2$, for example.

For values of n larger than 10 one can use approximations. In particular if p is moderate—neither close to 0 nor close to 1—then the distribution of Y is approximately normal, with mean np and variance npq. So Table A–1, which gives normal probabilities, can be used in this case. If p is close to 0 (or close to 1, in which case one again interchanges success and failure so that the p would be close to 0), one can use the following approximation:

$$\binom{n}{k}p^k(1 - p)^{n-k} \doteq e^{-np}\frac{(np)^k}{k!}, \quad \text{for large } n, \text{ small } p.$$

Table A–3 gives values of this function, which happens to define a family of probability distributions, useful in their own right, called *Poisson*.

Example 7–2. Let Y be binomial with $n = 10$ and $p = \frac{2}{3}$. Then $10 - Y$ is binomial with $n = 10$ and $p = \frac{1}{3}$. Thus, for instance,

$$P(Y = 4) = P(10 - Y = 6) = \binom{10}{6}\left(\frac{1}{3}\right)^6\left(\frac{2}{2}\right)^4 \doteq .2276,$$

the numerical value being obtained from Table A–2. Similarly,

$$P(Y < 3) = P(10 - Y > 7) = P(10 - Y = 8, 9, \text{ or } 10)$$

$$\doteq .0030 + .0003 + .000 = .0033.$$

Example 7–3. An ordinary fair die is cast 162 times. The probability of getting 5 or 6 on each throw is $p = \frac{1}{3}$. The mean number of successes (where "success" means getting a 5 or a 6) in the 162 trials is $\frac{162}{3} = 54$. The variance is

$$\text{var } Y = 162 \cdot \frac{2}{3} \cdot \frac{1}{3} = 36,$$

so the standard deviation is 6. The distribution of Y, the number of successes, is then approximately normal with mean 54 and variance 36. Because the normal is a continuous distribution, one approximates probabilities of intervals rather than single values. For instance,

$$P(Y \leq 42) \doteq \Phi\left(\frac{42 - 36}{6}\right) = \Phi(1) \doteq 0.84,$$

from Table A–1. If the probability of a single value is needed, it can be obtained as a difference; thus,

$$P(Y = 42) = P(Y \leq 42) - P(Y \leq 41)$$

$$\doteq \Phi\left(\frac{42 - 36}{6}\right) - \Phi\left(\frac{41 - 36}{6}\right)$$

$$\doteq 0.841 - 0.797 = 0.044.$$

One refinement of this approximation procedure, useful for an n that is only moderately large is to add .5 to the value of Y at the right endpoint of intervals of the form $Y \leq k$:

$$P(Y \leq 42) \doteq \Phi\left(\frac{42.5 - 36}{6}\right) \doteq 0.8614.$$

Although the difference is slight for $n = 162$, experience shows that the approximation is usually better with this correction than without it, especially for values of n below 100.

Example 7–4. A manufacturing process produces a certain simple part, which is acceptable with probability .98. In a batch of 100 such parts, what is the probability that there is at most one defective part?

The batch of 100 can be thought of as the result of 100 independent trials of Bernoulli type, and the number of defectives is therefore binomially distributed with $n = 100$ and $p = .02$. The probability of obtaining either 0 or 1 defective part (that is, at most one) is given by the binomial formula

$$P(Y = 0 \text{ or } 1) = (.98)^{100} + 100(.98)^{99}(.02)^{1}.$$

Since n is large and p small, with $np = 2$, this probability can be approximated using the probabilities in Table A–3 on page 281:

$$P(Y = 0 \text{ or } 1) \doteq e^{-2} + e^{-2}\frac{(2)^{1}}{1!} = \frac{3}{e^2} = .406,$$

which is a considerably easier calculation than raising .98 to the 99th power.

7.3 The Hypergeometric Distribution

When sampling from a finite Bernoulli population, the number Y of successes is not binomial if the objects drawn are not replaced. If there are M labeled 1 and $N - M$ labeled 0, the probability that $Y = k$ in a selection of n is given by the formula

$$P(Y = k) = \binom{n}{k} \frac{(M)_k (N - M)_{n-k}}{(N)_n},$$

as shown in Example 7–1 for a particular case. It can be shown that

$$E(Y) = np, \qquad \text{var } Y = np(1 - p) \frac{N - n}{N - 1}$$

where p is M/N (the probability of a 1 on a single draw).

Intuitively it is clear that if the population size N is very large compared to the sample size n, then it does not matter much whether the objects drawn are replaced or not. That is, the hypergeometric probabilities are almost equal to binomial probabilities. (This can be shown by passing directly to the limit as N becomes infinite with $M/N = p$ fixed.)

Example 7–5. Suppose that 5 per cent of the households in a certain city have a color TV set. What is the probability that a random selection of 60 includes at least 5 households with color TV?

The distribution of Y, the number of households among the 60 with color TV, is hypergeometric with mean $.05N$, where N is the number of households in the city. (The important problems of defining a "household" and of obtaining a "random selection" are conveniently bypassed.) Assuming the city to be quite large, the variable Y is approximately binomially distributed with $n = 60$ and $p = .05$. The probability of at least 5 successes in 60 trials is

$$1 - \sum_{k=0}^{4} \binom{60}{k} (.05)^k (.95)^{60-k}.$$

This in turn can be approximated using Poisson probabilities (with $np = 3$):

$$1 - \sum_{k=0}^{4} e^{-3} \frac{3^k}{k!} = 1 - .848 = .152.$$

Problems

7–1 Evaluate each of the following

    (a) $(6)_3$ **(b)** $\binom{12}{4}$ **(c)** $\binom{100}{98}$

7–2 A bowl contains four black and eight white chips. Five are drawn, one at a time, from the bowl. Determine the probability of the sequence W, B, B, W, B, **(a)** assuming no replacement of chips drawn, and **(b)** assuming replacement and mixing before each drawing. Determine also the probability of three black chips among the five drawn (no regard to order), **(c)** assuming no replacement, and **(d)** assuming replacement and mixing. Determine **(e)** the probability of the sequence W, B, B, W, B given that the selection of five chips includes exactly three black chips.

7–3 Compute the binomial probabilities for the case $n = 6$ and $p = \frac{1}{3}$, and then verify that the center of gravity of the distribution is $np = 2$.

7–4 Compute the probabilities for the number of black chips in a random selection (no replacement) of six chips from a bowl containing four black and eight white chips. As in Problem 7–3, verify that the center of gravity is $np = 2$.

7–5 Compare the binomial probabilities for $n = 10$ and $p = .1$ given in Table A-2 with the Poisson approximations obtained with the use of Table A-3.

7–6 Compare the binomial probabilities for $n = 10$ and $p = .3$ with the normal approximations obtained using Table A-1. Make the comparison with and without the continuity correction introduced in Example 7–3.

7–7 If 55 per cent of the voters of a large city are in favor of a given proposal, what is the probability that a random sample of 100 voters would not show a majority in favor?

7–8 A poll is taken to determine the number of people in a town of population 10,000 who have never left their state. In place of questioning the entire population, a sample of 100 people is selected from the population. Of these, three are found never to have left the state. What is the approximate probability of such a result, when in fact 5 per cent of the population have never left the state?

7.4 Posterior Distributions

Given a prior distribution for the Bernoulli parameter p (or M in the finite population case, where $p = M/N$), and given a certain number Y of successes in a sequence of observations, one can calculate (in principle) the corresponding posterior probabilities or density for M or p, respectively. Because the hypergeometric probability formula is rather complicated, and does not lend itself to simple calculations in a general case, this section will give only some results for the case of independent observations (binomially distributed Y).

A family of prior distributions for the Bernoulli parameter p that is easy to work with but which includes a sufficient variety to provide reasonable approximations to many prior configurations is the family of *beta distributions*, with density

$$g(p; a, b) = (\text{const})p^a(1 - p)^b, \qquad 0 \le p \le 1.$$

The graphs of these functions vanish at $p = 0$ and $p = 1$ (if a or b are positive) and have a single hump in between. If $a = b$, the graph is symmetrical; the hump is narrow and high if the common value is large, and broad and low if the common value is small. If a is larger than b, the curve has a higher order of tangency at $p = 0$ than at $p = 1$, and the maximum is closer to $p = 1$. Figure 7–1 shows some particular cases. Incidentally, the uniform, or constant, density is included as the case $a = b = 0$. If a or b is less than or equal to -1, the graph goes to infinity at the corresponding value of p in such a way that the area under the graph is not finite; one could not then make it into a density function in the ordinary sense, but it can be used (with any "const") as a prior weighting.

It has been stated already, and is here repeated, that the expected value of a distribution with a beta density of the above form is

$$\frac{a + 1}{a + b + 2}.$$

Notice that if $a = b$ this has the value $\frac{1}{2}$, the midpoint of $0 \le p \le 1$. Another result of interest (obtained by methods of calculus) is that the maximum of the beta density $g(p; a, b)$ occurs at the value $p = a/(a + b)$. This is the mode of the distribution. If $a = b$ this mode is $\frac{1}{2}$, the center of symmetry.

What makes the beta family convenient in the present context is that multiplication of the likelihood function for a random sample from a Bernoulli population by a beta prior distribution yields a function that is again (as far as p is concerned) of the beta type. For, given $Y = k$, and assuming a beta prior with parameters r and s,

$$f(k \mid p)g(p) = \binom{n}{k}p^k(1 - p)^{n-k}(\text{const.})p^r(1 - p)^s$$

$$= (\text{const.})p^{r+k}(1 - p)^{s+n-k}.$$

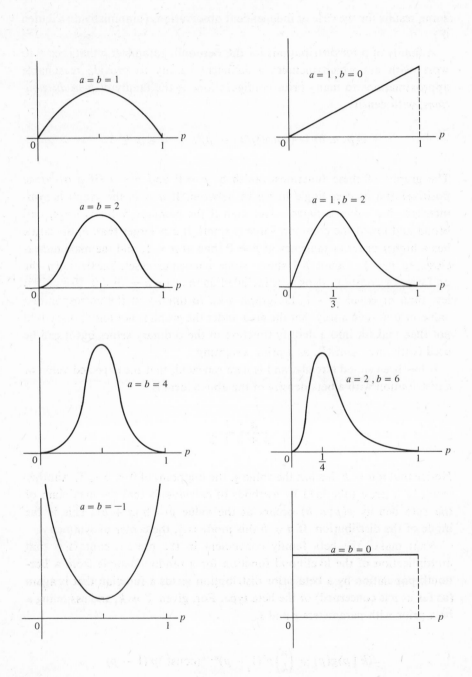

Figure 7–1

Because the denominator in the posterior density for p, which is just the unconditional probability for Y, does not involve p, the posterior density— given a beta prior—is proportional to the above product and is again a beta density:

$$h(p \mid k) = (\text{const.})p^{r+k}(1 - p)^{s+n-k}.$$

The mean or expected value of this posterior density is

$$p_B \equiv E_h(p) = \frac{k + r + 1}{n + r + s + 2},$$

which is then the *Bayes estimate* of p for the given prior, when a quadratic loss function is assumed.

The mode of the posterior distribution would be given by

$$p_{\text{mode}} = \frac{k + r}{n + r + s}.$$

For $r = s = 0$ the prior is uniform, and the mode (k/n) is the maximum likelihood estimate of p. Incidentally, this particular estimate would be obtainable as a Bayes estimate for beta priors only if $r = s = -1$, a case in which the prior is not a bona fide probability distribution.

Example 7–6. Suppose Y is the number of successes in 6 independent trials, and that a beta prior is assumed with $r = 1$ and $s = 4$. For $Y = k$, the maximum likelihood estimate is $k/6$, and the Bayes estimate is $(k + 2)/13$. A comparison is interesting:

k	0	1	2	3	4	5	6
Bayes Est.	0	$\frac{1}{6}$	$\frac{2}{6}$	$\frac{3}{6}$	$\frac{4}{6}$	$\frac{5}{6}$	1
Max.Lik.Est.	$\frac{2}{13}$	$\frac{3}{13}$	$\frac{4}{13}$	$\frac{5}{13}$	$\frac{6}{13}$	$\frac{7}{13}$	$\frac{8}{13}$

Prior convictions favor small values of p and make 7/13 reasonable if 6 successes are observed. But for 0 successes, $p = 0$ is still not a reasonable guess.

7.5 Mean Squared Error in Estimation

With the random Y replacing the specific k, the estimators obtained above become the following:

$$\text{Bayes:} \quad p_B = \frac{Y + r + 1}{n + r + s + 2} \quad \text{(for beta } (r, s) \text{ prior).}$$

$$\text{Max. Likelihood:} \quad p_{ml} = \frac{Y}{n}.$$

The mean squared errors for these estimators can be derived from the formula for the mean and variance of the binomial Y:

$$E(Y) = np, \quad \text{and} \quad \text{var } Y = np(1 - p).$$

To do this it is helpful to know that if $X = AY + B$, then in general

$$E(X) = E(AY + B) = AE(Y) + B,$$

and

$$\text{var } X = \text{var } (AY + B) = A^2 \text{ var } Y.$$

(These are not hard to prove from the defining formulas.)

Applying these results one obtains, for the maximum likelihood estimate

$$E(p_{ml}) = \frac{E(Y)}{n} = p,$$

and

$$E[(p_{ml} - p)^2] = \text{var } (p_{ml}) = \frac{\text{var } Y}{n^2} = \frac{pq}{n}.$$

And for the Bayes estimate:

$$E(p_B) = \frac{E(Y) + r + 1}{n + r + s + 2} = p + \frac{r + 1 - p(r + s + 2)}{n + r + s + 2},$$

and

$$\text{var } (p_B) = \frac{\text{var } Y}{(n + r + s + 2)^2} = \frac{np(1 - p)}{(n + r + s + 2)^2}.$$

The mean squared error for p_B is then the sum of its variance and $(Ep_B - p)^2$:

$$\text{m.s.e. } (p_B) = \frac{np(1 - p) + [r + 1 - p(r + s + 2)]^2}{(n + r + s + 2)^2}.$$

Example 7–7. For six independent trials, and a prior proportional to $p(1 - p)^4$, the Bayes estimate (see Example 7–6) is $(Y + 2)/13$. The mean squared error is obtainable from the general formula above:

$$\text{m.s.e. } (p_B) = \frac{6p(1 - p) + (2 - 7p)^2}{169}$$

$$= \frac{43p^2 - 22p + 4}{169}.$$

The graphs of this risk, and the risk for the maximum likelihood error (which is $p(1 - p)/6$) are shown in Figure 7–2. Notice that the risk for the Bayes estimate is small in the range of values of p emphasized in the prior distribution for p. It might be of interest to calculate the averages of these risks with respect to the prior distribution; this can be done with the aid of the information $E_g(p) = \frac{2}{7}$ and $E_g(p^2) = \frac{3}{28}$, where E_g denotes an averaging with respect to the prior distribution.:

Expected Bayes risk using Bayes estimator: .0030

Expected risk of m.l.e. (with respect to given prior):   .0298.

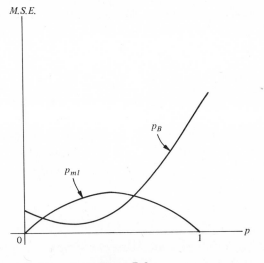

Figure 7–2

Thus, *if a prior is at hand*, it pays to take advantage of it, rather than use the uninformed Y/n; in this case the saving is a factor of about 10.

Problems

7–9 In estimating p one performs eight independent trials. Assuming a prior density for p proportional to $p^4(1 - p)^2$,

    (a) determine the Bayes and maximum likelihood estimates of p, given $Y = 5$, that is, given five successes in the eight trials;

    (b) determine the mean squared errors (as functions of p) for the Bayes and maximum likelihood estimators.

7–10 Obtain the specific expressions for the mean squared error using the Bayes estimator and the maximum likelihood estimator of p in the case of a "uniform" prior density for p ($r = s = 0$). Show that if $p = \frac{1}{2}$, the Bayes estimator is better, and if $p = 0$ or 1, the maximum likelihood estimator is better.

7–11 Suppose the loss function in the estimation problem is

$$l(p, a) = |p - a|.$$

The risk function for an estimator $t(Y)$ based on the number (Y) of successes in n trials is then

$$E|t(Y) - p| = \sum_{k=0}^{n} |t(k) - p| P(Y = k).$$

Calculate the risk when $t(Y)$ is the Bayes estimator, assuming a uniform prior for p, and when $t(Y)$ is the maximum likelihood estimator, in the particular case $n = 6$ and $p = \frac{1}{2}$.

7.6 Testing Hypotheses About p

Hypotheses concerning a Bernoulli population are defined in terms of the parameter p, the probability of success at a given trial. The most readily handled case is that of testing one particular value of p against another

$$H_0: \quad p = p_0 \quad \text{against} \quad H_1: p = p_1 \, (\neq p_0).$$

Here the most powerful tests are those with critical regions of the form $\Lambda < \text{const}$, where Λ denotes the likelihood ratio; in the case of independent identical trials, or sampling with replacement and mixing, this likelihood ratio is as follows, for Y successes in n trials:

$$\Lambda = \frac{p_0{}^Y(1 - p_0)^{n-Y}}{p_1{}^Y(1 - p_1)^{n-Y}} = \left[\frac{p_0(1 - p_1)}{p_1(1 - p_0)}\right]^Y \left[\frac{1 - p_0}{1 - p_1}\right]^n.$$

If $p_0 < p_1$, then $1 - p_1 < 1 - p_0$, and the fraction in the first set of brackets is less than 1. Small values of Λ then correspond to large values of Y, so the best critical regions of Y-values are of the form $Y > \text{const.}$ (If $p_0 > p_1$, they are of the form $Y < \text{const.}$) This is eminently reasonable—to act as though the larger p better describes the state of nature when a large number of successes is observed to occur.

The situation is similar in the case of sampling without replacement from a finite Bernoulli population. Given Y successes in n drawn from a population of size N with M objects marked success and $N - M$ marked failure (or 1 and 0, respectively), the likelihood ratio corresponding to $M = M_0$ and $M = M_1$ is as follows:

$$\Lambda(Y) = \frac{(M_0)_Y(N - M_0)_{n-Y}/(N)_n}{(M_1)_Y(N - M_1)_{n-Y}/(N)_n}.$$

It is not particularly difficult (although it is perhaps a trifle tricky) to show that this is either an increasing or decreasing function of Y according as $M_0 > M_1$ or $M_0 < M_1$. Therefore, if $M_0 < M_1$, the critical region $\Lambda < \text{const}$ is equivalent to a region of Y-values of the form $Y > \text{const.}$ These are the best tests, and are Bayes tests for some combination of prior probabilities and losses. As in the case of sampling with replacement, they are what one would expect intuitively—rejecting the larger value of M if there are few "successes" in the sample.

Having determined the class of best tests, one is still faced with selecting one of these for a particular situation. This is done in classical statistical practice by fixing α, the acceptable size of type I error, and then taking whatever β (or size of type II error) is associated with the corresponding test. That β will be smallest for the best test above when compared with β's of other tests with the same α. Example 5–10 and Problem 5–12, in an earlier chapter, illustrate the determination of a likelihood ratio test in the case of independent, Bernoulli trials. The following example presents a similar analysis in a case of sampling without replacement from a finite population. The population size used in the example is perhaps a bit on the unrealistic side, with respect to usual practical applications; this is done to make the computations easier.

Example 7–8. A sample of size 4 is drawn from a Bernoulli population of size 10. Let M denote the number of objects of one type (coded 1) in the population, and Y the number of this type in the sample. It is desired to test the hypothesis $M = 5$ against $M = 7$ (or, if $p = M/N$, $p = .5$ against $p = .7$, as in Example 5–10). The distributions of Y under these two hypotheses are shown in the following table, along with the likelihood ratio $\Lambda(Y)$ for each Y.

y	$P(Y = y \mid M = 5)$	$P(Y = y \mid M = 7)$	$\Lambda(y)$
0	$\dfrac{1}{42}$	0	∞
1	$\dfrac{10}{42}$	$\dfrac{1}{30}$	$\dfrac{450}{63}$
2	$\dfrac{20}{42}$	$\dfrac{9}{30}$	$\dfrac{100}{63}$
3	$\dfrac{10}{42}$	$\dfrac{15}{30}$	$\dfrac{30}{63}$
4	$\dfrac{1}{42}$	$\dfrac{5}{30}$	$\dfrac{9}{63}$

Notice, as asserted to be a general phenomenon, that the value of Λ decreases as Y increases, which means that $\Lambda <$ const corresponds to $Y >$ const. The six distinct critical regions (nonrandomized) defined by inequalities of this type are shown in the next table, along with the error sizes in each case, and the risks computed with the assumption of losses 2 for an error of type I, 1 for an error of type II, and 0 for a correct decision:

Critical values of Y	α	β	2α
empty set	0	1	0
{4}	$\dfrac{1}{42}$	$\dfrac{5}{6}$	$\dfrac{1}{21}$
{4, 3}	$\dfrac{11}{42}$	$\dfrac{1}{3}$	$\dfrac{11}{21}$
{4, 3, 2}	$\dfrac{31}{42}$	$\dfrac{1}{30}$	$\dfrac{31}{21}$
{4, 3, 2, 1}	$\dfrac{41}{42}$	0	$\dfrac{41}{21}$
{4, 3, 2, 1, 0}	1	0	2

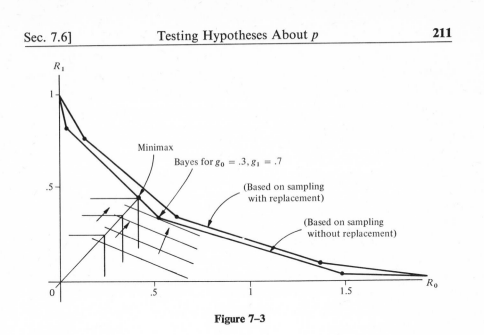

Figure 7–3

The risk points $(2\alpha, \beta)$ are plotted, for each test, in Figure 7–3. The straight line segments joining them are the randomized or mixed tests that are also best. Shown also in the same figure is a plot of the points corresponding to the same critical regions, but based on sampling with replacement, that is, on independent Bernoulli trials. Notice the slight advantage of sampling without replacement.

The minimax test (in the class of mixed tests) is a mixture of the critical region {4} and {4, 3}, namely, that mixture that weights the former with weight $\frac{8}{41}$ and the latter with weight $\frac{33}{41}$. To carry out such a mixed test one would reject $M = 5$ if $Y = 4$ and reject it with probability $\frac{33}{41}$ if $Y = 3$. The Bayes test for a particular prior distribution can be taken to be one of the pure tests; for $g_0 = .3$, for instance, the Bayes test is given by the critical region $Y = 3$ or 4, as shown in Figure 7–3.

In the one-sided problem of testing $p \le p^*$ against $p > p^*$, as in the preceding chapter, a standard approach is to pick a value of p in H_0 and a value in H_1 and set up of the best test for the former against the latter, that is, for simple hypothesis against simple. This critical region will usually perform well for the one-sided composite problem.

Example 7–9. It is desired to test $p \le \frac{1}{2}$ against $p > \frac{1}{2}$ in a Bernoulli population, where p is the probability of success at a single observation. The best tests for one value of p against a larger single value of p are of the form $Y > $ const, where Y is the number of successes in n observations—whether the observations are from independent trials, or are observations in a sample obtained without replacement (from a finite population). Suppose, then, that 25 independent trials are performed, and that the test with critical region $Y > 10$ is adopted. The power function of this test is the probability that $Y > 10$ is observed, as a function of p:

$$\pi(p) = P(Y > 10 \mid p) \doteq 1 - \Phi\left(\frac{10.5 - 25p}{\sqrt{25p(1 - p)}}\right).$$

The last expression, in terms of the function $\Phi(z)$ given in Table A–1, exploits the fact that binomial probabilities can be approximated by normal probabilities if n is even moderately large (and p is not too close to 0). The mean and variance of the normal distribution are taken to be the mean and variance of the distribution of Y, which (being binomial) has mean $25p$ and variance $25p(1 - p)$. The graph of $\pi(p)$ as given above is shown in Figure 7–4. Notice that it tends to be large for $p > \frac{1}{2}$ and small for $p \le \frac{1}{2}$, as is desired. (Ideally, one would want it to be 1 on the alternative and 0 on the null hypothesis.)

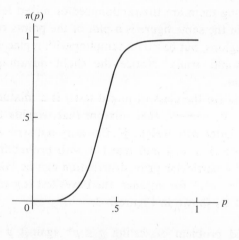

Figure 7–4

Example 7–10. A lot of 400 articles is considered acceptable if not more than 20 of them (5 per cent) are defective, otherwise unacceptable. A sample of 25 articles is drawn at random from the lot (without replacement), and a decision to accept or reject the lot is to be based on the number of defectives in that sample. In statistical language, it is desired to test the hypothesis $M \le 20$ against $M > 20$, where M is the number of defectives in the lot, based on the number Y of defectives in the sample. A one-sided test is appro-

priate, namely, to reject the lot if $Y >$ const. In particular consider the test
with critical region $Y \geq 2$. This test has the power function (with $p = M/400$)

$$\pi(p) = 1 - P(Y = 0 \text{ or } 1 \mid p)$$

$$\doteq 1 - [p^0(1 - p)^{25} + 25p^1(1 - p)^{24}]$$

$$\doteq 1 - e^{-25p}(1 + 25p).$$

(The first approximation, expressing the desired probability in terms of
binomial probabilities, stems from considering the population so large with
respect to the sample size that sampling with replacement and sampling
without replacement are practically equivalent. The second approximation is
the Poisson approximation to the binomial, used for large n and small p—
in this case, $n = 25$ and p small, at least for the kinds of lots expected.) This
power characteristic is shown in Figure 7–5, and appears to be reasonably
good—there is a high probability that very bad lots will be rejected and a
low probability that very good lots will be accepted, although marginally
good lots may often be rejected by the test.

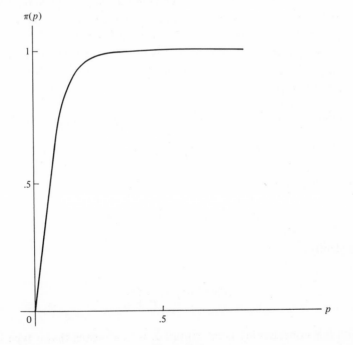

Figure 7–5

A loss function is usually neither simple to determine nor simple to specify or write down. One oversimplified loss function for the one-sided hypothesis testing problem is that which assigns a constant loss for all errors of type I and another constant loss for those of type II:

	$H_0: p \leq p^*$	$H_1: p > p^*$
Accept H_0	0	a
Reject H_0	b	0

The risk function is then simply related to the power function (see Section 5.7):

$$R(p; C) = \begin{cases} b\pi(p), & \text{for } p \leq p^*, \\ a[1 - \pi(p)], & \text{for } p > p^*, \end{cases}$$

where $\pi(p)$ is the power function of the test with critical region C. If a prior distribution for p is assumed, one can (in principle) determine the corresponding Bayes solution by choosing C to minimize the average risk with respect to that prior distribution—which is not usually a very simple process.

The Bayes action for an observed value $Y = k$ can also be determined by applying the posterior distribution to p in the original loss table; the action with the smaller expected posterior loss is the Bayes action. If $h(p)$ denotes the posterior density of p, and P_h denotes probability in this posterior distribution, then

Expected posterior loss for accepting $H_0 = aP_h(p > p^*)$,

Expected posterior loss for rejecting $H_0 = bP_h(p \leq p^*)$.

Thus, H_0 is to be rejected if

$$bP_h(p \leq p^*) < aP_h(p > p^*),$$

or equivalently

$$P_h(p > p^*) > \frac{b}{a + b}.$$

If the loss b is considerably greater than a, which means that a type I error (rejecting H_0 when it is true) is much more costly than a type II error, then

$b/(a + b)$ is close to 1, and for rejection one would have to have a posterior distribution that puts this large fraction of its "mass" to the right of p^*.

Example 7–11. Consider testing $p \le .6$ against $p > .6$ using as a test statistic the number Y of successes in five independent trials. Assume losses of 3 units for an error of type I and of 1 unit for an error of type II, and assume a beta prior distribution with $r = s = 1$

$$g(p) = 2p(1 - p) \qquad 0 \le p \le 1.$$

If the result $Y = 4$ is observed, the posterior distribution is also of the beta type, as follows

$$h(p \mid 4) = 168p^5(1 - p)^2, \qquad 0 \le p \le 1.$$

The graph of this density is given in Figure 7–6, which also indicates the probability that $p > p^* = .6$ in this posterior distribution, as the area under

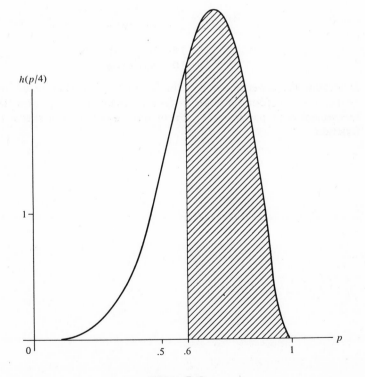

Figure 7–6

the graph to the right of .6. The area can be shown (by methods of calculus) to be about .696, which is less than the value of $b/(a + b) = \frac{3}{4}$. Thus, for the given prior and the given observation, the null hypothesis would be accepted. Note that if the losses had been $b = 2$ and $a = 1$, so that $b/(a + b) = \frac{2}{3}$, the same observation would call for rejection of H_0.

Problems

7–12 Referring to Example 7–8, repeat the various computations of Λ, α, β in case the sampling is done *with* replacement and mixing, and so verify the curve of Figure 7–3.

7–13 Referring to Example 7–10, obtain the power function for the test with critical region $Y \geq 3$, and compare the result with that shown in Figure 7–5.

7–14 Determine and sketch the power function of the test that rejects H_0 if 100 independent trials of a Bernoulli experiment result in more than 40 successes (see Example 7–9).

7–15 A loss function is defined as follows

$$l(p, A) = \begin{cases} 0, & \text{if } .4 < p < .6, \\ 2, & \text{otherwise,} \end{cases}$$

$$l(p, B) = \begin{cases} 3, & \text{if } .4 < p < .6, \\ 0, & \text{otherwise.} \end{cases}$$

Determine the power function of the test that calls for action B if there are no successes or four successes in four independent trials (of a Bernoulli experiment with parameter p). From this determine and sketch the risk function.

Chapter 8 Rectangular Games

In the decision problems considered so far, the decision maker has been groping in the dark—challenging the unknown, striving to make a wise decision without knowing a crucial fact about the situation, namely, the actual state of nature that is governing. Sometimes one is tempted to imagine that Nature is doing her best to outwit him, as reflected in the saying, "if something can go wrong, it will." But, aside from such moments of discouragement, people will generally be willing to agree that Nature is not malevolent, and is not trying her best to do them in.

On the other hand there are situations, in which decisions must be made, that involve actual living and breathing opponents—one or more. Through their own wise actions, these opponents are trying to maximize their profits, often at the expense of the others involved in the situation.

Example 8-1. Two firms are invited to bid on an order for 200 electric typewriters, the bids to be rounded to the nearest hundred dollars. The firm making the lower bid wins the contract if their bids are different, but the order is to be divided equally between the two firms if their bids happen to be the same. Each firm knows what its typewriters cost to produce, and each firm would naturally like to maximize its profits; but if it bids too high, the contract is lost, and if it bids too low, its margin of profit is small. For each firm the utility in winning the contract may be measured not only by the dollar profit in that transaction, but also in the prestige in having won it and in the increased probability of selling other of its products. With the assumption that this utility can be determined, the firm must set its bid, not knowing what the other firm will bid, but knowing that the other firm is going through a similar process of arriving at a bid that is best for that firm.

A theory of games has been developed to provide a mathematical framework in which to treat such problems as that given in the example above, and to consider the earlier decision problems—thought of as games played against Nature. Only the simplest elements of the simplest kinds of games will be considered here.

A *game* is a set of rules and conventions followed by people called *players*. A *play* of a game is one realization of the rules. A *move* is a point in the game at which a player selects one from a given set of alternatives. An *n*-person game involves just *n* players, although the "player" may actually be a partnership of two persons, as in bridge.

At the end of a play of a game there is an assignment of rewards according to the outcome of the play. If the net gain of player P_i is g_i $(i = 1, 2, \ldots, n)$, and if $g_1 + g_2 + \cdots + g_n = 0$, the game is said to be a *zero-sum* game. In such a game, the total capital of the players remains fixed, the winnings of one player coming from the losses of other players.

A game with several moves per player can be reduced to an equivalent game with one move per player, by interpreting a "move" as a *plan of action* that includes a choice of an alternative at each actual move of the game, that is, as what is usually thought of as a *strategy*. For this reason the various alternatives for each player are referred to as *strategies*.

A two person, zero-sum game with one move (or strategy) for each player is called a *rectangular game*. Only such games in which each player can choose from a finite number of moves will be considered.

It is convenient to denote the *m* alternatives available to player P_1 by the integers $1, 2, \ldots, m$, and the alternatives available to player P_2 by the integers $1, 2, \ldots, n$. Thus, each player chooses an integer from the set of integers available to him, and a payoff to each player is then determined (according to the rules of the game). The notation will be as follows: If player P_1 chooses i and player P_2 chooses j, the payoff to player P_1 is a_{ij}. Because the game is assumed to be a zero-sum game, the payoff to player P_2 is automatically $-a_{ij}$, so the game is determined or characterized by the array of payoffs a_{ij} to player P_1:

		P_2's alternatives				
		1	2	3	$\cdots$	n
	1	a_{11}	a_{12}	a_{13}	$\cdots$	a_{1n}
P_1's	2	a_{21}	a_{22}	a_{23}	$\cdots$	a_{2n}
alternatives	$\vdots$	$\vdots$				$\vdots$
	m	a_{m1}	a_{m2}	a_{m3}	$\cdots$	a_{mn}

The problem facing each player is somehow to select a strategy so that his gain is as large as possible; what makes the problem awkward is that he doesn't know what his opponent is going to do.

Example 8–2. Perhaps the reader has played the following game in his youth. Two players simultaneously bring their right forearms down onto a table, with hands in one of three configurations: fist closed, representing *stone*, hand flat, representing *paper*, or only middle and forefingers extended, representing *scissors*. The payoff is according to the scheme that *stone* beats *scissors*, that *scissors* beats *paper*, and that *paper* beats *stone*. Although the payoff may be some kind of corporal punishment, when played by youngsters, it could be that the loser pays the winner one unit. The payoff table would then be as follows, for player P_1

| | | P_2's alternatives | | |
		Stone	Paper	Scissors
P_1's alternatives	Stone	0	-1	1
	Paper	1	0	-1
	Scissors	-1	1	0

This is a zero-sum game because one player pays the other—no source of outside funds increases the total capital of the two players.

8.1 Minimax Strategies

Upon examining each of the strategies available to him, P_1 will observe that if he chooses i, the least he will gain is the minimum of the entries in that ith row: $\min_j a_{ij}$. Looking at these various minima in the rows, he sees that one (or more) has the largest minimum; by choosing that row, he can be assured of gaining at least that amount:

$$\max_i \left(\min_j a_{ij} \right).$$

This choice of row would be termed his *maximin gain strategy*. This maximum minimum gain may not be very large—not as large as P_1 would like it to be, but in playing against an opponent who is also trying to win it's an amount that he can at least be sure of.

If the payoff table had been given in terms of losses, instead of gains, it would look the same except that all the signs would be changed; that is, the loss l_{ij} incurred by P_1 when he chooses i and P_2 chooses j is just $-a_{ij}$. Notice then that

$$\min_j a_{ij} = -\max_j l_{ij},$$

and that

$$\max_i \left(\min_j a_{ij} \right) = \max_i \left(-\max_j l_{ij} \right) = -\min_i \left(\max_j l_{ij} \right),$$

the corresponding maxima and minima occurring in precisely the same rows and columns. That is, the same choice of row for P_1 assures him of a minimum maximum loss as assures him a maximum minimum gain—and these amounts are the negatives of each other.

Now, what about player P_2? The array of payoffs to him is obtained from that for player P_1 by changing all of the signs, since P_1's loss is precisely P_2's gain. That is, the loss table for P_1 is the gain table or payoff table for P_2. If P_2 looks at his payoff table in the same way P_1 looked at his, P_2 will be led to choose the column (strategy) j that maximizes his minimum gain, thereby assuring himself of at least

$$\max_j \left(\min_i (-a_{ij}) \right) = -\min_j \left(\max_i a_{ij} \right).$$

Thus, he plays to minimize P_1's maximum gain—which is $\min_j (\max_i a_{ij})$.

Example 8–3. Consider a rectangular game with the following array of payoffs to player P_1:

		P_2's alternatives			$\min\limits_j$
		1	2	3	
P_1's	1	2	0	-4	-4
alternatives	2	-1	3	1	-1
	$\max\limits_i$	2	3	1	

If P_1 chooses 1, the minimum gain he will experience is -4; if he chooses 2, the minimum is -1. Of these, -1 is the larger minimum:

$$\max_i \left(\min_j a_{ij} \right) = -1.$$

If player P_2 chooses 1, the maximum that P_1 will get is 2; if he chooses 2, the maximum is 3; if he chooses 3, the maximum is 1. Of these maximum payoffs to P_1, the smallest is 1, corresponding to P_2's choosing 3. That is, by choosing 3, player P_2 keeps P_1 from getting more than 1:

$$\min_j \left(\max_i a_{ij} \right) = 1.$$

It would seem to be in P_1's best interest to play 2, and in P_2's best interest to play 3. (Let it be observed for future discussion, however, that if P_2 tosses a coin between 2 and 3, the expected payoff to P_1 is -2, if P_1 happens to play 1, and 0 if P_1 happens to play 2; thus, by introducing this randomization, P_2 can keep P_1 from getting an average or expected payoff of more than zero, which is better for P_2 than if he simply chooses 3.)

In Example 8–3 it was seen that the amount that P_1 could assure himself of, by maximizing his minimum payoff, was not as large as the amount that P_2 could keep him from getting more than, by minimizing the maximum payoff. This is true generally:

$$\max_i \left(\min_j a_{ij} \right) \leq \min_j \left(\max_i a_{ij} \right).$$

To see that this is the case, notice first that for all i' and j',

$$\min_j a_{i'j} \leq a_{i'j'} \leq \max_i a_{ij'}.$$

Since the left-most member of these inequalities is not larger than the right-most member for all i', the maximum of the left-most member over i' also is bounded by the same quantity:

$$\max_i \left(\min_j a_{ij} \right) \leq \max_i a_{ij'}.$$

But this in turn is true for all j', and in particular for the j' that minimizes the right-hand member; and this is what was to be shown.

If it should happen (and it sometimes does) that the amount that P_1 can assure himself of by maximizing his minimum payoff is precisely equal to the limit that P_2 can impose on his gain:

$$\max_i \left(\min_j a_{ij} \right) = \min_i \left(\max_j a_{ij} \right),$$

then certainly each player should play to achieve these ends—that is, each should adopt the minimax loss (or maximin gain) strategy. In this case,

$$v \equiv \max_i \left(\min_j a_{ij} \right)$$

or the amount P_1 is willing to settle for and which P_2 is willing to give him, is called the *value* of the game (to player P_1). Notice that so long as P_2 must be assumed to be an intelligent opponent who is likely to be minimaxing, player P_1 would not be likely to improve his lot by playing other than his minimax loss strategy (and conversely).

Example 8–4. Player A is to choose from (0, 1) and Player B is also to choose from (0, 1), with payoffs according to the following table:

		B's choice 0	B's choice 1	min j
A's choice	0	-1	0	-1
	1	2	1	1
	max i	2	1	

The maximum minimum, for A, is 1; the minimum maximum, for B, is 1. Thus, the value of the game (to A) is 1. The optimum strategies are for A to choose 1 and for B to choose 1.

8.2 Saddle Points

It will be convenient to alter the notation slightly and to use the functional notation $f(i, j)$ in place of the matrix notation a_{ij}. (The value of a_{ij} is, of course, a function of i and j, and the f-notation simply calls attention to this.) The following definition will then apply either to a function $f(i, j)$ defined for integers i and j, or to a function $f(x, y)$ defined for real numbers x and y.

DEFINITION *A point (x_0, y_0) is a saddle point of the function $f(x, y)$ if and only if $f(x_0, y_0)$ is the maximum of $f(x, y_0)$ as x varies and simultaneously the minimum of $f(x_0, y)$ as y varies.*

The geometric interpretation of a function $f(x, y)$ as a surface is what gives rise to the name saddle point; this is accomplished by plotting all triples (x, y, z), where $z = f(x, y)$, as points in three-dimensional space. Thus, above each (x, y) in the xy-plane, there is a point on the locus or graph z units up, with $z = f(x, y)$. Figure 8–1 shows a saddle-shaped surface, and the saddle-point (x_0, y_0), which is below the peak, coming up from the sides of the

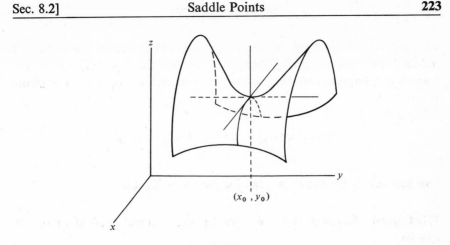

Figure 8–1

saddle and which is simultaneously below a low point, coming down from the front and back.

When $f(i, j)$ denotes the entry in a payoff table (corresponding to P_1's choice of i and P_2's choice of j), a saddle point is a combination of strategies such that the corresponding payoff is a maximum in its column and a minimum in its row. That is, (i_0, j_0) is a saddle point if when i_0 is held fixed (which means attention is fixed on the i_0th row), the minimum entry is $f(i_0, j_0)$, and when j_0 is held fixed (attention is fixed on the j_0th column), the maximum entry is $f(i_0, j_0)$. Not all payoff matrices have saddle points, but some do.

Example 8–5. The matrix of payoffs for the stone-paper-scissors game of Example 8–2 does not have a saddle point; examination of each of the nine entries will show that none of them is simultaneously a maximum in its column and minimum in its row. On the other hand, the matrix of Example 8–4:

$$\begin{pmatrix} -1 & 0 \\ 2 & 1 \end{pmatrix},$$

does have a saddle point, namely $(1, 1)$, since $f(1, 1) = 1$ is the larger value in the column corresponding to P_2's choice of 1 and is the smaller value in the row corresponding to P_1's choice of 1.

It may be noticed that of the two payoff matrices mentioned in Example 8–5, the one with no saddle point is one in which the maximum minimum is *not* equal to the minimum maximum, whereas in the case of the one with a saddle point there is equality. Moreover, in the case of a saddle point, the maximum minimum and the minimum maximum are attained at the saddle point:

$$\max_i \left(\min_j a_{ij} \right) = \min_j \left(\max_i a_{ij} \right) = a_{i_0 j_0}.$$

This happens to be true in general, for functions $f(x, y)$:

THEOREM *Provided that the maxima and minima involved exist, the equality*

$$\max_x \min_y f(x, y) = \min_y \max_x f(x, y)$$

holds if and only if $f(x, y)$ has a saddle point. Moreover, the common value, if there is one, is just $f(x_0, y_0)$, where (x_0, y_0) is the saddle point.

There are two parts to this theorem: one part asserting that equality of the maximin and the minimax implies that there is a saddle point, and the other asserting that existence of a saddle point implies equality. First, then, assume that (x_0, y_0) is a saddle point:

$$f(x, y_0) \le f(x_0, y_0) \le f(x_0, y), \quad \text{for all } x, y.$$

If this is true for *all* x and y, then it remains true for the x that maximize the left member and for the y that minimizes the right member:

$$\max_x f(x, y_0) \le \min_y f(x_0, y).$$

But the *minimum* maximum is no larger than the left member here, and the *maximum* minimum is no smaller than the right member:

$$\min_y \max_x f(x, y) \le \max_x f(x, y_0) \le \min_y f(x_0, y) \le \max_x \min_y f(x, y).$$

Because the minimax is known to be at least as big as the maximin, this last string of inequalities demonstrates that they must be equal.

Second, assume equality of the minimax and maximin, and denote by x_0 the value of x for which the function $\min_y f(x, y)$ has its maximum, and by y_0 the value of y for which the function $\max_x f(x, y)$ has its minimum. Then

$$f(x_0, y_0) \le \max_x f(x, y_0) = \min_y \max_x f(x, y)$$

$$= \max_x \min_y f(x, y) = \min_y f(x_0, y) \le f(x_0, y_0).$$

Clearly, each of these quantities is equal to $f(x_0, y_0)$, so that

$$\begin{cases} \max_x f(x, y_0) = f(x_0, y_0) \\ \min_y f(x_0, y) = f(x_0, y_0), \end{cases}$$

these conditions being what define (x_0, y_0) to be a saddle point. This completes the proof of the theorem.

Problems

8–1 Consider the rectangular game defined by the following payoff matrix for P_1:

		P_2's alternatives			
		1	2	3	4
	1	0	7	0	2
P_1's alternatives	2	3	6	2	−2
	3	8	5	4	7
	4	2	−1	3	5

(a) Determine $\max_i \min_j a_{ij}$ and $\min_i \max_j a_{ij}$.

(b) Is there a saddle point? If so, what is the value of the game?

(c) Would it be possible to eliminate any of P_1's choices by considerations of dominance?

8–2 Show that the game matrix

$$\begin{pmatrix} 1 & 4 & 0 \\ 7 & -2 & 2 \\ 2 & -1 & 6 \end{pmatrix}$$

has no saddle point. Determine P_1's optimal strategy. Show also that by tossing a fair coin to choose between 1 and 2, P_1 can improve his payoff. (Explain the sense in which this is an improvement.)

8-3 Verify that in the stone-paper-scissors game of Example 8–2, the maximin and minimax are not equal—and that there is no saddle point.

8-4 Mr. A and Mr. B own jointly a property worth N units of utility, and each has (privately) assets worth 4 units of utility. They agree that each will make a sealed bid of 0, 1, 2, 3, or 4 units for sole ownership of the property. The higher bidder takes possession of it and pays the other the amount he bid, but if the bids are equal the ownership is decided by the toss of a coin (with no other transfer of assets.) Set up the game matrix in terms of N and determine any saddle points for the various possible values of N.

8.3 Mixed Strategies

In an earlier example (Example 8–3) it was seen parenthetically that P_1 could do better, on the average, with a *mixed* strategy than he could using his maximin pure strategy. This is not the case if the game has a saddle point (i_0, j_0), for by playing j_0, player P_2 can keep P_1 from getting more than v, the value of the game, and strategy i_0 assures P_1 of at least v. So the possibility of improving on a maximin pure strategy exists only in the case of a payoff matrix that does not have a saddle point.

The terminology of *pure* and *mixed* carries over from the earlier usage in connection with decision problems: A *mixed strategy* for P_1 is a probability vector $X = (x_1, \ldots, x_m)$. To carry out such a strategy he performs the experiment leading to X and selects the alternative i if the result is the outcome with probability x_i. That is, he selects alternative 1 with probability x_1, 2 with probability $x_2, \ldots,$ and m with probability x_m. The particular mixed strategy of the form $(0, 0, \ldots, 1, 0, \ldots, 0)$, which puts all of the probability at alternative i (say), is equivalent to just playing i, and is called a *pure strategy*.

Player P_2, of course, may also realize that a mixed strategy may be more effective than a pure strategy; for him a mixed strategy is a probability vector $Y = (y_1, y_2, \ldots, y_n)$; with it he selects alternative j with probability y_j.

If P_1 uses a mixed strategy X and P_2 uses a mixed strategy Y, the payoff is a random variable. With the usual assumption that gain is measured in utility, the appropriate quantity is the expected value of this random variable, to be denoted by $\mathscr{E}(X, Y)$:

$$\mathscr{E}(X, Y) = \sum_j \sum_i a_{ij} x_i y_j.$$

If one player, say P_1, uses a pure strategy i, the notation for expected payoff to P_1 will be as follows:

$$\mathscr{E}(i, Y) = \sum_j a_{ij} y_j.$$

Although more complicated mathematically, the situation facing the two players is basically the same as when only pure strategies were permitted; each player has a set of strategies from which to choose, and corresponding to each choice X of P_1 and choice Y of P_2, there is a corresponding payoff, namely, the expected gain, $\mathscr{E}(X, Y)$. The reasoning that led to the maximization of the minimum gain for pure strategies would apply equally well to the expected gain for mixed strategies, but now the players have a much wider selection. [The set of mixed strategies is the set of points on a diagonal plane of the unit cube of m dimensions, for P_1—that is, points $(x_1, \ldots, x_m)$ such that $0 \le x_i \le 1$ and $x_1 + \cdots + x_m = 1$.]

The function $\mathscr{E}(X, Y)$ may or may not have, as far as is yet evident, a saddle point (X_0, Y_0). If it does, then the maximum minimum (over X and Y respectively) is equal to the minimum maximum (over Y and X), and the corresponding value $\mathscr{E}(X_0, Y_0)$ is the value of the game. Such a point is called a *strategic saddle point* and is in a sense the *solution* of the game. For, by using strategy X_0 player P_1 can assure himself of at least v, the value of the game, and by using strategy Y_0 player P_2 can keep P_1 from getting more than v (all this on the average!).

Example 8–6. Consider again the paper-stone-scissors game of Example 8–2, defined by the following payoff matrix (for P_1):

		x Stone	y Paper	$1 - x - y$ Scissors
r	Stone	0	-1	1
s	Paper	1	0	-1
$1 - r - s$	Scissors	-1	1	0

If P_1 adopts the strategy $(r, s, 1 - r - s)$ and P_2 the strategy $(x, y, 1 - x - y)$, the expected payoff is calculated as the weighted sum of the various possible payoffs, the weight for a given combination of P_1's and P_2's moves being the probability of that combination (which in turn is a product of the probabilities assigned in the mixed strategies):

$$\mathscr{E}(r, s; x, y) = -1 \cdot yr + 1 \cdot r(1 - x - y) + 1 \cdot xs - 1 \cdot s(1 - x - y)$$
$$- 1 \cdot x(1 - r - s) + 1 \cdot y(1 - r - s)$$
$$= -3ry + 3xs + r - s + y - x$$
$$= r(1 - 3y) - s(1 - 3x) + (y - x)$$
$$= y(1 - 3r) - x(1 - 3s) + (r - s).$$

It is clear from the last representation of this expected payoff that P_1 can assure himself of 0 by adopting the mixed strategy $(\frac{1}{3}, \frac{1}{3}, \frac{1}{3})$, which makes the expected payoff 0 no matter what strategy P_2 uses, pure or mixed. Similarly, if $y = x = \frac{1}{3}$, the expected payoff is 0 no matter what strategy P_1 adopts; so by using $(\frac{1}{3}, \frac{1}{3}, \frac{1}{3})$ player P_2 can keep player P_1 from getting more than 0, on the average. Indeed, these strategies for P_1 and P_2 constitute a saddle point for the function $\mathscr{E}(r, s; x, y)$, considering this as a function of the two variables (r, s) and (x, y). They are then also maximin and minimax strategies, respectively, and the value of the game is 0.

It is evident, in this last example, that the introduction of mixed strategies can turn a problem with no saddle point into a problem for which a saddle point solution exists. This was not just the result of a fortuitous selection of numbers—it always happens. And this is the content of the fundamental theorem for rectangular games:

THEOREM *Every finite rectangular game has a "solution" (strategic saddle point) in mixed strategies.*

The theorem is not trivial to prove, depending essentially on certain results in the theory of convex sets, and the proof will not be given here. (It may be found, for instance, in McKinsey's *Theory of Games* (McGraw-Hill).)

8.4 Relation to the Decision Problem

The decision problem has been viewed as a game—a two-person game in which the lineup of players is as follows:

Player P_1:   Statistician,

Player P_2:   Nature.

Such a viewpoint assumes that Nature is a conscious opponent who is trying to outwit the statistician, and this assumption is sufficiently untenable to cause statisticians to shun it. However, certain theoretical lights are cast on the decision problem by viewing it as a game against Nature.

The minimax approach to a decision problem was that of minimizing the maximum loss, which is equivalent to maximizing the minimum gain or payoff, to put it in the language of game theory. But this minimum payoff was determined for each action, or mixed action, over the various *pure* states of nature; that is, for each strategy one determined

$$\min_{j} \mathscr{E}(X, j),$$

and then maximized this minimum over strategies X. The maximum gain or pay-off was then

$$\max_{X} \min_{j} \mathscr{E}(X, j).$$

It will be shown next that

$$\max_{X} \min_{Y} \mathscr{E}(X, Y) = \max_{X} \min_{j} \mathscr{E}(X, j),$$

which means that the strategy X^* for P_1 (the statistician) which is part of a strategic saddle point of $\mathscr{E}(X, Y)$, is also a maximin strategy (minimax loss strategy) for the statistician in the decision problem approach, and conversely.

Let (X^*, Y^*) be a strategic saddle point for a game with expected payoff $\mathscr{E}(X, Y)$; in particular this means that

$$v = \max \min \mathscr{E}(X, Y)$$
$$= \mathscr{E}(X^*, Y^*) \leq \mathscr{E}(X^*, Y),$$

for all Y, where v is the value of the game. Since this inequality holds for all Y, it holds in particular for all pure strategies j for P_2:

$$\mathscr{E}(X^*, Y^*) \leq \mathscr{E}(X^*, j), \qquad j = 1, \ldots, n.$$

But then it must hold for the j that produces the minimum on the right

$$v = \mathscr{E}(X^*, Y^*) \leq \min_{j} \mathscr{E}(X^*, j).$$

Now, if $\mathscr{E}(X^*, j)$ is *strictly* greater than v for some j', then

$$v = \sum \sum x_i^* y_j^* a_{ij} = \sum y_j^* \mathscr{E}(X^*, j) > v \sum y_j^* = v,$$

unless $y_{j'}^* = 0$; and if $\mathscr{E}(X^*, j) > v$ for all j, then *all* $y_j^* = 0$, which cannot be, since the y_j^* add up to 1 (being probabilities). Hence it follows that $v = \min_j \mathscr{E}(X^*, j)$. It remains to show that

$$\max_X \min_j \mathscr{E}(X, j) = \min_j \mathscr{E}(X^*, j),$$

which can be deduced by exploiting the other side of the strategic saddle point condition:

$$\sum y_j^* \mathscr{E}(X, j) = \mathscr{E}(X, Y^*) \le \mathscr{E}(X^*, Y^*) = v.$$

If for given X the smallest $\mathscr{E}(X, j)$ exceeded v, then each $\mathscr{E}(X, j)$ would exceed v, and so would $\mathscr{E}(X, Y^*)$. Hence, for every X,

$$\min_j \mathscr{E}(X, j) \le v.$$

And then also the maximum of the left member cannot exceed v:

$$\max_X \min_j \mathscr{E}(X, j) \le v = \max_X \min_Y \mathscr{E}(X, Y).$$

Finally, because the set of all mixed Y's includes all pure j's:

$$\min_Y \mathscr{E}(X, Y) \le \min_j \mathscr{E}(X, j),$$

so that

$$v = \max_X \min_Y \mathscr{E}(X, Y) \le \max_X \min_j \mathscr{E}(X, j),$$

and the desired equality is established.

Example 8–7. Consider again (as in Example 8–3) the game with payoff matrix as follows:

		P₂'s alternatives		
		1	2	3
P₁'s	1	2	0	−4
alternatives	2	−1	3	1

This game does not have a saddle point in pure strategies, but consider the mixed strategies $X = (r, 1 - r)$ and $Y = (a, b, c)$ for P_1 and P_2, respectively. The expected payoff, when these strategies are employed, is

$$\mathscr{E}(X, Y) = 2ar - 4cr - a(1 - r) + 3b(1 - r) - c(1 - r)$$

$$= r(2a - 4c) + (1 - r)(-a + 3b + c)$$

$$= a(3r - 1) + b(3 - 3r) + c(1 - 5r)$$

Treating this problem as a decision problem, with P_1 as the decision maker and P_2 as the state of nature, and using the graphical techniques of Example 3–8, yields $X^* = (\frac{1}{4}, \frac{3}{4})$. This X^* is then part of a strategic saddle point. Treating the problem as a decision problem with P_1 as the state of nature and P_2 the decision maker, and using the graphical technique of Example 3–7, yields $Y^* = (\frac{5}{8}, 0, \frac{3}{8})$. This is the other part of the strategic saddle point. The following can now be calculated, by substituting for X and Y in the expression above for $\mathscr{E}(X, Y)$:

$$\mathscr{E}(X^*, j) = \begin{cases} -1/4, & \text{if } j = 1, \\ 1/4, & \text{if } j = 2, \\ -1/4, & \text{if } j = 3, \end{cases}$$

and

$$\mathscr{E}(i, Y^*) = \begin{cases} -1/4, & \text{if } i = 1, \\ -1/4, & \text{if } i = 2. \end{cases}$$

(Recall that "$j = 1$," for example, means the special mixed strategy $(1, 0, 0)$ for P_2). Clearly,

$$v = \min_j \mathscr{E}(X^*, j) = \max_i \mathscr{E}(i, Y^*) = -\frac{1}{4}.$$

Notice also that

$$\mathscr{E}(X, Y^*) \le \mathscr{E}(X^*, Y^*) \le \mathscr{E}(X^*, Y),$$

and that for $j = 2$, for which $\mathscr{E}(X^*, j) > v$, the corresponding component of Y^* is 0.

In Section 3.6 the notion of "least favorable distribution" was introduced. This is the prior distribution for the state of nature, in a decision problem, for which the minimum Bayes loss, that is, the Bayes loss using the Bayes procedure for a given prior, is largest. In the interpretation of a decision problem as a game against Nature, the prior distributions for Nature are Nature's mixed strategies; and when the statistician (P_1) uses strategy X and Nature (P_2) uses strategy Y, the Bayes loss is simply the negative of the expected payoff to the statistician, namely $\mathscr{E}(X, Y)$. The minimum Bayes loss becomes the negative of the maximum expected payoff.

Suppose then that (X^*, Y^*) is a strategic saddle point for the rectangular game defined by a given decision problem with finitely many actions and finitely many stages of nature. It has been seen that X^* is a minimax loss solution for the decision problem. But the fact that X^* is part of a strategic saddle point means that for all mixed actions X, $\mathscr{E}(X^*, Y^*) \geq \mathscr{E}(X, Y^*)$, and this in turn says that X^* maximizes the expected payoff, or minimizes the Bayes loss against the prior distribution Y^*. Thus, the minimax mixed action X^* is Bayes for the prior distribution Y^*. And that prior distribution is least favorable, in that it maximizes the minimum Bayes loss to the statistician.

Problems

8–5 For each of the following payoff matrices of zero-sum games determine the optimal strategies following the procedure of Example 8–6. (Does either have a saddle point? And if so, does it agree with the strategic saddle point?)

(a)

		P_2	
		0	1
P_1	0	-1	0
	1	2	1

(b)

		P_2	
		0	1
P_1	0	-1	1
	1	1	-1

8–6 In Problems 5–16 and 5–17 the following table of risks was encountered, in testing $H_0: M = 1$ against $H_1: M = 3$:

	Risk	
	under H_0	under H_1
Test 1	0	2
Test 2	1	4/5
Test 3	5	0

Treat the situation as a game and show that the minimax strategy for the statistician and the least favorable prior distribution for Nature constitute a strategic saddle point. Observe that the value of the game is the minimax risk, 10/11. (Note the fact that the entries in the table are in terms of *loss* rather than *payoff*.)

8.5 Linear Programming

Perhaps it has not been completely unnoticed that our examples and problems calling for minimax solutions—both in the case of decision problems and in the case of rectangular games—have involved at most two or three states of nature, or at most two or three available actions. That is, the number of alternatives or strategies for at least one player has been at most three, and usually two (except for a few examples in which there was a saddle point in pure strategies). This is not just a pedagogical desire for simplicity, for it seems that the geometrical representations and the solutions exploiting the coordinate geometry of two or three dimensions do not lend themselves to practical generalizations.

In this section the problem of determining a strategic saddle point for a rectangular game will be reformulated as a problem in what is called *linear programming*. Algorithms have been developed for solving linear programming problems that can then be used for the determination of minimax strategies for games with more than two or three alternatives for each player—and hence for the determination of minimax decision rules.

In the preceding section the following result was obtained: If (X^*, Y^*) is a strategic saddle point for a finite rectangular game with value v, then

$$v = \min_j \mathscr{E}(X^*, j) = \max_i \mathscr{E}(i, Y^*).$$

(The last expression involving "max" over i was not derived explicitly there, but it follows in exactly the same way—or simply by interchanging the roles of the two players.) It now follows that v is the largest number such that

$$v \le \mathscr{E}(X^*, j), \quad \text{for } j = 1, 2, \ldots, n,$$

and that it is also the smallest number such that

$$v \ge \mathscr{E}(i, Y^*), \quad \text{for } i = 1, 2, \ldots, m.$$

If this were not so, then there would be a larger number v_1 such that

$$v < v_1 \leq \mathscr{E}(X^*, j),$$

for all j. But then the inequality holds also for the minimum

$$v < v_1 \leq \min_j \mathscr{E}(X^*, j) = v,$$

which is a contradiction. A similar contradiction is seen to follow if there were assumed to be a number v_2 larger than v such that $v_2 \geq \mathscr{E}(i, Y^*)$.

Example 8–8. Consider the rectangular game defined by the following matrix of payoffs to player P_1:

	1	2
1	2	4
2	3	0

For a given strategy $X = (x_1, x_2)$, one can compute $\mathscr{E}(X, j)$, for $j = 1, 2$:

$$\begin{cases} \mathscr{E}(X, 1) = 2x_1 + 3x_2 \\ \mathscr{E}(X, 2) = 4x + 0x_2. \end{cases}$$

The solution (X, Y) and value v of the game will then be such that

$$\begin{cases} x_1 + x_2 = 1 \\ x_1 \geq 0, x_2 \geq 0, \\ 2x_1 + 3x_2 \geq v \\ 4x_1 + 0x_2 \geq v \\ v \text{ is a maximum, subject to the above constraints.} \end{cases}$$

A graphical solution is found with the aid of Figure 8–2, in which the condition $2x_1 + 3x_2 \geq v$ is replaced by the equivalent condition $2 + x_2 \geq v$ (which follows from $x_1 + x_2 = 1$). The maximum v subject to the stated constraints is clearly $v = \frac{12}{5}$, and occurs for $x_1 = \frac{3}{5}$, $x_2 = \frac{2}{5}$. A similar

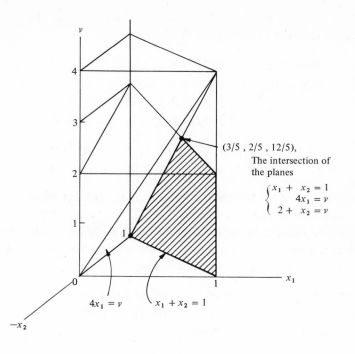

Figure 8–2

application of the fact that v is the smallest number for which $\mathscr{E}(i, Y^*) \leq v$ yields $y_1 = \frac{4}{5}$ and $y_2 = \frac{1}{5}$. Thus, the vectors $X^* = (\frac{3}{5}, \frac{2}{5})$ and $Y^* = (\frac{4}{5}, \frac{1}{5})$ make up the saddle point, and the value of the game is $\frac{12}{5}$.

The reduction of the game problem to a problem in linear programming is as follows. The value v and the solution vector $(x_1, \ldots, x_m)$ for P_1 are such that v is the largest number for which

$$\begin{cases} \mathscr{E}(X, 1) \geq v, \\ \mathscr{E}(X, 2) \geq v, \\ \quad \vdots \\ \mathscr{E}(X, n) \geq v. \end{cases}$$

Let $z_1, \ldots, z_n$ be introduced as nonnegative *slack variables*, representing the amount by which the inequalities are not equalities:

$$\begin{cases} \mathscr{E}(X, 1) + z_1 = v \\ \quad \vdots \qquad \vdots \quad \vdots \\ \mathscr{E}(X, n) + z_n = v. \end{cases}$$

and then subtract (say) the first equation from each of the others. The problem is then the following:

Maximize: $v = \mathscr{E}(X, 1) + z_1$

Subject to:
$$\begin{cases} x_1 + x_2 + \cdots + x_m = 1 \\ \mathscr{E}(X, 2) - \mathscr{E}(X, 1) + z_2 - z_1 = 0 \\ \mathscr{E}(X, 3) - \mathscr{E}(X, 1) + z_3 - z_1 = 0 \\ \quad\vdots \qquad\qquad \vdots \\ \mathscr{E}(X, n) - \mathscr{E}(X, 1) + z_n - z_1 = 0. \\ x_1 \geq 0, \ldots, x_m \geq 0, z_1 \geq 0, \ldots, z_n \geq 0. \end{cases}$$

Since $\mathscr{E}(X, j)$ is a linear function of $x_1, \ldots, x_m$, the equations here are all linear equations in the variables $x_1, \ldots, x_m, z_1, \ldots, z_n$, and the "objective function" v is also a linear function of those variables. Such a problem— maximizing a linear function subject to linear constraints and constraints of nonnegativity—is called a problem of *linear programming*.

Example 8–9. The solution of the game in Example 8–8 above was found to be such that the strategy (x_1, x_2) for P_1 and the value v of the game satisfied the following conditions:

$$\begin{cases} x_1 + x_2 = 1, \\ x_1 \geq 0, x_2 \geq 0 \\ 2x_1 + 3x_2 \geq v \\ 4x_1 + 0x_2 \geq v \\ v \text{ is a maximum.} \end{cases}$$

With the introduction of slack variables z_1 and z_2, the inequalities for v become

$$\begin{cases} 2x_1 + 3x_2 + z_1 = v \\ 4x_1 + z_2 = v, \end{cases}$$

and subtraction of the first from the second yields

$$2x_1 - 3x_2 + z_2 - z_1 = 0.$$

Thus, the problem can now be stated as follows

Maximize: $v = z_1 + 2x_1 + 3x_2$

subject to
$$\begin{cases} x_1 \geq 0, x_2 \geq 0, z_1 \geq 0, z_2 \geq 0, \\ x_1 + x_2 = 1 \\ 2x_1 - 3x_2 + z_2 - z_1 = 0. \end{cases}$$

The formulation of a general linear programming problem can be given in terms of constraints that are inequalities.

$$\text{Maximize:} \quad c_1x_1 + \cdots + c_mx_m$$

$$\text{subject to} \quad \begin{cases} x_1 \geq 0, \ldots, x_m \geq 0, \\ a_{11}x_1 + \cdots + a_{1m} \geq 0 \\ \vdots \qquad\qquad \vdots \\ a_{n1}x_n + \cdots + a_{nm}x_m \geq 0, \end{cases}$$

simply by noting that an equality $A = 0$ is equivalent to two inequalities: $A \geq 0$ and $A \leq 0$. For, with this one can transform equality constraints into inequalities; inequalities can be replaced by equalities, on the other hand, by the introduction of slack variables.

In the form above, the *constraint set*, or set of points $(x_1, \ldots, x_m)$ satisfying the constraint conditions, can be shown to be a convex set—or more specifically, a convex polyhedron, having a finite number of extreme points or corners. It is not hard to see, intuitively, that a *linear* function must achieve its maximum (subject to the constraints) at an extreme point of the constraint set. In the case of two x's, for instance, the constraint set would be a convex polygon in the x_1x_2 plane, and the linear objective function $z = c_1x_1 + c_2x_2$ would be represented by a plane; the highest point on the plane within the cylinder defined by the constraint polygon is clearly on the boundary of the polygon, at a corner. For, if one thinks he has a maximum at some other point, he can clearly increase the value of z by moving a little in some direction but without leaving the constraint set.

This discussion suggests that the way to solve a linear programming problem is to locate the extreme points of the constraint polygon and to evaluate the objective function at each such point; the maximum such value would be the solution to the problem. Unfortunately, although this may be practical when the number of variables is quite small, it turns out to be impractical for real problems, owing to the rate at which the number of corners increases with the dimensions of the problem.

8.6 The Simplex Method

The *simplex technique* or *method*, devised by George Dantzig, is a scheme for locating the solution to a linear programming problem by checking, not all of the finitely many possible points described at the end of the preceding section, but an efficiently chosen subset of them—and doing it in an efficient sequence of steps. Since it is not the purpose here to give the student a mastery of the simplex technique, a procedure that is easily learned and easily forgotten, all that will be presented is the geometrical approach to the problem that gave rise to the name "simplex method" and that shows intuitively why it works. This approach will be explained with the aid of a specific problem rather than in generality.

Consider then the following linear programming problem: Maximize the linear function

$$w = u_1 + u_4 + 2u_5$$

subject to the constraints

$$\begin{cases} u_i \geq 0, & i = 1, \ldots, 5 \\ u_1 + u_2 + u_3 + u_4 + u_5 = 1 \\ 2u_1 + 2u_2 + 2u_5 = \dfrac{1}{2} \\ 2u_2 + u_3 + 2u_4 = 1. \end{cases}$$

This is not typical of the most general problem that might be encountered, having a constraint of a very special type, namely, that the u's add up to 1. This particular constraint is what makes the geometrical derivation possible, although the formal algorithm to which it leads is not so restricted.

It will be convenient to have some notation: Let P_i denote the column of coefficients of u_i in the constraint equations:

$$P_1 = \begin{pmatrix} 1 \\ 2 \\ 0 \end{pmatrix}, \quad P_2 = \begin{pmatrix} 1 \\ 2 \\ 2 \end{pmatrix}, \quad P_3 = \begin{pmatrix} 1 \\ 0 \\ 1 \end{pmatrix}, \quad P_4 = \begin{pmatrix} 1 \\ 0 \\ 2 \end{pmatrix}, \quad P_5 = \begin{pmatrix} 1 \\ 2 \\ 0 \end{pmatrix}$$

and let P_0 denote the column of right-hand members of those equations:

$$P_0 = \begin{pmatrix} 1 \\ 1/2 \\ 1 \end{pmatrix}.$$

The constraint conditions can then be written in terms of the P's:

$$u_1 P_1 + \cdots + u_5 P_5 = P_0.$$

Let Q_i's be defined from the P_i's by replacing the first element by the coefficient of u_i in the objective function, that is, the linear function of the u's being maximized:

$$Q_1 = \begin{pmatrix} 1 \\ 2 \\ 0 \end{pmatrix}, \quad Q_2 = \begin{pmatrix} 0 \\ 2 \\ 2 \end{pmatrix}, \quad Q_3 = \begin{pmatrix} 0 \\ 0 \\ 1 \end{pmatrix}, \quad Q_4 = \begin{pmatrix} 1 \\ 0 \\ 2 \end{pmatrix}, \quad Q_5 = \begin{pmatrix} 2 \\ 2 \\ 0 \end{pmatrix},$$

Then the point

$$Q = u_1 Q_1 + \cdots + u_5 Q_5$$

is a linear combination of $(Q_1, \ldots, Q_5)$ with probability coefficients, that is, a convex combination of the Q's. As such it lies in the convex set generated by the Q's, called a "polytope." Moreover, the coordinates of this convex combination Q are as follows:

$$Q = \begin{pmatrix} u_1 + u_4 + 2u_5 \\ 2u_1 + 2u_2 + 2u_5 \\ 2u_2 + u_3 + 2u_4 \end{pmatrix}$$

and what is being sought is a probability vector $(u_1, \ldots, u_5)$ such that the second coordinate of Q is $\frac{1}{2}$, the third coordinate is 1, and the first coordinate is as large as possible.

The condition that the second and third coordinates of a point in 3-space are fixed defines a line parallel to the axis of the first coordinate; what is wanted is a point on that line as far as possible in the positive direction of the first coordinate axis. Figure 8–3 shows (if one overlooks the inadequacies of a flat drawing of a three-dimensional figure) the polytope defined by the Q's of the present example, and the line L defined by $x_2 = \frac{1}{2}$ and $x_3 = 1$, where (x_1, x_2, x_3) are the coordinates being used in the representation. The first coordinate, x_1, is shown with its positive direction to the right, and what is wanted is the point on the line L that is as far to the right as possible but still in the set of convex combinations of the Q's. That point will clearly lie on the "simplex" defined by some one of the $\binom{5}{3} = 10$ combinations of three points chosen from the five Q's.

To locate that simplex containing the right-most point on line L, one selects arbitrarily some one simplex, and then by a process of replacing vertices one at a time, works his way across the polytope to the optimal simplex.

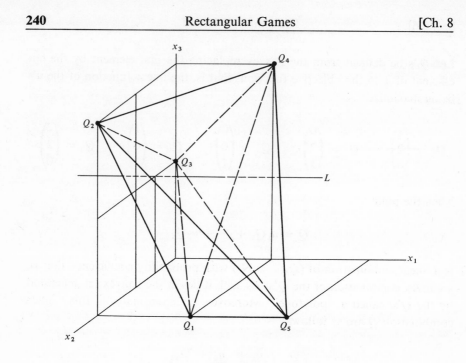

Figure 8–3

Consider, then, the selection Q_1, Q_2, and Q_3. The line L may or may not pass through the simplex defined by these Q's—and this is what is checked first. We look for τ_1, τ_2, τ_3, such that $\tau_1 + \tau_2 + \tau_3 = 1$, $\tau_i \geq 0$, and

$$\begin{pmatrix} x_1 \\ 1/2 \\ 1 \end{pmatrix} = \tau_1 Q_1 + \tau_2 Q_2 + \tau_3 Q_3 = \begin{pmatrix} \tau_1 \\ 2\tau_1 + 2\tau_2 \\ 2\tau_2 + \tau_3 \end{pmatrix}$$

Solving simultaneously the system

$$\begin{cases} \tau_1 + \tau_2 + \tau_3 = 1 \\ 2\tau_1 + 2\tau_2 = \dfrac{1}{2} \\ \phantom{2\tau_1 +{}} 2\tau_2 + \tau_3 = 1 \end{cases}$$

one obtains

$$\tau_1 = \frac{1}{8}, \qquad \tau_2 = \frac{1}{8}, \qquad \tau_3 = \frac{3}{4},$$

which are indeed nonnegative, and yield

$$x_1 = \tau_1 = \frac{1}{8};$$

this is the x_1 coordinate of the point in which L meets the simplex $Q_1Q_2Q_3$. These τ's can be interpreted as the first three u's, so that what has been found is a "feasible" solution: a set of u's that satisfy the constraints, but that do not necessarily maximize the objective function; that set is $(\frac{1}{8}, \frac{1}{8}, \frac{3}{4}, 0, 0)$ and the value of the objective function for these u's is $\frac{1}{8}$.

The remaining Q's, Q_4 and Q_5, can be checked to see whether they lie to the left or to the right of the plane determined by the first three Q's, whose points are all represented in the form

$$\sigma_1 Q_1 + \sigma_2 Q_2 + \sigma_3 Q_3, \quad \text{where } \sigma_1 + \sigma_2 + \sigma_3 = 1.$$

The line through Q_4 parallel to the x_1-axis (defined by $x_2 = 0$ and $x_3 = 2$) meets the above plane in that point for which

$$\begin{cases} \sigma_1 + \sigma_2 + \sigma_3 = 1 \\ 2\sigma_1 + 2\sigma_2 \qquad = 0 \\ \qquad 2\sigma_2 + \sigma_3 = 2, \end{cases}$$

which yields $\sigma_1 = -\frac{1}{2}$, $\sigma_2 = \frac{1}{2}$, $\sigma_3 = 1$. Since the x_1-coordinate of $-\frac{1}{2}Q_1 + \frac{1}{2}Q_2 + Q_3$ is $-\frac{1}{2}$, and of Q_4 is 1, Q_4 is to the right (that is, positive x_1-direction) of the plane. This means that the tetrahedron $Q_1Q_2Q_3Q_4$ lies to the right of the simplex $Q_1Q_2Q_3$ and therefore that some other face of the tetrahedron is pierced by the line L in a point with x_1-coordinate larger than $\frac{1}{8}$.

So the next step is to throw out one of the points Q_1, Q_2, Q_3 and replace it by Q_4. The question is, which one?

It has been seen that $(\frac{1}{8}, \frac{1}{8}, \frac{3}{4}, 0, 0)$ satisfies the constraints

$$P_0 = u_1 P_1 + \cdots + u_5 P_5,$$

so that

$$P_0 = \frac{1}{8} P_1 + \frac{1}{8} P_2 + \frac{3}{4} P_3.$$

The point P_4 can be represented as a linear combination of P_1, P_2, P_3:

$$P_4 = \alpha_1 P_1 + \alpha_2 P_2 + \alpha_3 P_3$$

or

$$\begin{pmatrix} 1 \\ 0 \\ 2 \end{pmatrix} = \alpha_1 \begin{pmatrix} 1 \\ 2 \\ 0 \end{pmatrix} + \alpha_2 \begin{pmatrix} 1 \\ 2 \\ 2 \end{pmatrix} + \alpha_3 \begin{pmatrix} 1 \\ 0 \\ 1 \end{pmatrix},$$

which condition is satisfied by

$$\alpha_1 = -\frac{1}{2}, \qquad \alpha_2 = \frac{1}{2}, \qquad \alpha_3 = 1.$$

To the expression above for P_0 is then added $-\theta P_4 + \theta P_4$, with the result

$$P_0 = \left[\frac{1}{8} - \theta\left(-\frac{1}{2}\right)\right]P_1 + \left[\frac{1}{8} - \theta\left(-\frac{1}{2}\right)\right]P_2 + \left[\frac{3}{4} - \theta\right]P_3 + \theta P_4.$$

One of these coefficients can be made 0, and the others kept nonnegative, by choosing θ to be the smallest positive ratio from among the various τ_i/α_i

$$\left\{\frac{1/8}{-1/2}, \ \frac{1/8}{1/2}, \ \frac{3/4}{1}\right\},$$

or $\theta = \frac{1}{4}$. Then

$$P_0 = \frac{1}{4}P_1 + 0 \cdot P_2 + \frac{1}{2}P_3 + \frac{1}{4}P_4.$$

This implies a new feasible solution, $(\frac{1}{4}, 0, \frac{1}{2}, \frac{1}{4}, 0)$, corresponding to the simple $Q_1 Q_3 Q_4$. That is, Q_2 is out and Q_4 has replaced it. The objective function has the value

$$u_1 + u_4 + 2u_5 = \frac{1}{4} + \frac{1}{4} = \frac{1}{2},$$

which is larger than its value on the simplex $Q_1 Q_2 Q_3$.

The location of Q_5 with respect to $Q_1 Q_3 Q_4$ can be checked as before; the line through Q_5 parallel to the x_1-axis meets the plane of Q_1, Q_3, Q_4 in the point $\rho_1 Q_1 + \rho_3 Q_3 + \rho_4 Q_4$ for which

$$\begin{cases} \rho_1 + \ \rho_2 + \rho_3 = 1 \\ 2\rho_1 + 2\rho_2 \qquad\ = 2 \\ \qquad\ 2\rho_2 + \rho_4 = 0, \end{cases}$$

which equations imply $\rho_1 = 1$, $\rho_2 = \rho_4 = 0$. That is, the x_1-coordinate is 1, compared with the x_1-coordinate of Q_5, which is 2; the point Q_5 is therefore to the right of the plane through Q_1, Q_3, Q_4, and a further increase in the objective function value is possible.

So Q_5 (and hence P_5) will enter and replace one of Q_1, Q_3, Q_4 (respectively P_1, P_3, P_4), as before. Starting with

$$P_0 = \frac{1}{4}P_1 + \frac{1}{2}P_3 + \frac{1}{4}P_4,$$

one adds and subtracts θP_5, where

$$P_5 = \beta_1 P_1 + \beta_3 P_3 + \beta_4 P_4,$$

or

$$\begin{cases} \beta_1 + \beta_3 + \beta_4 = 1 \\ 2\beta_1 \qquad\qquad = 2 \\ \qquad \beta_3 + 2\beta_4 = 0, \end{cases}$$

from which $\beta_1 = 1$, $\beta_3 = \beta_4 = 0$. The choice

$$\theta = \min\left\{\frac{1/4}{1}, \frac{1/2}{0}, \frac{1/4}{0}\right\} = \frac{1}{4}$$

yields

$$P_0 = 0P_1 + \frac{1}{2}P_3 + \frac{1}{4}P_4 + \frac{1}{4}P_5.$$

Thus, a new feasible solution is $(0, 0, \frac{1}{2}, \frac{1}{4}, \frac{1}{4})$, and the new value of $u_1 + u_4 + 2u_5$ is $\frac{3}{4}$. There are no more points to consider, and the process is finished. The desired maximum is $\frac{3}{4}$ and is achieved for $u_1 = 0$, $u_2 = 0$, $u_3 = \frac{1}{2}$, $u_4 = u_5 = \frac{1}{4}$.

The process described for the particular problem considered above can be adapted to the general linear programming problem. The essential computations are those of linear representations of points P_k in terms of a set of m P_i's, where m is the number of constraint equations; these are ordinarily given in the form of tables, or *simplex tableaus*, so constructed as to facilitate the determination of which P to throw out and which to replace it by, at each step.*

---

* The simplex technique is presented in numerous books entitled *Linear Programming*.

Problems

8–7 Set up the paper-scissors-stone game as a problem in linear programming. Verify that the solution of the game found in Example 8–6 provides "feasible solution" of the programming problem.

8–8 Brand A of a vitamin pill costs 5¢ each and contains 1 unit of vitamin B_1 and 5 units of vitamin B_2. Brand B costs 15¢ per pill, and each one contains 4 units of vitamin B_1 and 1 unit of vitamin B_2. Determine how many tablets of each brand to take in order to fulfill a requirement of 25 units of vitamin B_1 and 24 units of vitamin B_2 at the lowest possible cost.

Chapter 9 Sequential Procedures

The statistical procedures considered so far have been based on samples of fixed size. This was not always made perfectly explicit, yet it has been assumed that the number of observations to be obtained was to be fixed ahead of time, and that no decision would be reached before all of the planned observations were actually at hand. The size of the sample to be used may, indeed, be chosen by the statistician as part of the design of the experiment he will use as part of a decision procedure; but having specified the sample size, he does not change his mind during the course of (and as a result of) the sampling, as to how much data is needed.

Various considerations suggest that it may be possible to design better procedures if one is not restricted by the assumption of a fixed sample size. *Multi-stage* procedures are those in which, after each observation or group of observations, a decision is made as to whether to stop and make a decision at that point or to obtain more data. In the most general such procedure, one would also want the freedom to choose at each stage the experiment from which to obtain the next piece of data.

Suppose for instance, that one is designing an experiment in which the precision of the information it will yield depends on the inherent population variability, as well as on the sample size. For a specified degree of precision, one could specify the sample size if he knew the population variability, but in many practical situations this is not known—even approximately. In such a case it may be desirable to take a preliminary exploratory or pilot sample of small size, from which might be obtained a rough idea as to the population variability; with this approximate information one can presumably do a better job of picking an overall sample size for a given degree of precision, and so determine how many additional observations to take.

As another motivation for considering sampling in stages, suppose that observations are being obtained in sequential fashion, one after another, and that the observations are available and recorded as they are obtained. If the "early returns" suggest strongly that the decision is going to have to turn out to be made in a certain way, one is tempted to stop the sampling process and make the decision early—thereby saving the cost of the additional observations without appreciably sacrificing precision.

Example 9–1. A lot of 100 capillary tubes, to be used in the manufacture of electric freezers, is to be sampled to determine whether the average pressure drop between the two ends of the tube is at an acceptable level. Suppose that specified error sizes are such that a sample of size ten is indicated. Suppose further that as the tubes are tested, one by one, it is apparent that the first four, say, show a pressure drop considerably in excess of 130 pounds per square inch (the acceptable or desired level). At this point one might profitably conclude that the lot is not meeting specifications, and save the cost of completing the tests on all ten tubes of the sample.

When observations are not obtained and available sequentially, one after another (or one group after another), a multi-stage or sequential procedure is not possible. There are situations where the sequential generation of data would be most awkward, and certainly not worth the potential saving of a sequential procedure.

Example 9–2. Suppose it is desired to compare a new treatment for protection against a certain environment with an old, standard treatment. One of the countless illustrations of such problems is that of comparing a new paint for highway striping with an old one. The test procedure is to paint a stripe of the old and a stripe of the new, side by side at a certain point on a roadway, and to check on the relative wear after a period of several months. If (to increase the reliability) a sample of several such comparisons is needed, perhaps using different cans of each type of paint, and at different spots on the roadway, it is a simple matter to paint these several stripes at once, rather than wait for the results of the test on the first pair before painting the second pair, and so on. A sequential collection of data would drag out over many years.

The kind of multi-stage or sequential procedure to be considered here is that in which the same (predetermined) experiment is performed at each stage, or in which at least the variation of experiment from stage to stage is fixed ahead of time. An example of the latter type is the selection of one article at a time from a lot of articles for the determination of the acceptability of the lot. The experiment changes from draw to draw, since the population is reduced with each draw—but in a known way.

9.1 Basic Definitions

It will be assumed that there is a stream of potential observations X_1, X_2, ..., generally infinite, but sometimes finite, as in the case of sampling from a finite population. The distribution of each finite segment $(X_1, \ldots, X_k)$ of the stream will be assumed to be known, and to depend in a known way on the state of nature. In the simplest case the variables $X_1, \ldots, X_k$ will be independent observations from a fixed population, with joint density (or probability function, in the discrete case)

$$f_k(x_1, \ldots, x_k \mid \theta) = f(x_1 \mid \theta)f(x_2 \mid \theta)\cdots f(x_k \mid \theta),$$

where $f(x \mid \theta)$ is the "population" density (or probability) function.

An optimum decision procedure is one that would minimize the overall expected loss (or maximize the expected utility), as usual. But an ingredient of the loss structure in a sequential problem that is not encountered in the case of problems involving samples of fixed size is the cost of obtaining observations—the cost of sampling. This is not to say that sampling is necessarily free in the case of samples of fixed size, but rather that the cost of sampling in such a case is the same for all competing procedures; it disappears in the computation of the regret function. In the sequential case the cost of sampling must be added to the loss ordinarily associated with the consequences of taking a certain action. In general the cost of sampling would depend on the state of nature, on the number of observations, and possibly on the values of those observations

$$\text{Cost of obtaining } (X_1, \ldots, X_k) = C(\theta; k; X_1, \ldots, X_k).$$

The simplest kind of assumption that might be analyzed, and one that is quite realistic, is that the observations all cost the same amount to obtain, independent of the state of nature

$$\text{Cost of obtaining } (X_1, \ldots, X_k) = kC,$$

where C is a fixed constant. That is, the cost is proportional to the number of observations. This is the only cost function that will be considered in what follows.

The most general decision procedure can be quite complicated, involving a *stopping rule* and a *terminal decision rule*. As the terminology implies, the stopping rule says when to stop sampling, and the terminal decision rule says what action to take on the basis of the information contained in the data that are available at the time of stopping.

A *terminal decision rule* is simply a collection of decision rules of the type used in problems with samples of fixed size, that is, a family of functions $d_i(X_i, \ldots, X_i)$, each of which assigns one of the available actions to each possible outcome $(X_1, \ldots, X_i)$, given that i observations and only i observations are at hand. Thus, a terminal decision rule is

$$d = \{d_0, d_1(X_1), d_2(X_1, X_2), \ldots\},$$

where d_0 is of course not a function, but one of the available actions, as selected by the rule when no data is at hand.

A *stopping rule* can be characterized by a family of functions of the form

$$\varphi = \{\varphi_0, \varphi_1(X_1), \varphi_2(X_1, X_2), \ldots\},$$

where in the nonrandomized case

$$\varphi_0 = \begin{cases} 0, & \text{if and only if the rule says to take the first observation,} \\ 1, & \text{if and only if the rule says to take no observations,} \end{cases}$$

and

$$\varphi_k(X_1, \ldots, X_k) = \begin{cases} 0, & \text{if and only if the rule says to take another observation, given that } X_1, \ldots, X_k \text{ are at hand,} \\ 1, & \text{if and only if the rule says to take no more observations, given that } X_1, \ldots, X_k \text{ are at hand.} \end{cases}$$

That is, given the functions φ_k one can determine (from the stream of observations) when to stop; and if the rule is given in other terms, one can determine the functions φ_k from the rule.

Alternatively, a stopping rule can be characterized by the family of functions

$$s = \{s_0, s_1(X_1), s_2(X_1, X_2), \ldots\},$$

where

$$s_0 = \varphi_0,$$

and

$$s_k(X_1, \ldots, X_k)$$
$$= (1 - \varphi_0)[1 - \varphi_1(X_1)] \cdots [1 - \varphi_{k-1}(X_1, \ldots, X_{k-1})]\varphi_k(X_1, \ldots, X_k)$$

$$= \begin{cases} 0, & \text{if the rule either stopped the sampling prior to the } k\text{th} \\ & \text{observation or says to go on after it,} \\ 1, & \text{if the rule calls for stopping sampling for the first time at} \\ & X_k, \text{ given the stream } X_1, X_2, \ldots. \end{cases}$$

Again, given the functions s_k one can determine when to stop, and given the stopping rule one can write down the functions s_k.

The number of observations that are actually obtained, when following a given stopping rule, is a random variable, since it depends on the values of the observations obtained up to the time of stopping; call it N. Given a stream of observations $X_1, X_2, X_3, \ldots$, the function s_k gives the conditional probability that precisely k observations are called for:

$$P(N = k \mid X_1, X_2, \ldots) = s_k(X_1, \ldots, X_k).$$

And the probability of stopping at the kth observation, computed before any observations are known, is the expected value, as computed assuming a particular state φ and a particular stopping rule s:

$$P_{s,\varphi}(N = k) = E[s_N(X_1, \ldots, X_N)].$$

Incidentally, nothing so far would prevent $N = \infty$, but in applying sequential rules one would usually want a rule for which $P(N < \infty) = 1$.

Example 9–3. One important example of a sequential procedure is that defined by the following pair (s, d) of families of functions: Let A, B, and M be given constants, with $A < M < B$, and let $\Lambda_n = \Lambda_n(X_1, \ldots, X_n)$ denote the following likelihood ratio

$$\Lambda_n = \frac{f_0(X_1)f_0(X_2) \cdots f_0(X_n)}{f_1(X_1)f_1(X_2) \cdots f_1(X_n)},$$

where $f_0(x)$ and $f_1(x)$ are density (or probability) functions that characterize the two states of nature (H_0 and H_1, respectively) in a hypothesis-testing problem. Then define

$$d_n(X_1, \ldots, X_n) = \begin{cases} \text{reject } H_0 \text{ if } \Lambda_n < M \\ \text{accept } H_0 \text{ if } \Lambda_n \geq M. \end{cases}$$

Define further the functions φ_n as follows: let $\varphi_0 = 0$, and for $n > 0$,

$$\varphi_n(X_1, \ldots, X_n) = \begin{cases} 0, & \text{if } A < \Lambda_n < B, \\ 1, & \text{if } \Lambda_n \leq A \text{ or } \Lambda_n \geq B. \end{cases}$$

These φ's then lead to a family of s's, and the s's and d's, or (s, d), define a sequential decision procedure for the problem of testing a simple hypothesis against a simple alternative—but which can also be used for testing a composite, one-sided hypothesis against a composite, one-sided alternative.

9.2 Bayesian Procedures

Suppose that, apart from sampling costs, a loss of $L(\theta, a)$ is incurred when action a is taken and Nature is in state θ. If a sequence of observations $X_1, X_2, \ldots$, is available, for the drawing, at cost kC, for k observations, and if a sequential procedure (s, d) is used, the loss incurred will be

$$L(\theta, d_N(X_1, \ldots, X_N)) + NC,$$

where N is the random variable (with distribution determined by θ and the stopping rule s) whose value is the number of observations actually used in reaching a decision. The expected loss, or risk function, is then

$$R(\theta, (s, d)) = E[L(\theta, d_N(X_1, \ldots, X_N)) + NC],$$

and the Bayes risk for a prior $g(\theta)$ is obtained by a further averaging with respect to that prior

$$B(s, d) = E[R(\theta, (s, d))].$$

(It is usually by no means as simple actually to compute the indicated averages as it is to write them as indicated computations.)

An approach to finding the procedure—that is, the pair (s, d) which minimizes the Bayes risk—is to determine the minimizing d for each stopping rule, and then to choose the stopping rule that produces the overall minimum. The choice of stopping rule is almost never a simple matter, but the choice of the terminal decision rule is rather straightforward. The following theorem can be established by means of a judicious manipulation of conditional expectations. (Since this technique is not assumed here, the proof will not be given.)

THEOREM   *If s is a given stopping rule and $g(\theta)$ a given prior, then the Bayes risk $B(s, d)$ is minimized (for that s) by the decision rule $d_B = (d_{0B}, d_{1B}, d_{2B}, \ldots)$, where d_{iB} is the Bayes rule based on the first i observations considered as a sample of fixed size i.*

It is worth remarking that the minimizing d for a given s does not depend on the s. This is useful to know in cases where the stopping rule is not necessarily chosen optimally, perhaps being chosen by someone other than the statistician. Even in such cases one would want to choose a terminal decision rule d that minimizes $B(s, d)$ for whatever s has been used; and since the minimizing d is independent of s, he need not know what stopping rule was actually used.

Sometimes a sequential problem has but a finite number of stages. A limit to the number of stages may occur naturally, as when one runs out of data (which happens if one samples without replacement from a finite population), or it may be decreed arbitrarily, possibly as the result of practical considerations. When the number of stages is finite, the theorem above can be used in a process of backward induction to determine the stopping rule s_B that is part of the Bayes procedure (s_B, d_B) for a given prior distribution, as follows.

Suppose there are potentially n stages (and no more), corresponding to observations $X_1, \ldots, X_n$. If the Bayes rule (s_B, d_B) happens to call for taking all n observations in a particular application, the terminal decision is made (so says the theorem) according to the Bayes criterion; that is, the posterior distribution determined by the n observed values is applied to the given loss function to obtain averages in terms of which the available actions are ordered and the optimum one chosen. If the stopping rule s_B calls for at least $n - k$ observations, the question of whether to stop (and use the Bayes terminal decision for those observations) or to obtain more data is answered by comparing two conditional expected losses, given the values of the first $n - k$ observations: the conditional expected loss if only those observations are used, and the conditional expected loss (including costs for future observations as required) if one takes more observations and behaves optimally.

Having determined the optimum procedure for $k = 0$, the computations and comparison can be made for $k = 1$, so as to determine what is optimal among rules calling for at least $n - 1$ observations. Next the computations and comparison can be made for $k = 2$, to determine the optimum among rules calling for at least $n - 2$ observations, and so on. Since n is finite, the induction stops, and the Bayes rule is completely determined.

The following example, in the case of estimation, will illustrate the fact that a Bayesian procedure in a family of finite or truncated procedures, although theoretically relatively simple, may be rather involved and tedious to determine in a particular case. On the other hand, a Bayes sequential procedure that is not truncated sometimes becomes simple to describe and determine, although the theory is much deeper. This will be seen in the remaining sections of this chapter, in the case of the problem of testing a simple hypothesis versus a simple alternative.

Example 9–4. Consider the problem of estimating the parameter p of a Bernoulli population, with quadratic loss:

$$l(p, a) = 2400(p - a)^2,$$

given a uniform prior distribution on $0 \leq p \leq 1$, and using any or all of the finite sequence X_1, X_2, X_3 of independent observations, each observation costing 21 units of utility. It is desired to obtain the Bayes sequential estimator under these conditions. For the following computations it will be necessary to know that for a distribution for p defined by a beta density:

$$f(p; r, s) = (\text{const})p^r(1 - p)^s, \qquad 0 < p < 1,$$

the first few moments are as follows:

$$E(p) = \frac{r + 1}{r + s + 2}, \qquad E(p^2) = \frac{(r + 1)(r + 2)}{(r + s + 2)(r + s + 3)},$$

$$\text{var}(p) = \frac{(s + 1)(r + 1)}{(r + s + 2)^2(r + s + 3)},$$

$$E(p^3) = \frac{(r + 1)(r + 2)(r + 3)}{(r + s + 2)(r + s + 3)(r + s + 4)}.$$

Step 1. Suppose that *two* observations have been obtained (by following the Bayes rule), with the result $X_1 + X_2 = y$. Should the sampling stop, or should X_3 be obtained? The prior, for use at this stage, looking ahead to X_3, is the posterior after the first two observations, namely

$$g_2(p) = (\text{const})p^y(1 - p)^{2-y}, \quad 0 < p < 1.$$

The mean and variance of this distribution are respectively

$$E_{g_2}(p) = \frac{y+1}{4} \quad \text{and} \quad \text{var}_{g_2}(p) = \frac{(3-y)(y+1)}{80}.$$

A. NO MORE OBSERVATIONS: If X_3 is not obtained, the Bayes estimate is the mean of the distribution defined by $g_2(p)$, namely, $(y + 1)/4$, and the expected loss, given $X_1 + X_2 = y$, is proportional to the variance:

$$30(3 - y)(y + 1) = \begin{cases} 90, & \text{if } y = 0 \text{ or } 2, \\ 120, & \text{if } y = 1. \end{cases}$$

B. TAKE OBSERVATION x_3: The posterior distribution after X_3, given the prior $g_2(p)$, is the same as the posterior after (X_1, X_2, X_3), given the initial uniform prior, with $X_1 + X_2$ replaced by y; the Bayes estimate is the mean of this posterior distribution, $(y + X_3 + 1)/5$ and the conditional expected loss (including the cost of obtaining X_3) is

$$2400E_{g_2}\left\{(1 - p)\left(\frac{y+1}{5} - p\right)^2 + p\left(\frac{y+2}{5} - p\right)^2\right\} + 21$$

$$= 24(y + 1)(3 - y) + 21 = \begin{cases} 93, & \text{if } y = 0 \text{ or } 2, \\ 117, & \text{if } y = 1. \end{cases}$$

Since for $y = 0$ or 2 the latter is greater than the 90 that results when the third observation is not taken, one should *not* take X_3 if $X_1 + X_2 = 0$ or 2. But since $117 < 120$, one *should* take X_3 if $X_1 + X_2 = 1$.

Step 2. Suppose that *one* observation has been obtained (by following the Bayes rule), with the result $X_1 = z$. Again a comparison can be made to determine whether to stop and make the estimate based only on X_1 or to take more data. The prior distribution to be used in looking ahead is the posterior after X_1 is obtained, namely, that defined by the density

$$g_1(p) = 2p^z(1 -)p^{1-z}, \quad 0 < z < 1,$$

which has moments

$$E_{g_1}(p) = \frac{z+1}{3}, \qquad \text{var } p = \frac{(z+1)(2-z)}{36}, \qquad E_{g_1}(p^3) = \frac{z+1}{10}.$$

A. If no more observations are obtained, the Bayes estimate base on the one observation at hand is used, that is, $(z+1)/3$, and the expected loss (given $X_1 = z$) is proportional to the variance of the distribution g_1:

$$\text{Expected conditional loss} = 2400 \frac{(2-z)(z+1)}{36}$$

$$= \frac{400}{3}, \quad \text{for either } z = 0 \text{ or } z = 1.$$

B. If more observations are obtained, and if $X_1 = X_2$, the sampling should stop after the second observation—according to the result of Step 1. Thus, the possible sequences, if $X_1 = 0$, are as given here, with corresponding estimates and losses:

Sequence	Prob, given $X_1 = 0$	Estimate	Loss
0, 0	$1 - p$	$\frac{1}{4}$	$2400\left(\frac{1}{4} - p\right)^2 + 21$
0, 1, 1	p^2	$\frac{3}{5}$	$2400\left(\frac{3}{5} - p\right)^2 + 42$
0, 1, 0	$p(1 - p)$	$\frac{2}{5}$	$2400\left(\frac{2}{5} - p\right)^2 + 42$

The conditional expected loss is then

$$E(\text{Loss } X_1 = 0) = E_{g_1}\left\{2400\left(\frac{1}{4} - p\right)^2(1 - p) + \left(\frac{3}{5} - p\right)^2 p^2 \right.$$

$$\left. + \left(\frac{2}{5} - p\right)^2 p(1 - p) + 21(1 - p) + 42p\right)$$

$$= 120.$$

A similar computation for $X_1 = 0$ yields the same conditional expected loss, so that whatever the outcome of X_1, one should take more data, the conditional expected loss of proceeding being less (120) than that incurred by stopping ($\frac{400}{3}$).

Step 3. Suppose that *no* observations are at hand; should one take any data at all? The prior is now the initial prior, $g(p) = 1$ $(0 < p < 1)$, with $E(p) = \frac{1}{2}$, $E(p^2) = \frac{1}{3}$, and $E(p^3) = \frac{1}{4}$.

A. If no data are obtained, then the Bayes estimate is $\frac{1}{2}$, and the expected loss is

$$2400 E_{g_0}\left[\left(p - \frac{1}{2}\right)^2\right] = 200.$$

B. If at least one observation is taken, Steps 1 and 2 show how to proceed according to the Bayes procedure. In particular, they show that the sampling should not stop after one observation, but should stop after two observations if and only if they are equal. Thus, the sequences that might be obtained are as shown in the following table, together with the probabilities (given p), the estimates, and the corresponding losses (including sampling costs):

Sequence	Probability	Estimate	Loss
0, 0	$(1 - p)^2$	$\frac{1}{4}$	$2400\left(\frac{1}{4} - p\right)^2 + 42$
1, 1	p^2	$\frac{3}{4}$	$2400\left(\frac{3}{4} - p\right)^2 + 42$
0, 1, 0	$p(1 - p)^2$	$\frac{2}{5}$	$2400\left(\frac{2}{5} - p\right)^2 + 63$
0, 1, 1	$p^2(1 - p)$	$\frac{3}{5}$	$2400\left(\frac{3}{5} - p\right)^2 + 63$
1, 0, 0	$p(1 - p)^2$	$\frac{2}{5}$	$2400\left(\frac{2}{5} - p\right)^2 + 63$
1, 0, 1	$p^2(1 - p)$	$\frac{3}{5}$	$2400\left(\frac{3}{5} - p\right)^2 + 63$

Multiplying the losses by the probabilities, summing, and averaging with respect to the distribution of p defined by $g_0(p)$ yields expected loss, including sampling costs, of 157, which is less than 200. Thus, it pays to do some sampling.

In summary, the Bayes sequential procedure, among those using at most three observations, is to take two observations and stop sampling if they are equal, with the estimate $\frac{1}{4}$ if $X_1 = X_2 = 0$ and estimate $\frac{3}{4}$ if $X_1 = X_2 = 1$, but to obtain a third observation if $X_1 \neq X_2$, estimating p to be $\frac{2}{5}$ if the third observation is 0, and to be $\frac{3}{5}$ if it is 1.

9.3 Hypothesis Testing—One More Observation?

Consider now the problem of testing a simple hypothesis against a simple alternative, using a sequence of independent, identically distributed observations $X_1, X_2, \ldots$. The idea, encountered in the preceding section, of balancing the potential reduction in expected loss with the cost of the observation being considered, was introduced in Example 4–6. The first of the two following examples takes up that situation again.

Example 9–5. The regret table of Examples 4–1 through 4–6 (and earlier examples) was as follows:

	θ_1	θ_2
a_1	0	1
a_2	1	0

In Example 4–1 an observation Z was introduced, whose distributions under the two states of nature were used in Example 4–4 to obtain the following table of risks or expected regrets for the eight possible decision rules defined in Example 4–2:

	d_1	d_2	d_3	d_4	d_5	d_6	d_7	d_8
θ_1	1	.9	.7	.4	.6	.3	.1	0
θ_2	0	.5	.4	.1	.9	.6	.5	1

In Example 4–6 it was seen that without the observation Z the minimum Bayes regret for an assumed prior probability of .8 for θ_1 is 0.2, whereas by using one of the rules based on the observation Z one can reduce this to a minimum Bayes regret of 0.18. Clearly, if the observation costs more than 0.02 to obtain, it is not worth obtaining, since the total cost would be more, rather than less than what can be achieved without the observation. This same kind of computation can be performed for a more general prior distribution, defined by $g(\theta_1) = w$, $g(\theta_2) = 1 - w$. For this prior distribution the average expected regrets are as follows:

For d_1: $w + 0(1 - w) = w$,

for d_2: $.9w + .5(1 - w) = .5 + .4w$,

for d_3: $.7w + .4(1 - w) = .4 + .3w$,

for d_4: $.4w + .1(1 - w) = .1 + .3w$,

for d_5: $.6w + .9(1 - w) = .9 - .3w$,

for d_6: $.3w + .6(1 - w) = .6 - .3w$,

for d_7: $.1w + .5(1 - w) = .5 - .4w$,

for d_8: $0w + 1(1 - w) = 1 - w$.

These are plotted in Figure 9–1, and for each w the minimum of these is a point on the heavy broken line, representing the minimum Bayes risk, $\rho(w)$. The total cost, if one does make the observation Z and use it according to the Bayes principle, is the minimum Bayes risk $\rho(w)$ plotted in Figure 9–1 plus the cost of obtaining the observation Z. That total cost is shown in Figure 9–2 for the case in which the cost of the observation Z is 0.1. Also shown in

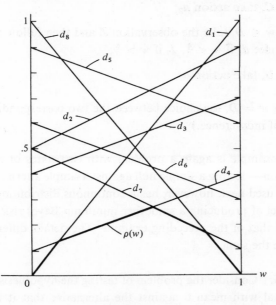

Figure 9–1

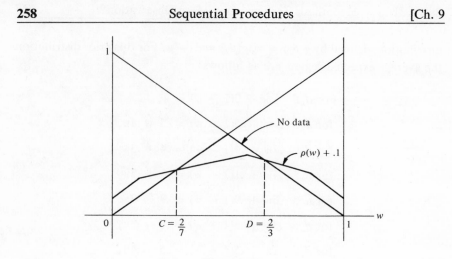

Figure 9–2

that figure is the minimum Bayes regret when the observation is not taken, namely, the minimum of the regret $1 - w$ for action a_1 and the regret w for action a_2. Notice that for some prior distributions (that is, for some values of w) the total cost is less if no observation is taken, but that for others the reverse is true. The Bayes procedure for this simple problem is therefore as follows:

(1)   If $w \le C$, take action a_2;

(2)   if $C \le w \le D$, take the observation Z and then follow the appropriate Bayes rule: d_4 if $w < \frac{4}{7}$, d_7 if $w > \frac{4}{7}$;

(3)   if $w \ge D$, take action a_1.

(If $w = C$ or $w = D$, the choice between the two corresponding possibilities is a matter of indifference.)

The next example is again a problem with two states of nature and two possible actions—testing a simple null against a simple alternative hypothesis. The statistic used next, however, has a continuous distribution; and this will have the effect of producing a smoother minimum Bayes risk curve, in comparison with that of the preceding example. The details differ, but the basic result will be the same.

Example 9–6.   Consider the problem of testing the hypothesis that a population is normal with mean 0 against the alternative that it is normal with mean 2, the variance being 1 in both cases. The actions are A, to accept H_0, and B, to reject H_0, with regrets as in the following table (in which a and b are positive constants):

	H_0	H_1
A	0	a
B	b	0

With no data, the Bayes action is chosen on the basis of the Bayes risks

$$\begin{cases} B_w(A) = a(1 - w), \\ B_w(B) = bw. \end{cases}$$

The minimum of these determines the proper action, as usual.

But now suppose that an observation from the population is being contemplated, at a certain cost. The cost of observation being fixed, the Bayes decision rule for a given observation is the one that minimizes the Bayes risk, namely the likelihood ratio rule:

$$\begin{cases} \text{Reject } H_0 \text{ if } \dfrac{f_0}{f_1} < \dfrac{a(1 - w)}{bw}, \\ \text{accept } H_0, \text{ otherwise,} \end{cases}$$

(as in Section 5.6), where f_i denotes the density of the observation under H_i. Since

$$\frac{f_0}{f_1} = \frac{e^{-x^2/2}}{e^{-(x-2)^2/2}} = e^{2-2x},$$

the inequality for rejecting H_0 can be expressed in terms of x, as

$$x > 1 - \frac{1}{2}\log\frac{a}{b} + \frac{1}{2}\log\frac{w}{1-w} \equiv K(w).$$

(For example, if $a(1 - w) = bw$, act as though the mean is 0 if the observation is closer to 0 than to 2, otherwise to act as though the mean is 2.) The minimum Bayes risk for given $w = g(H_0)$, which implies the rejection limit $K(w)$, is then

$$\rho(w) \equiv bw\alpha + a\beta(1 - w)$$

$$= bw[1 - \Phi(K)] + a(1 - w)\Phi(K - 2),$$

where $\Phi(z)$ is the probability distribution function given in Table A-1. The values of this function for the case $a = 2$ and $b = 1$ are in part as shown in the following table:

w	$K(w)$	$1 - \Phi(K)$	$\Phi(K - 2)$	$\rho(w)$
.1	-1.544	.939	0	.09
.3	-.194	.577	.014	.193
.5	.16	.16	.16	.24
.7	1.5	.069	.3085	.233
.9	2.85	.0022	.8023	.162
.95	3.6	0	.945	.0945

The total cost of taking an observation and using the Bayes rule for that observation is the value of $\rho(w)$ plus the cost of the observation; this total is also the minimum of the sum of the observation cost plus the Bayes risk taken over arbitrary rules that use one observation. The minimum Bayes risk, over all rules that use *either* no observations or one observation, is again found graphically: Figure 9–3 shows $\rho(w)$ with zero cost of observation, and also with two other constant costs of observation; shown also are the Bayes regrets for procedures using no observations. In one case, the cost of an observation is so high that the minimum average risk is obtained by using procedures with no observations, that is, reject H_0 or accept it according as the prior w is smaller or larger than M. For a more moderate cost, there is again a region where it pays to sample. The Bayes rule for that situation is as follows:

(1) If $w \leq C$, reject H_0, with no observation;

(2) if $C \leq w \leq D$, take the observation and use the appropriate Bayes rule;

(3) if $w \geq D$, accept H_0, with no observation.

The examples above are typical of the situation in a general problem of testing a simple null hypothesis against a simple alternative. The function $\rho(w)$, the minimum Bayes risk not counting the cost of the additional observation, is a concave function of w which is zero for $w = 0$ and for $w = 1$. The comparison of that function plus a constant cost for the observation with the minimum Bayes regret for the no data situation yields a rule of the same form as that encountered in the examples: Make a decision without taking the observation if $w > C$ or $w < D$, but take the observation (and then follow the usual Bayes rule) if $C \leq w \leq D$.

The argument above can also be adapted for the study of a sequential problem in which at most $n + 1$ steps are permitted, and in particular to

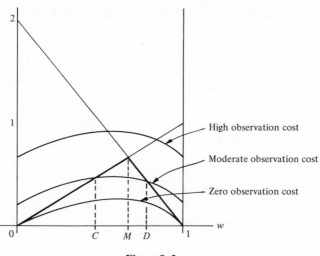

Figure 9–3

determine the Bayes procedures in the class of procedures requiring either n or $n + 1$ steps. Thus, suppose one considers only stopping rules that called for taking at least n observations; if such a stopping rule is to be part of a Bayes procedure, the associated terminal decision rule, wherever the sampling stops, is an ordinary (fixed sample size) Bayes decision rule. For stopping rules that call for exactly n observations, with a terminal decision at that point, the decision rule (being Bayesian) is obtained by applying the posterior probabilities for H_0 and H_1 directly to the original regret table. Thus, if at least n observations (and at most $n + 1$) are assumed, one is in almost exactly the same position as in the examples above, namely, that of deciding whether to make a decision with no (further) observations, or to take one (more) observation and then choose an action; the difference is simply that in place of the prior w of those examples one now uses the posterior probabilities based on the first n observations.

Given the data vector $Z = (X_1, \ldots, X_n)$, that is, the first n observations, and the original prior probabilities $w = P(H_0)$ and $1 - w = P(H_1)$, the posterior probabilities $w = P(H_0)$ and $1 - w = P(H_1)$, the posterior probabilities (as calculated in Section 5.6) are

$$\begin{cases} h_0 = \dfrac{wf_0(z)}{p(z)} \\[2mm] h_1 = \dfrac{(1 - w)f_1(z)}{p(z)}, \end{cases}$$

where $f_i(z)$ denotes the probability function (or density function) of the data Z and

$$p(z) = wf_0(z) + (1 - w)f_1(z).$$

The inequality that determines whether or not the $(n + 1)$st observation is to be taken, namely $C < h_0 < D$, where C and D are determined as in Examples 9–5 and 9–6, can be expressed in terms of the likelihood ratio, upon substitution for the posterior probability h_0:

$$C < \frac{wf_0(z)}{wf_0(z) + (1 - w)f_1(z)} < D.$$

Turning this upside down yields

$$\frac{1}{C} < 1 + \frac{1 - w}{w}\frac{f_1(z)}{f_0(z)} < \frac{1}{D},$$

or, in terms of $\Lambda_n = f_0(z)/f_1(z)$

$$A < \Lambda_n < B,$$

where

$$A = \frac{1 - w}{w}\frac{C}{1 - C}, \qquad B = \frac{1 - w}{w}\frac{D}{1 - D}.$$

Thus, among procedures calling for either n or $n + 1$ observations, the Bayes procedure is as follows: Calculate the likelihood ratio based on n observations; if it falls in the interval from A to B, take one more observation and use the Bayes test for $n + 1$ observations. If the likelihood ratio for the n observations is less than A, reject H_0; if it exceeds B, accept H_0 without taking the $(n + 1)$st observation.

The backwards induction process, outlined in the preceding section, could be used in principle to obtain the Bayes procedure in the class of sequential tests using at most $n + 1$ observations. One would find, it turns out, that the graph used to determine the "C" and "D" at each stage (and hence the "A" and the "B") is again concave down—so that the constants can be determined as above, but that this curve is different at each stage. This is to be expected, since the additional information potentially available from future observations, at each stage, becomes less and less as the number of future observations decreases. So the process is rather involved and will not be carried out here.

9.4 The Bayes Sequential Test—Two Actions

The availability of a potentially infinite stream of identically distributed observations, upon which to base a sequential test of a simple hypothesis against a simple alternative, makes it easier to determine the form of the Bayes procedure than it is when the problem is truncated. At least such is the case if the Bayes stopping rule can be determined, stage by stage, by comparing at each stage the conditional expected loss involved in stopping at that point with the conditional expected loss incurred by taking more observations. It turns out that this is correct, but not at all simple to prove.

The simplification of having a potentially infinite supply of observations lies in the fact that at every stage the future looks exactly as it does at every other stage! Hence, the conditional expected loss, given the observations already at hand, is exactly the same function of the corresponding posterior probabilities at each stage. Those posterior probabilities, of course, will depend on the observations already at hand, but the observations at hand enter the decision process only through the posterior distribution.

First will be considered the problem of whether to take any observations at all. The approach will be essentially that used in Example 9–6, except that the alternative to no sampling is now *at least one*, rather than *exactly* one observation. For a given procedure (s, d), where s is a stopping rule and d is a terminal decision rule, and for given losses a and b corresponding respectively to erroneous acceptance and erroneous rejection of the null hypothesis, the expected loss is

$$R(\theta; s, d) = \begin{cases} b\alpha + cE(N \mid H_0) \equiv R_0, & \text{if } \theta = H_0 \\ a\beta + cE(N \mid H_1) \equiv R_1, & \text{if } \theta = H_1, \end{cases}$$

where α and β are the usual error sizes (see Section 5.6), where c is the cost per observation, and where N is the number of observations used in making a decision (according to the stopping rule and the particular sequence of observations encountered). The quantities denoted by R_0 and R_1 depend on the procedure, (s, d). If one assumes a given prior distribution, as defined by the probability w assigned to H_0, the Bayes risk is

$$B_w(s, d) = wR_0 + (1 - w)R_1,$$

and the Bayes procedure (s_B, d_B) is the one that minimizes this quantity over all procedures (s, d). (It will be assumed that such a minimizing procedure exists).

If no observations are permitted by the stopping rule s, the minimum Bayes risk is just its value when the no-data Bayes procedure is used:

$$\rho_0(w) = \min_{\substack{\text{(no data rules)}}} B_w(s, d) = \begin{cases} bw, & \text{if } w \le \dfrac{a}{a + b}, \\ a(1 - w), & \text{if } w > \dfrac{a}{a + b}. \end{cases}$$

This is the sort of thing obtained in Chapter 3 (Example 3–10, Figure 3–9); the graph is shown in Figure 9–4, the heavy line representing $\rho_0(w)$.

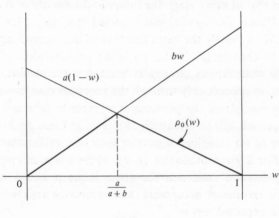

Figure 9–4

Consider next the class $\mathscr{C}_1$ of rules calling for at least one observation, and denote by $\rho_1(w)$ the minimum Bayes risk in this class:

$$\rho_1(w) = \min_{\mathscr{C}_1} [wR_0 + (1 - w)R_1].$$

The graph of this function of w will be somewhat as shown in Figure 9–5, having the properties:

(a) $\rho_1(w) \ge c,$

(b) $\rho_1(0) = \rho_1(1) = c,$

(c) the graph of $\rho_1(w)$ is concave down.

Property (a) is a result of the requirement that at least one observation, at cost c, must be taken. Property (b) follows from the fact that if the prior is

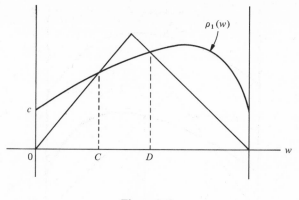

Figure 9–5

as strong as $w = 0$ or $w = 1$, no amount of sampling will alter the distribution, so the cost is just c plus the 0 of the no-data curve at those values of w. Property (c) is clear intuitively, since the curve $\rho_1(w)$ is the lower envelope of a family of line segments joining pairs of points $(0, R_0)$ and $(1, R_1)$. (For each procedure (s, d) the function $B_w(s, d)$ is such a line segment.) The concavity can also be established more formally, as follows: Take any two points w' and w'' between 0 and 1, and consider the value of $\rho_1(w)$ at the intermediate point $\lambda w' + (1 - \lambda)w''$, where $0 < \lambda < 1$:

$$\rho_1(\lambda w' + (1 - \lambda)w'')$$

$$= \min_{\mathscr{C}} \{(\lambda w' + (1 - \lambda)w'')R_0 + (1 - \lambda w' - (1 - \lambda)w'')R_1\}$$

$$= \min_{\mathscr{C}} \{\lambda(w'R_0 + (1 - w')R_1) + (1 - \lambda)(w'' + (1 - w'')R_1)\}$$

$$= \min_{\mathscr{C}} \{\lambda B_{w'}(s, d) + (1 - \lambda)B_{w''}(s, d)\}$$

$$\geq \lambda \rho_1(w') + (1 - \lambda)\rho_1(w'').$$

This shows that the graph of ρ_1 at the intermediate point is higher than the chord between the points corresponding to w' and w''. (It was essential in obtaining the inequality to know that the minimum of a sum is at least as great as the sum of the minima.)

Now that the properties of $\rho_0(w)$ and $\rho_1(w)$ are established, a general comparison of these functions can be made graphically, as in Figure 9–6, in which the two curves are plotted on common axes, for two values of c. Now, either the cost c is so large that the graph of $\rho_1(w)$ lies entirely above that of $\rho_0(w)$—in which case one would take no observations at all, or there are precisely

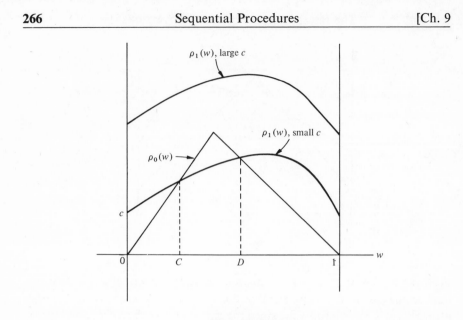

Figure 9–6

two points of intersection. Denote by C and D the abscissas of the two points of intersection, in the interesting case in which some observations may be worth while. It is clear that if $C < w < D$, the first observation, at least, should be taken, whereas if $w < C$ or $w > D$, no observations should be taken.* In the latter case, of course, the action to be taken is according to the Bayes rule for the no-data problem: reject H_0 if $w < C$ and accept H_0 if $w > D$.

Suppose next that n observations have been taken; the question is whether to take any more observations or to stop and make a decision with only the information in the n observations at hand. It is observed now that the problem is precisely as it was at the beginning, except that in place of a prior probability w there is a posterior probability h_n corresponding to the observations $X_1, \ldots, X_n$ (and to the prior w). Thus, the analysis made at the outset, to determine whether or not to take any observations at all, is applicable here, intact, except for the change of w to h_n. Moreover, exactly as in the discussion of the preceding section (following Example 9–6), the inequality $C < h_n < D$, which is the condition for continuing with the sampling, can be expressed in terms of the likelihood ratio for the first n observations:

$$A < \Lambda_n < B,$$

* If $w = C$ or $w = D$, it doesn't matter whether observations are taken or not.

where

$$A = \frac{1 - w}{w} \frac{C}{1 - C}, \quad \text{and} \quad B = \frac{1 - w}{w} \frac{D}{1 - D}.$$

The Bayes sequential procedure can thus be summarized in the following steps:

(1) Given losses a and b, and cost c per observation, determine from the graphs of $\rho_0(w)$ and $\rho_1(w)$ the values of C and D, as in Figure 9–5. (If $\rho_1(w) \geq \rho_0(w)$ for all w, let $C = D = a/(a + b)$.)

(2) If $w \leq C$, reject H_0, and if $w \geq D$, accept H_0; otherwise begin sampling, and determine A and B (from C and D and w) as above.

(3) After each observation X_n determine the corresponding likelihood ratio Λ_n for $X_1, \ldots, X_n$; if $\Lambda_n \leq A$, reject H_0, and if $\Lambda_n \geq B$, accept H_0. If $A < \Lambda_n < B$, take another observation.

The flaw, perhaps all too obvious, in this procedure, is that the function $\rho_1(w)$ is not generally known. On the other hand, it has been seen that because of the characteristics of $\rho_1(w)$, the *form* of the Bayes sequential procedure must be as given.

9.5 The Classical Sequential Likelihood Ratio Test

The sequential likelihood ratio test (SLRT), sometimes called the sequential probability ratio test (SPRT), for testing a simple hypothesis H_0 against a simple alternative H_1, is usually defined outside the framework of decision theory, as follows. For a test that is to achieve error sizes α and β, define constants

$$A = \frac{\alpha}{1 - \beta}, \qquad B = \frac{1 - \alpha}{\beta},$$

and use these as limits for the likelihood ratio Λ_n computed after each observation is taken. If $\Lambda_n \leq A$, the sampling stops and the null hypothesis is rejected; if $\Lambda_n \geq B$, the sampling stops and the null hypothesis is accepted. If $A < \Lambda_n < B$, another observation is taken. The test assumes the availability of observations $X_1, X_2, \ldots$, and that at least one observation is taken. It can be shown that although the error sizes actually achieved with the test are not exactly those specified, they are close enough for practical purposes.

Example 9–7. Suppose it is desired to test between $H_0: p = .5$ and $H_1: p = .7$ with specified error sizes $\alpha = .05$ and $\beta = .10$. The inequality for continuing sampling is then defined by the constants

$$A = \frac{.05}{1 - .10} = \frac{1}{18} \qquad B = \frac{1 - .05}{.10} = 9.5.$$

After n observations the likelihood ratio is

$$\Lambda_n = \left(\frac{.5}{.7}\right)^k \left(\frac{.5}{.3}\right)^{n-k}$$

and the value of Λ_{n+1} can be obtained from Λ_n by multiplying in the factor $\frac{5}{7}$ if the $(n + 1)$st observation is success, or the factor $\frac{5}{3}$ if it is failure. Thus, if a sequence of observations is as follows: $H, T, T, H, H, H, T, T, H, H, T, T, T, H, H, T, T, T, H, H, \ldots$, the first few Λ's are

$$\Lambda_1 = \frac{5}{7} \qquad \Lambda_2 = \frac{5}{7}\frac{5}{3} \qquad \Lambda_3 = \frac{5}{7}\frac{5}{3}\frac{5}{3} \qquad \Lambda_4 = \frac{5}{7}\frac{5}{3}\frac{5}{3}\frac{5}{7}, \ldots$$

Continuing in this manner one would find $\Lambda_{18} = 11$, which exceeds 9.5 (for the first time in the sequence), and so after eighteen observations $p = .5$ is accepted in preference to $p = .7$. (The remaining two observations given need not be obtained, of course.)

The computations, as the sampling proceeds, can be made a little less tedious by rewriting the inequality for continuing sampling in terms of some simpler statistic, in many cases. In testing a probability p_0 against an alternative probability p_1 for the Bernoulli model, with

$$\Lambda_n = \left(\frac{p_0}{p_1}\right)^k \left(\frac{1 - p_0}{1 - p_1}\right)^{n-k}$$

the inequality can be expressed in terms of k, the number of successes. This is done by taking the logarithms of each term in the inequality (which preserves the order):

$$\log A < k \log \frac{p_0}{p_1} + (n - k) \log \frac{1 - p_0}{1 - p_1} < \log B,$$

and manipulating further to obtain, for $p_0 > p_1$,

$$\frac{\log A - n \log \dfrac{1 - p_0}{1 - p_1}}{\log \dfrac{p_0}{p_1} - \log \dfrac{1 - p_0}{1 - p_1}} < k < \frac{\log B - n \log \dfrac{1 - p_0}{1 - p_1}}{\log \dfrac{p_0}{p_1} - \log \dfrac{1 - p_0}{1 - p_1}}.$$

The extremes of this extended inequality are linear functions of n, easily computed and graphed once and for all at the beginning of the test; the value of k can then be plotted as the test proceeds, and when it strays outside the region between the two straight lines, the test stops, the decision depending on which line is crossed. In case $p_0 < p_1$, the inequalities above are reversed.

Example 9–8.   Consider the problem of Example 9–7 above. Since $p_0 = .5$ and is less than $p_1 = .7$, the inequality for continued sampling is

$$\frac{\log 18}{\log \left(\dfrac{7}{3}\right)} + n \frac{\log \left(\dfrac{5}{3}\right)}{\log \left(\dfrac{7}{3}\right)} > k > -\frac{\log 9.5}{\log \left(\dfrac{7}{3}\right)} + n \frac{\log \left(\dfrac{5}{3}\right)}{\log \left(\dfrac{7}{3}\right)}$$

or

$$3.41 + .603n > k > -2.63 + .603n.$$

The graphs of the linear functions of n in the extremes of this inequality are shown (as though n were continuous) in Figure 9–7, along with a record of the number of successes as given in the sequence of outcomes of Example 9–7. Notice that the lower line (corresponding to the right member of the above inequality) is crossed with the eighteenth observation, calling for acceptance of $H_0(p = .5)$ at that point in the sequence.

  Carrying out a sequential test such as above, one might well wonder whether in some cases the test might never terminate, with Λ_n remaining indefinitely between A and B. It was shown by A. Wald, in his pioneering book *Sequential Analysis* (John Wiley and Sons, 1947), that the test will terminate with probability one. Moreover, the number of observations required to reach a decision (a random variable) has an expected value that is usually less than needed for a test with comparable detecting power based on a fixed sample size. In individual cases, of course, a sequential test *can* require a great many observations.

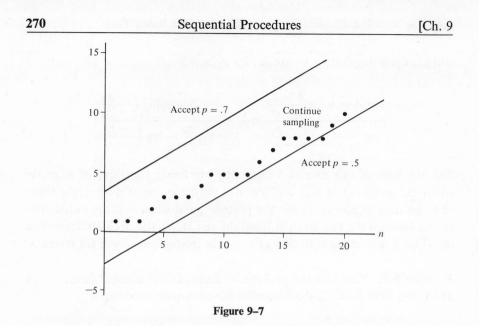

Figure 9–7

It can be shown that the expected number n of observations required for a decision using a sequential likelihood ratio test is

$$E(n) = \frac{E(\log \Lambda_n)}{EZ},$$

where Z is the logarithm of the likelihood ratio for a single observation, and where the numerator is given approximately by

$$E(\log \Lambda_n) \doteq (\log A)P(\text{reject } H_0) + (\log B)P(\text{accept } H_0).$$

For the Bernoulli population, given the observation x,

$$\log \frac{L(p_0 \mid x)}{L(p_1 \mid x)} = \log \left(\frac{p_0}{p_1}\right)^x \left(\frac{1 - p_0}{1 - p_1}\right)^{1-x}$$

$$= x \log \frac{p_0(1 - p_1)}{p_1(1 - p_0)} + \log \frac{1 - p_0}{1 - p_1},$$

for $x = 0, 1$. This function of x defines a function of the Bernoulli random variable X, and this is what was called Z above. Thus

$$EZ = p \log \frac{p_0(1 - p_1)}{p_1(1 - p_0)} + \log \frac{1 - p_0}{1 - p_1}.$$

Example 9-9. Referring again to the situation in Examples 9–7 and 9–8 one finds the following expected sample sizes. Under H_0,

$$E_{H_0}(n) \doteq \frac{-.05 \log 18 + .95 \log 9.5}{.5 \log \left(\frac{3}{7}\right) + \log \left(\frac{5}{3}\right)} \doteq 26,$$

and under H_1,

$$E_{H_1}(n) \doteq \frac{-.9 \log 18 + .1 \log 9.5}{.7 \log \left(\frac{3}{7}\right) + \log \left(\frac{5}{3}\right)} \doteq 31.$$

It is of interest to observe that for a sample of fixed size 26 and an α of .05, the corresponding β is .173, considerably larger than the .10 of the above sequential test.

The sequential likelihood ratio test is constructed for testing p_0 against p_1, given the desired sizes of the type I and type II errors. But as in the case of fixed-size tests, the test constructed for choosing between two simple hypotheses can also be used in testing between composite hypotheses in the one-sided case: $p \leq p^*$ versus $p > p^*$. The power function of the test defined by the inequality $A < \Lambda_n < B$ (as the criterion for continuing the sampling), although nontrivial to derive, can easily be roughly sketched using five points, as follows. First, of course, it should be realized that the notation Λ_n has been used as denoting the likelihood ratio corresponding to p-values p_0 and p_1. What is usually done is to select arbitrarily a p_0 in H_0 ($p \leq p^*$) and a p_1 in H_1 ($p > p^*$) and to specify α and β such that

$$\begin{cases} \alpha = P(\text{reject } H_0 \mid p_0) \\ \beta = P(\text{accept } H_0 \mid p_1). \end{cases}$$

The power function $\pi(p)$ of the test so specified has these* values

$$\pi(0) = 0,$$
$$\pi(1) = 1,$$
$$\pi(p_0) = \alpha,$$
$$\pi(p_1) = 1 - \beta,$$
$$\pi(p_2) = \frac{\log B}{\log B - \log A},$$

---

* The derivation of these results can be found in B. W. Lindgren, *Statistical Theory* (2nd ed.), Macmillan, 1968.

where

$$p_2 = -\frac{\log\left[\frac{(1 - p_0)}{(1 - p_1)}\right]}{\log\left(\frac{p_0}{p_1}\right) - \log\left[\frac{(1 - p_0)}{(1 - p_1)}\right]}.$$

Example 9–10. If it is desired to conduct a sequential test between $p \leq .6$ and $p > .6$, one might specify that the test is to reject $p \leq .6$ with probability .05 when $p = .5$ and to accept $p \leq .6$ with probability .10 when $p = .7$. This reduces the problem to that of Example 9–7, 9–8, and 9–9, with $p_0 = .5$, $p_1 = .7$, $\alpha = .05$, and $\beta = .10$. The power function of the test for this situation, as given in Example 8-h, has the values $\pi(0) = 0$, $\pi(1) = 1$, $\pi(.5) = .05$, $\pi(.7) = .90$; for the fifth point, in the above notation,

$$p_2 = \frac{\log \frac{5}{3}}{\log\left(\frac{5}{3}\right) - \log\left(\frac{5}{7}\right)} = .603,$$

and

$$\pi(p_2) = \frac{\log 9.5}{\log 9.5 - \log\left(\frac{1}{18}\right)} = .438.$$

Figure 9–8 shows the power function as sketched from these five points on its graph.

The SLRT looks very much like the Bayes sequential procedure defined in the preceding section. The essential difference is that there is no zero stage in the SLRT, with the possibility of making a decision with no data at all,

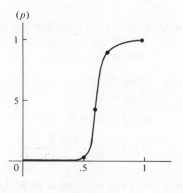

Figure 9–8

because a specific loss structure is not assumed. It can be shown, however, that given any SLRT (which means: given any constants A and B with $A < 1 < B$), there exist losses a and b and a sampling cost c per observation such that the Bayes sequential test for some prior distribution (and, in particular, one that permits the sampling to begin) is precisely the given SLRT.

In a sense, then, the family of SLRT's has an optimality property, but it is not really clear how to pick a test from this family. In the classical approach, without expressed losses and prior probabilities, one can achieve arbitrarily small error sizes—but only at the expense of increasing the expected sample size; there is no clear way to balance these competing factors. In the decision theoretic approach one can balance the losses and the cost of sampling—but only by means of the relationship provided by the function $\rho_1(w)$, which may not be readily obtainable.

Problems

9–1 Toss a coin repeatedly to test between $p = .5$ and $p = .7$ with the aid of the graph given in Example 9-8 (Let $p = P(\text{Heads})$.)

9–2 How many tosses would be required to make the decision between $p = .5$ and $p = .7$, if the coin used has two Heads? Two Tails?

9–3 Construct the sequential likelihood ratio test for $H_0:P = .5$ against $H_1:p = .1$, using $\alpha = \beta = .2$. Use a coin to carry out the test, with $p = P(\text{Heads})$. Carry out the test again using a die, with $p = P(1 \text{ or } 2)$.

9–4 Determine the expected number of trials necessary to reach a decision in Problem 9-3, under H_0 and under H_1.

9–5 Sketch the power function for the test of Problem 9-3 using the five point method illustrated in Example 9-10. (Because $p_1 < p_0$, it is necessary to make slight changes: $\pi(0) = 1, \pi(1) = 0$.)

References

Blackwell, D., and M. A. Girshicck, *Theory of Games and Statistical Decisions*, Wiley, New York, 1954.

Chernoff, H., and L. Moses, *Elementary Decision Theory*, Wiley, New York, 1959.

De Groot, Morris H., *Optimal Statistical Decisions*, McGraw-Hill, New York, 1970.

Ferguson, T. S., *Mathematical Statistics*, Academic Press, New York, 1967.

Lehmann, E. L., *Testing Statistical Hypotheses*, Wiley, New York, 1959.

McKinsey, J. C. C., *Introduction to the Theory of Games*, McGraw-Hill, New York, 1952.

von Neumann, J., and O. Morgenstern, *Theory of Games and Economic Behaviour* (3rd ed), Princeton U. Press, Princeton, N.J., 1944.

Savage, L. J., *The Foundations of Statistics*, Wiley, New York, 1954.

Wald, A., *Sequential Analysis*, Wiley, New York, 1947.

Wald, A., *Statistical Decision Functions*, Wiley, New York, 1950.

Appendix—Tables

Table A–1. Values of the Standard Normal Distribution Function

$$\Phi(z) = \int_{-\infty}^{z} \frac{1}{\sqrt{2\pi}} e^{-u^2/2} \, du = P(Z \le z)$$

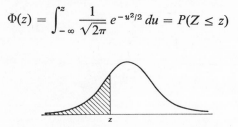

z	0	1	2	3	4	5	6	7	8	9
− 3.	.0013	.0010	.0007	.0005	.0003	.0002	.0002	.0001	.0001	.0000
− 2.9	.0019	.0018	.0017	.0017	.0016	.0016	.0015	.0015	.0014	.0014
− 2.8	.0026	.0025	.0024	.0023	.0023	.0022	.0021	.0021	.0020	.0019
− 2.7	.0035	.0034	.0033	.0032	.0031	.0030	.0029	.0028	.0027	.0026
− 2.6	.0047	.0045	.0044	.0043	.0041	.0040	.0039	.0038	.0037	.0036
− 2.5	.0062	.0060	.0059	.0057	.0055	.0054	.0052	.0051	.0049	.0048
− 2.4	.0082	.0080	.0078	.0075	.0073	.0071	.0069	.0068	.0066	.0064
− 2.3	.0107	.0104	.0102	.0099	.0096	.0094	.0091	.0089	.0087	.0084
− 2.2	.0139	.0136	.0132	.0129	.0126	.0122	.0119	.0116	.0113	.0110
− 2.1	.0179	.0174	.0170	.0166	.0162	.0158	.0154	.0150	.0146	.0143
− 2.0	.0228	.0222	.0217	.0212	.0207	.0202	.0197	.0192	.0188	.0183
− 1.9	.0287	.0281	.0274	.0268	.0262	.0256	.0250	.0244	.0238	.0233
− 1.8	.0359	.0352	.0344	.0336	.0329	.0322	.0314	.0307	.0300	.0294
− 1.7	.0446	.0436	.0427	.0418	.0409	.0401	.0392	.0384	.0375	.0367
− 1.6	.0548	.0537	.0526	.0516	.0505	.0495	.0485	.0475	.0465	.0455
− 1.5	.0668	.0655	.0643	.0630	.0618	.0606	.0594	.0582	.0570	.0559
− 1.4	.0808	.0793	.0778	.0764	.0749	.0735	.0722	.0708	.0694	.0681
− 1.3	.0968	.0951	.0934	.0918	.0901	.0885	.0869	.0853	.0838	.0823
− 1.2	.1151	.1131	.1112	.1093	.1075	.1056	.1038	.1020	.1003	.0985
− 1.1	.1357	.1335	.1314	.1292	.1271	.1251	.1230	.1210	.1190	.1170
− 1.0	.1587	.1562	.1539	.1515	.1492	.1469	.1446	.1423	.1401	.1379
− .9	.1841	.1814	.1788	.1762	.1736	.1711	.1685	.1660	.1635	.1611
− .8	.2119	.2090	.2061	.2033	.2005	.1977	.1949	.1922	.1894	.1867
− .7	.2420	.2389	.2358	.2327	.2297	.2266	.2236	.2206	.2177	.2148
− .6	.2743	.2709	.2676	.2643	.2611	.2578	.2546	.2514	.2483	.2451
− .5	.3085	.3050	.3015	.2981	.2946	.2912	.2877	.2843	.2810	.2776
− .4	.3446	.3409	.3372	.3336	.3300	.3264	.3228	.3192	.3156	.3121
− .3	.3821	.3783	.3745	.3707	.3669	.3632	.3594	.3557	.3520	.3483
− .2	.4207	.4168	.4129	.4090	.4052	.4013	.3974	.3936	.3897	.3859
− .1	.4602	.4562	.4522	.4483	.4443	.4404	.4364	.4325	.4286	.4247
− 0	.5000	.4960	.4920	.4880	.4840	.4801	.4761	.4721	.4681	.4641

(Continued)

Table A–1. Values of the Standard Normal Distribution Function (*continued*)

z	0	1	2	3	4	5	6	7	8	9
.0	.5000	.5040	.5080	.5120	.5160	.5199	.5239	.5279	.5319	.5359
.1	.5398	.5438	.5478	.5517	.5557	.5596	.5636	.5675	.5714	.5753
.2	.5793	.5832	.5871	.5910	.5948	.5987	.6026	.6064	.6103	.6141
.3	.6179	.6217	.6255	.6293	.6331	.6368	.6406	.6443	.6480	.6517
.4	.6554	.6591	.6628	.6664	.6700	.6736	.6772	.6808	.6844	.6879
.5	.6915	.6950	.6985	.7019	.7054	.7088	.7123	.7157	.7190	.7224
.6	.7257	.7291	.7324	.7357	.7389	.7422	.7454	.7486	.7517	.7549
.7	.7580	.7611	.7642	.7673	.7703	.7734	.7764	.7794	.7823	.7852
.8	.7881	.7910	.7939	.7967	.7995	.8023	.8051	.8078	.8106	.8133
.9	.8159	.8186	.8212	.8238	.8264	.8289	.8315	.8340	.8365	.8389
1.0	.8413	.8438	.8461	.8485	.8508	.8531	.8554	.8577	.8599	.8621
1.1	.8643	.8665	.8686	.8708	.8729	.8749	.8770	.8790	.8810	.8830
1.2	.8849	.8869	.8888	.8907	.8925	.8944	.8962	.8980	.8997	.9015
1.3	.9032	.9049	.9066	.9082	.9099	.9115	.9131	.9147	.9162	.9177
1.4	.9192	.9207	.9222	.9236	.9251	.9265	.9278	.9292	.9306	.9319
1.5	.9332	.9345	.9357	.9370	.9382	.9394	.9406	.9418	.9430	.9441
1.6	.9452	.9463	.9474	.9484	.9495	.9505	.9515	.9525	.9535	.9545
1.7	.9554	.9564	.9573	.9582	.9591	.9599	.9608	.9616	.9625	.9633
1.8	.9641	.9648	.9656	.9664	.9671	.9678	.9686	.9693	.9700	.9706
1.9	.9713	.9719	.9726	.9732	.9738	.9744	.9750	.9756	.9762	.9767
2.0	.9772	.9778	.9783	.9788	.9793	.9798	.9803	.9808	.9812	.9817
2.1	.9821	.9826	.9830	.9834	.9838	.9842	.9846	.9850	.9854	.9857
2.2	.9861	.9864	.9868	.9871	.9874	.9878	.9881	.9884	.9887	.9890
2.3	.9893	.9896	.9898	.9901	.9904	.9906	.9909	.9911	.9913	.9916
2.4	.9918	.9920	.9922	.9925	.9927	.9929	.9931	.9932	.9934	.9936
2.5	.9938	.9940	.9941	.9943	.9945	.9946	.9948	.9949	.9951	.9952
2.6	.9953	.9955	.9956	.9957	.9959	.9960	.9961	.9962	.9963	.9964
2.7	.9965	.9966	.9967	.9968	.9969	.9970	.9971	.9972	.9973	.9974
2.8	.9974	.9975	.9976	.9977	.9977	.9978	.9979	.9979	.9980	.9981
2.9	.9981	.9982	.9982	.9983	.9984	.9984	.9985	.9985	.9986	.9986
3.	.9987	.9990	.9993	.9995	.9997	.9998	.9998	.9999	.9999	1.0000

Note 1: If a normal variable X is not "standard," its values must be "standardized": $Z = (X - \mu)/\sigma$, that is, $P(X \le x) = \Phi[(x - \mu)/\sigma]$.

Note 2: For "two-tail" probabilities, see Table Ic.

Note 3: For $z \ge 4$, $\Phi(z) = 1$ to four decimal places; for $z \le -4$, $\Phi(z) = 0$ to four decimal places.

Note 4: Entries opposite 3 and -3 are for 3.0, 3.1, 3.2, etc., and -3.0, -3.1, etc., respectively.

Table A–2. Binomial Probabilities

$$b(x, n, p) = \binom{n}{x} p^x(1 - p)^{n-x}$$

Binomial probabilities $\quad b(x, n, p) = \binom{n}{x} p^x(1 - p)^{n-x}$

n	x	p .01	.05	.10	.15	.20	.25	.30	$\frac{1}{3}$	.35	.40	.45	.50
4	0	.9606	.8145	.6561	.5220	.4096	.3164	.2401	.1975	.1785	.1296	.0915	.0625
	1	.0388	.1715	.2916	.3685	.4096	.4219	.4116	.3951	.3845	.3456	.2995	.2500
	2	.0006	.0135	.0486	.0975	.1536	.2109	.2646	.2963	.3105	.3456	.3675	.3750
	3	.0000	.0005	.0036	.0115	.0256	.0469	.0756	.0988	.1115	.1536	.2005	.2500
	4	.0000	.0000	.0001	.0005	.0016	.0039	.0081	.0123	.0150	.0256	.0410	.0625
5	0	.9510	.7738	.5905	.4437	.3277	.2373	.1681	.1317	.1160	.0778	.0503	.0312
	1	.0480	.2036	.3280	.3915	.4096	.3955	.3601	.3292	.3124	.2592	.2059	.1562
	2	.0010	.0214	.0729	.1382	.2048	.2637	.3087	.3292	.3364	.3456	.3369	.3125
	3	.0000	.0011	.0081	.0244	.0512	.0879	.1323	.1646	.1811	.2304	.2757	.3125
	4	.0000	.0000	.0004	0022	.0064	.0146	.0283	.0412	.0488	.0768	.1128	.1562
	5	.0000	.0000	.0000	.0001	.0003	.0010	.0024	.0041	.0053	.0102	.0185	.0312
6	0	.9415	.7351	.5314	.3771	.2621	.1780	.1176	.0878	.0754	.0467	.0277	.0156
	1	.0571	.2321	.3543	.3993	.3932	.3560	.3025	.2634	.2437	.1866	.1359	.0938
	2	.0014	.0305	.0984	.1762	.2458	.2966	.3241	.3292	.3280	.3110	.2780	.2344
	3	.0000	.0021	.0146	.0415	.0819	.1318	.1852	.2195	.2355	.2765	.3032	.3125
	4	.0000	.0001	.0012	.0055	.0154	.0330	.0595	.0823	.0951	.1382	.1861	.2344
	5	.0000	.0000	.0001	.0004	.0015	.0044	.0102	.0165	.0205	.0369	.0609	.0938
	6	.0000	.0000	.0000	.0000	.0001	.0002	.0007	.0014	.0018	.0041	.0083	.0156
7	0	.9321	.6983	.4783	.3206	.2097	.1335	.0824	.0585	.0490	.0280	.0152	.0078
	1	.0659	.2573	.3720	.3960	.3670	.3115	.2471	.2049	.1848	.1306	.0872	.0547
	2	.0020	.0406	.1240	.2097	.2753	.3115	.3177	.3073	.2985	.2613	.2140	.1641
	3	.0000	.0036	.0230	.0617	.1147	.1730	.2269	.2561	.2679	.2903	.2918	.2734
	4	.0000	.0002	.0026	.0109	.0287	.0577	.0972	.1280	.1442	.1935	.2388	.2734
	5	.0000	.0000	.0002	.0012	.0043	.0115	.0250	.0384	.0466	.0774	.1172	.1641
	6	.0000	.0000	.0000	.0001	.0004	.0013	.0036	.0064	.0084	.0172	.0320	.0547
	7	.0000	.0000	.0000	.0000	.0000	.0001	.0002	.0005	.0006	.0016	.0037	.0078
8	0	.9227	.6634	.4305	.2725	.1678	.1001	.0576	.0390	.0319	.0168	.0084	.0039
	1	.0746	.2793	.3826	.3847	.3355	.2670	.1977	.1561	.1373	.0896	.0548	.0312
	2	.0026	.0515	.1488	.2376	.2936	.3115	.2965	.2731	.2587	.2090	.1569	.1094
	3	.0001	.0054	.0331	.0839	.1468	.2076	.2541	.2731	.2786	.2787	.2568	.2187
	4	.0000	.0004	.0046	.0185	.0459	.0865	.1361	.1707	.1875	.2322	.2627	.2734
	5	.0000	.0000	.0004	.0026	.0092	.0231	.0467	.0683	.0808	.1239	.1719	.2187
	6	.0000	.0000	.0000	.0002	.0011	.0038	.0100	.0171	.0217	.0413	.0703	.1004
	7	.0000	.0000	.0000	.0000	.0001	.0004	.0012	.0024	.0033	.0079	.0164	.0312
	8	.0000	.0000	.0000	.0000	.0000	.0000	.0001	.0002	.0002	.0007	.0017	.0039
9	0	.9135	.6302	.3874	.2316	.1342	.0751	.0404	.0260	.0207	.0101	.0046	.0020
	1	.0830	.2985	.3874	.3679	.3020	.2253	.1556	.1171	.1004	.0605	.0339	.0176
	2	.0034	.0629	.1722	.2597	.3020	.3003	.2668	.2341	.2162	.1612	.1110	.0703
	3	.0001	.0077	.0446	.1069	.1762	.2336	.2668	.2731	.2716	.2508	.2119	.1641
	4	.0000	.0006	.0074	.0283	.0661	.1168	.1715	.2048	.2194	.2508	.2600	.2461
	5	.0000	.0000	.0008	.0050	.0165	.0389	.0735	.1024	.1181	.1672	.2128	.2461
	6	.0000	.0000	.0001	.0006	.0028	.0087	.0210	.0341	.0424	.0743	.1160	.1641
	7	.0000	.0000	.0000	.0000	.0003	.0012	.0039	.0073	.0098	.0212	.0407	.0703
	8	.0000	.0000	.0000	.0000	.0000	.0001	.0004	.0009	.0013	.0035	.0083	.0176
	9	.0000	.0000	.0000	.0000	.0000	.0000	.0000	.0001	.0001	.0003	.0008	.0020
10	0	.9044	.5987	.3487	.1969	.1074	.0563	.0282	.0173	.0135	.0060	.0025	.0010
	1	.0914	.3151	.3874	.3474	.2684	.1877	.1211	.0867	.0725	.0403	.0207	.0098
	2	.0042	.0746	.1937	.2759	.3020	.2816	.2335	.1951	.1757	.1209	.0763	.0439
	3	.0001	.0105	.0574	.1298	.2013	.2503	.2668	.2601	.2522	.2150	.1665	.1172
	4	.0000	.0010	.0112	.0401	.0881	.1460	.2001	.2276	.2377	.2508	.2384	.2051
	5	.0000	.0001	.0015	.0085	.0264	.0584	.1029	.1366	.1536	.2007	.2340	.2461
	6	.0000	.0000	.0001	.0012	.0055	.0162	.0368	.0569	.0689	.1115	.1596	.2051
	7	.0000	.0000	.0000	.0001	.0008	.0031	.0090	.0163	.0212	.0425	.0746	.1172
	8	.0000	.0000	.0000	.0000	.0001	.0004	.0014	.0030	.0043	.0106	.0229	.0439
	9	.0000	.0000	.0000	.0000	.0000	.0000	.0001	.0003	.0005	.0016	.0042	.0098
	10	.0000	.0000	.0000	.0000	.0000	.0000	.0000	.0000	.0000	.0001	.0003	.0010

Taken from I. Richard Savage, *Statistics: Uncertainty and Behavior,* Houghton Mifflin Company, 1968. Used by permission.

Table A–3. Poisson Distribution Function: $F(c) = \displaystyle\sum_{k-0}^{c} \dfrac{m^k e^{-m}}{K!}$

m (Expected value)

c	.02	.04	.06	.08	.10	.15	.20	.25	.30	.35	.40
0	.980	.961	.942	.923	.905	.861	.819	.779	.741	.705	.670
1	1.000	.999	.998	.997	.995	.990	.982	.974	.963	.951	.938
2		1.000	1.000	1.000	1.000	.999	.999	.998	.996	.994	.992
3						1.000	1.000	1.000	1.000	1.000	.999
4											1.000

c	.45	.50	.55	.60	.65	.70	.75	.80	.85	.90	.95
0	.638	.607	.577	.549	.522	.497	.472	.449	.427	.407	.387
1	.925	.910	.894	.878	.861	.844	.827	.809	.791	.772	.754
2	.989	.986	.982	.977	.972	.966	.959	.953	.945	.937	.929
3	.999	.998	.998	.997	.996	.994	.993	.991	.989	.987	.984
4	1.000	1.000	1.000	1.000	.999	.999	.999	.999	.998	.998	.997
5					1.000	1.000	1.000	1.000	1.000	1.000	1.000

c	1.0	1.1	1.2	1.3	1.4	1.5	1.6	1.7	1.8	1.9	2.0
0	.368	.333	.301	.273	.247	.223	.202	.183	.165	.150	.135
1	.736	.699	.663	.627	.592	.558	.525	.493	.463	.434	.406
2	.920	.900	.879	.857	.833	.809	.783	.757	.731	.704	.677
3	.981	.974	.966	.957	.946	.934	.921	.907	.891	.875	.857
4	.996	.995	.992	.989	.986	.981	.976	.970	.964	.956	.947
5	.999	.999	.998	.998	.997	.996	.994	.992	.990	.987	.983
6	1.000	1.000	1.000	1.000	.999	.999	.999	.998	.997	.997	.995
7					1.000	1.000	1.000	1.000	.999	.999	.999
8									1.000	1.000	1.000

c	2.2	2.4	2.6	2.8	3.0	3.2	3.4	3.6	3.8	4.0	4.2
0	.111	.091	.074	.061	.050	.041	.033	.027	.022	.018	.015
1	.355	.308	.267	.231	.199	.171	.147	.126	.107	.092	.078
2	.623	.570	.518	.469	.423	.380	.340	.303	.269	.238	.210
3	.819	.779	.736	.692	.647	.603	.558	.515	.473	.433	.395
4	.928	.904	.877	.848	.815	.781	.744	.706	.668	.629	.590
5	.975	.964	.951	.935	.916	.895	.871	.844	.816	.785	.753
6	.993	.988	.983	.976	.966	.955	.942	.927	.909	.889	.867
7	.998	.997	.995	.992	.988	.983	.977	.969	.960	.949	.936
8	1.000	.999	.999	.998	.996	.994	.992	.988	.984	.979	.972
9		1.000	1.000	.999	.999	.998	.997	.996	.994	.992	.989
10				1.000	1.000	1.000	.999	.999	.998	.997	.996
11							1.000	1.000	.999	.999	.999
12									1.000	1.000	1.000

(*continued*)

c	4.4	4.6	4.8	5.0	5.2	5.4	5.6	5.8	6.0	6.2	6.4
0	.012	.010	.008	.007	.006	.005	.004	.003	.002	.002	.002
1	.066	.056	.048	.040	.034	.029	.024	.021	.017	.015	.012
2	.185	.163	.143	.125	.109	.095	.082	.072	.062	.054	.046
3	.359	.326	.294	.265	.238	.213	.191	.170	.151	.134	.119
4	.551	.513	.476	.440	.406	.373	.342	.313	.285	.259	.235
5	.720	.686	.651	.616	.581	.546	.512	.478	.446	.414	.384
6	.844	.818	.791	.762	.732	.702	.670	.638	.606	.574	.542
7	.921	.905	.887	.867	.845	.822	.797	.771	.744	.716	.687
8	.964	.955	.944	.932	.918	.903	.886	.867	.847	.826	.803
9	.985	.980	.975	.968	.960	.951	.941	.929	.916	.902	.886
10	.994	.992	.990	.986	.982	.977	.972	.965	.957	.949	.939
11	.998	.997	.996	.995	.993	.990	.988	.984	.980	.975	.969
12	.999	.999	.999	.998	.997	.996	.995	.993	.991	.989	.986
13	1.000	1.000	1.000	.999	.999	.999	.998	.997	.996	.995	.994
14				1.000	1.000	1.000	.999	.999	.999	.998	.997
15							1.000	1.000	.999	.999	.999
16									1.000	1.000	1.000

c	6.6	6.8	7.0	7.2	7.4	7.6	7.8	8.0	8.5	9.0	9.5
0	.001	.001	.001	.001	.001	.001	.000	.000	.000	.000	.000
1	.010	.009	.007	.006	.005	.004	.004	.003	.002	.001	.001
2	.040	.034	.030	.025	.022	.019	.016	.014	.009	.006	.004
3	.105	.093	.082	.072	.063	.055	.048	.042	.030	.021	.015
4	.213	.192	.173	.156	.140	.125	.112	.100	.074	.055	.040
5	.355	.327	.301	.276	.253	.231	.210	.191	.150	.116	.089
6	.511	.480	.450	.420	.392	.365	.338	.313	.256	.207	.165
7	.658	.628	.599	.569	.539	.510	.481	.453	.386	.324	.269
8	.780	.755	.729	.703	.676	.648	.620	.593	.523	.456	.392
9	.869	.850	.830	.810	.788	.765	.741	.717	.653	.587	.522
10	.927	.915	.901	.887	.871	.854	.835	.816	.763	.706	.645
11	.963	.955	.947	.937	.926	.915	.902	.888	.849	.803	.752
12	.982	.978	.973	.967	.961	.954	.945	.936	.909	.876	.836
13	.992	.990	.987	.984	.980	.976	.971	.966	.949	.926	.898
14	.997	.996	.994	.993	.991	.989	.986	.983	.973	.959	.940
15	.999	.998	.998	.997	.996	.995	.993	.992	.986	.978	.967
16	.999	.999	.999	.999	.998	.998	.997	.996	.993	.989	.982
17	1.000	1.000	1.000	.999	.999	.999	.999	.998	.997	.995	.991
18				1.000	1.000	1.000	1.000	.999	.999	.998	.996
19								1.000	.999	.999	.998
20									1.000	1.000	.999
21											1.000

c	10.0	10.5	11.0	11.5	12.0	12.5	13.0	13.5	14.0	14.5	15.0
2	.003	.002	.001	.001	.001	.000					
3	.010	.007	.005	.003	.002	.002	.001	.001	.000		
4	.029	.021	.015	.011	.008	.005	.004	.003	.002	.001	.001
5	.067	.050	.038	.028	.020	.015	.011	.008	.006	.004	.003
6	.130	.102	.079	.060	.046	.035	.026	.019	.014	.010	.008
7	.220	.179	.143	.114	.090	.070	.054	.041	.032	.024	.018
8	.333	.279	.232	.191	.155	.125	.100	.079	.062	.048	.037
9	.458	.397	.341	.289	.242	.201	.166	.135	.109	.088	.070
10	.583	.521	.460	.402	.347	.297	.252	.211	.176	.145	.118
11	.697	.639	.579	.520	.462	.406	.353	.304	.260	.220	.185
12	.792	.742	.689	.633	.576	.519	.463	.409	.358	.311	.268
13	.864	.825	.781	.733	.682	.628	.573	.518	.464	.413	.363
14	.917	.888	.854	.815	.772	.725	.675	.623	.570	.518	.466
15	.951	.932	.907	.878	.844	.806	.764	.718	.669	.619	.568
16	.973	.960	.944	.924	.899	.869	.835	.798	.756	.711	.664
17	.986	.978	.968	.954	.937	.916	.890	.861	.827	.790	.749
18	.993	.988	.982	.974	.963	.948	.930	.908	.883	.853	.819
19	.997	.994	.991	.986	.979	.969	.957	.942	.923	.901	.875
20	.998	.997	.995	.992	.988	.983	.975	.965	.952	.936	.917
21	.999	.999	.998	.996	.994	.991	.986	.980	.971	.960	.947
22	1.000	.999	.999	.998	.997	.995	.992	.989	.983	.976	.967
23		1.000	1.000	.999	.999	.998	.996	.994	.991	.986	.981
24				1.000	.999	.999	.998	.997	.995	.992	.989
25					1.000	.999	.999	.998	.997	.996	.994
26						1.000	1.000	.999	.999	.998	.997
27								1.000	.999	.999	.998
28									1.000	.999	.999
29										1.000	1.000

Answers to Problems

Chapter 1

1–2 (b) $\frac{1}{2}$, (c) $\frac{3}{10}$, (d) $\frac{1}{5}$.

1–3 (a) $P(Y = k) = \frac{9}{13}$ for $k = 0$, $= \frac{1}{13}$ for $k = 1, 2, 3$, or 4.
(b) $\frac{11}{13}$, (c) $\frac{10}{13}$.

1–4 (a) $\frac{2}{3}$, (b) $\frac{15}{16}$, (c) $\frac{1}{8}$.

1–6 5.5.

1–7 (a) $\frac{10}{13}$, (b) 0.

1–8 $EX = 1$ in either model.

1–9 3.5.

1–10 4.

1–11 Yes; no.

1–12 $x + \mathit{ll}y = 7$.

1–13 (a) Not unless $P_3 = k\left(\begin{smallmatrix}2\\-1\end{smallmatrix}\right)$, in which case any a, b such that $a - 2b = k$ will work.
(b) $x + 2y = 0$ (passes through origin).

1–16 Not convex: **(a)**, **(b)**, **(d)**, **(e)**, **(f)**, **(g)**.

Chapter 2

2–8 (a) $\frac{1}{4}$, (b) $-\frac{1}{3}$, (c) 4.

2–9 $\frac{5}{4}$.

2–10 (a) Any $p < 1/101$.

2–11 $[F, B]_p$, with $p > .99$.

2–12 (a) $u_A(4 \text{ wks.}) = \frac{8}{7}$,
(b) Let $u_B(\text{none}) = 0$, $u_B(\text{status quo}) = 1$, $u_B(4 \text{ wks.}) > 8$.

2–13 He should play.

2–14 (a) \$11, (b) \$2.414, (c) \$2.

2–15 $u(N) = 2u(5)$, $u(M) = 6u(5)$.

2–16 $u(b_A) = .308$, $u(b_B) = .45$.

2–17 0.2.

2–18 (a) yes, (b) no.

2–19 *Money odds:* Approximately 1:30,000, or 1:150,000 if processing cost considered. *Probability odds:* Approximately 1:667,000.

2–20 No.

2–21 No.

2–22 (a) $\frac{1}{2}$, (b) no, (c) $\frac{2}{3}$.

2–23 Yes; yes.

Chapter 3

3–1 $r(\theta_1, a_1) = r(\theta_2, a_2) = 0$, $r(\theta_1, a_2) = r(\theta_2, a_1) = 1$.

3–2 $(\frac{1}{2}, \frac{1}{2})$; no.

3–4 $(\frac{1}{14}, \frac{5}{14}, \frac{8}{14})$.

3–5 $(\frac{1}{3}, \frac{1}{3}, \frac{1}{3})$.

3–6 *Possible answers:* $(\frac{2}{7}, \frac{2}{7}, 0, 0, \frac{3}{7})$, $(\frac{4}{7}, 0, 0, \frac{2}{7}, \frac{1}{7})$.

3–7 *Loss:* Pure—a_2, mixed—$(0, 1)$.
  Regret: Pure—a_1 or a_2, mixed—$(\frac{1}{2}, \frac{1}{2})$.

3–8 *Loss:* Pure—a_2 or a_3, mixed—$(\frac{7}{10}, \frac{3}{10}, 0)$.
  Regret: Pure—a_1, mixed—$(\frac{3}{5}, \frac{2}{5}, 0)$.

3–9 *Loss:* a_2 or a_3, *regret:* a_2.

3–10 $(\frac{1}{3}, \frac{2}{3})$.

3–12 a_1 for $w \leq \frac{5}{7}$, a_2 for $w \geq \frac{5}{7}$.

3–13 a_2.

3–14 a_1.

3–15 $(\frac{5}{7}, \frac{2}{7})$.

3–16 $(\frac{1}{2}, \frac{1}{2})$.

3–18 Mixtures of a_1, a_2.

3–19 $(\frac{5}{7}, \frac{2}{7})$.

3–20 (a) a_1 strictly dominates a_2, (b) a_1, (c) any prior distribution which assigns zero probability to θ_3.

Chapter 4

4–1

	d_1	d_2	d_3	d_4	d_5	d_6	d_7	d_8
θ_1	1	.1	.9	1	0	.1	.9	0
θ_2	5	5	5.2	5.8	5.2	5.8	6	6

4–2 (a) $f(z_1; M) = 1 - M/5, f(z_2; M) = M/5$.
  (b) $R(M, d_1) = 5 - M$, $R(M, d_2) = \frac{1}{5}(25 - 10M + 3M^2)$,
    $R(M, d_3) = \frac{3}{5}M(5 - M)$, $R(M, d_4) = 2M$.

4–3 $R(M, d_1) = 5$, $R(M, d_2) = 2M^2 - 7M + 5$.
  $R(M, d_3) = -2M^2 + 15M - 20$, $R(M, d_4) = 10M - 25$.

4–4 Take action a_i if $Z = z_i$ $(i = 1, 2, 3)$.

4–5 (a) 27, 8.

(b)

		d_1	d_2	d_3	d_4	d_5	d_6	d_7	d_8
Action if $Z =$	z_1	a_1	a_1	a_1	a_2	a_2	a_2	a_2	a_1
	z_2	a_1	a_1	a_2	a_1	a_2	a_2	a_1	a_2
	z_3	a_1	a_2	a_1	a_1	a_2	a_1	a_2	a_2
Risk, if $\Theta =$	θ_1	2	1	1.4	1.6	0	1	.6	.4
	θ_2	-1	$-.5$	.5	2	4	3.5	2.5	1

4–6 (a) 0.16, (b) 0.43.

4–7 d_3; value = 0.1.

4–8 1.4.

4–9 $\frac{1}{4}, \frac{4}{7}$ (if mixed strategies are used).

4–10 $P(Z = 0) = .16$, $P(Z = 1) = .12$, $P(Z = 2) = .72$.

4–11

	0	1	2	3	4	5
$h(m \mid 1)$	0	$\frac{2}{7}$	$\frac{2}{7}$	$\frac{3}{7}$	0	0
$h(m \mid 0)$	$\frac{30}{43}$	$\frac{8}{43}$	$\frac{3}{43}$	$\frac{2}{43}$	0	0

4–12 $f(z) = f(z \mid \theta_m)$.

4–13 1/46.

4–14 (a) 10/15, 4/15, 1/15, 0, 0, 0) for $z = 0$
  (0, 3/5, 2/5, 0, 0, 0) for $z = 1$
  (b) $h(m \mid 1) = m/15$, $h(m \mid 0) = (5 - m)/15$, $m = 0, 1, 2, 3, 4, 5$.

4–15 $h(\theta \mid z) \equiv g(\theta)$ (for all z).

4–18

	Posterior probabilities, given					
	$Z = 0$	$Z = 1$	$Z = 2$	$Y = 0$	$Y = 1$	$Y = 2$
θ_1	$\frac{14}{15}$	$\frac{7}{11}$	$\frac{7}{22}$	0	$\frac{7}{13}$	1
θ_2	$\frac{1}{15}$	$\frac{4}{11}$	$\frac{15}{22}$	1	$\frac{6}{13}$	0

4–19 Pass the lot if $Z = 0$, reject if $Z = 1$.

4–20 a_1 if $Z = 0$ or 1; a_1 if $Y = 1$ or 2.

4–21 (a) $\frac{7}{37}, \frac{30}{37}$, (b) a_2, (c) same.

4–22 1.2.

Chapter 5

5–1 3.

5–2 (a) $T = 5$; (b) $T = 0$ (abs. error loss), $T = 1$ (squared error loss).

5–3 (a) $\frac{1}{8}$, (b) $\frac{2}{9}$, (c) $\frac{5}{9}$.

5–4 (a) $\frac{3}{4}$, (b) $\frac{1}{2}$, (c) 0.6.

5–5 $\frac{1}{2}, \frac{1}{2}, \frac{2}{3}, a/2, \frac{1}{2}, \frac{1}{3}$.

5–6 $\frac{2}{3}$.

5–7 $\frac{2}{3}, \frac{1}{3}$.

5–8

M	0	1	2	3	4	5
Risk	25	16	8.5	5.5	10	25

(T_3 is not admissible, being strictly dominated by T_2 or T_1)

5–9 Announce $\frac{3}{4}$ (1) if $Z = 0$, $\frac{17}{4}$ (4) if $Z = 2$.

5–10 $\frac{19}{7}$ (3).

5–11 0.49.

5–13 $13M(5 - M)/25$.

5–14 5 or 6.

5–15

Rule	α	β
Reject θ_1 if $Z = z_1, z_2$, or z_3	1	0
Reject θ_1 if $Z = z_1$ or z_2	.5	.1
Reject θ_1 if $Z = z_1$	.2	.4
Do not reject θ_1	0	1

5–16 Reject $M = 1$ if $Z = 1$, accept if $Z = 0$.

5–17 Reject $M = 1$ with prob. 10/11 if $Z = 1$; Bayes against the prior $(\frac{6}{11}, \frac{5}{11})$.

5–18

Critical Z-values	α	β
–	0	1
4	$\dfrac{1}{16}$	$\dfrac{175}{256}$
4, 3	$\dfrac{5}{16}$	$\dfrac{67}{256}$
4, 3, 2	$\dfrac{11}{16}$	$\dfrac{13}{256}$
4, 3, 2, 1	$\dfrac{15}{16}$	$\dfrac{1}{256}$
4, 3, 2, 1, 0	1	0

5–19 H_0: $M = 0$ or 1, H_1: $M = 2, 3, 4$, or 5.

5–20

θ	θ_1	θ_2	θ_3	θ_4	θ_5
Risk for C_3	2.5	1.0	.4	.2	.6
Risk for $Z = z_2$	2.5	4.0	1.6	1.8	1.4

5–22

z	0	1	2	3	4
$\Lambda(z)$	$\dfrac{27}{8}$	$\dfrac{2187}{2048}$	$\dfrac{64}{81}$	$\dfrac{512}{2187}$	$\dfrac{1}{81}$

Critical regions of form $Z > $ const.

Chapter 6

6–1 .1587, .0013, .1574, .9974, .0556.

6–2 .0062, .8904, .8641.

6–3 6′ 4.16″.

6–4 1.68%, 127.3, 85.3%.

6–6 $\frac{3}{2}$, $\frac{1}{2}$.

6–7 $\exp(-2\sum X_i + 2)$.

6–8 Normal, mean $\bar{X}$ and variance σ^2/n.

6–9 $\frac{1}{2}(X + m)$, where m is the mean of the prior.

6–10 .6826.

6–11 .686.

6–12 If $\mu_0 < \mu_1$, reject μ_0 when $\bar{X} > (\mu_0 + \mu_1)/2$. Bayes against prior $(\frac{1}{2}, \frac{1}{2})$.

6–13 $n \doteq 7$, $K = 12.8$, $\pi(\mu) = \Phi((\mu - 12.8)/1.69)$.

6–14 $R(\mu) = 2\pi(\mu)$ for $|\mu - 10| < .1$, $(1 - \pi(\mu))$ for $|\mu - 10| > 2$, and 0 elsewhere, where $\pi(\mu) = 1 - \Phi(22 - 2\mu) + \Phi(18 - 2\mu)$.

6–15 $\alpha = .10$.

6–16 0.527.

Chapter 7

7–1 120, 495, 4950.

7–2 $\frac{7}{495}$, $\frac{4}{243}$, $\frac{70}{495}$, $\frac{40}{243}$, $\frac{1}{10}$.

7–3 $\binom{6}{k}\left(\frac{1}{3}\right)^k\left(\frac{2}{3}\right)^{6-k}$, $k = 0, 1, \ldots, 6$.

7–4 $\binom{4}{k}\binom{8}{6-k} \big/ \binom{12}{k}$, $k = 0, 1, 2, 3, 4$.

7–5

k	0	1	2	3	4	5	6
Binomial	.3487	.3874	.1937	.0574	.0112	.0015	.0001
Poisson	.368	.368	.184	.061	.015	.003	.001

7–6

	0	1	2	3	4	5	6	7	8
Binomial	.028	.121	.233	.267	.200	.103	.037	.009	.001
Normal	.016	.065	.161	.255	.255	.161	.065	.016	.003
Normal with corr.	.034	.100	.223	.270	.223	.100	.034	.007	.001

7–7 0.18.

7–8 0.14.

7–9 (a) $\frac{5}{8}$, $\frac{5}{8}$; (b) $[8p(1 - p) + (5 - 8p)^2]/256$, $p(1 - p)/8$.

7–10 m.s.e $(p_B) = [np(1 - p) + (1 - 2p)^2]/(n + 2)^2$.

For $p = \frac{1}{2}$, m.s.e. $(p_B) = \left(\dfrac{n}{n + 2}\right)^2$ m.s.e. (p_{ml}).

7–11 0.117.

7–12 $\Lambda = 7.7, 3.3, 1.42, .61, .26$ resp.

7–13 $1 - e^{-25p}(1 + 25p + (25p)^2/2)$.

7–14 $\Phi\left(\dfrac{100p - 40.5}{10\sqrt{p(1 - p)}}\right)$

7–15 Risk $= 3[(1 - p)^4 + p^4]$ if $.4 < p < .6$, $= 2[1 - p^4 - (1 - p)^4]$, otherwise.

Chapter 8

8–1   (a) both $= 4$, (b) yes, value $= 4$, (c) alternative 4 dominated by alternative 3

8–2   maximin $a_{ij} = 0 \neq 4 =$ minimax a_{ij}.

8–4   Saddle point is $(4, 4)$ if $N > 8$; $(3, 3)$ if $6 < N < 8$; $(2, 2)$ if $4 < N < 6$; $(1, 1)$ if $2 < N < 4$; $(0, 0)$ if $N < 2$.

8–5   (a) $(1, 1)$ is a s.p. as well as a s.s.p.

      (b) $(\frac{1}{2}, \frac{1}{2})$ is a s.s.p.

8–7   *Maximize:* $v = x_2 - x_3 + z_1$ subject to

$$-x_1 - \ x_2 + 2x_3 + z_2 - z_1 = 0$$
$$x_1 - 2x_2 + \ x_3 + z_3 - z_1 = 0$$
$$x_i \geq 0, \ z_i \geq 0$$

8–8   Ignoring requirement of integer solution, min. cost for $\frac{71}{19}$ pills of Brand A, $\frac{101}{19}$ pills of Brand B. Integer solution is 6 of Brand A, 5 of Brand B.

Chapter 9

9–2   9, 5.

9–3   Continue sampling if $|k - .2675n| < .631$.

9–4   1.63, 2.26.

Index

291